W9-BLR-214

# The Basics
## *of*
# Introductory Statistics

### REVISED SECOND EDITION

James L. Walker, Jr.
James K. Esser
Edythe E. Kirk

**Lamar University**

*Copley Custom Textbooks*

An imprint of XanEdu Publishing, Inc.

Copyright © 2004 by James L. Walker, James K. Esser, and Edythe E. Kirk. All rights reserved
Printed in the United States of America

Revised Second Edition
Reprinted June 2010

ISBN 13: 978-1-58152-317-1
ISBN 10: 1-58152-317-3

No part of this book may be reproduced in any manner without written permission from the publisher.

*Copley Custom Textbooks*

An imprint of XanEdu Publishing, Inc.
138 Great Road
Acton, Massachusetts 01720
800-562-2147

# Contents

# Contents

# Contents

# CHAPTER ONE

# Introduction

## Why Study Statistics?

You may be wondering why you have to take a course in statistics. Rest assured; you are not alone. Very few students in a beginning statistics course are there by choice. Usually a first statistics course is required – as part of a university core program or as part of a major program of study.

You also may be more than a little nervous about how difficult statistics will be. Rest assured; you are not alone in this either. However, although the development of statistical methods was the work of mathematical geniuses, understanding basic statistical tools well enough to use them effectively is something that normal people can do. Furthermore, once learned, the knowledge of statistics repays the effort it took to learn.

Statistics are useful in a lot of ways. First, statistical applications are so common in the contemporary world that those who are without statistical knowledge are at a competitive disadvantage. For example, in industry statistically based quality control methods are in widespread use. Second, an educated person must be able to evaluate statistical information to make informed decisions. For example, over the last 30 years scores on college entrance exams have dropped. A knowledge of statistics is necessary to form an informed opinion about questions such as "Is this drop in scores something to worry about?" or "Are college entrance exam scores related to anything important?" Third, many different professional disciplines use statistics. A partial list includes medicine, education, business, industrial engineering, and, of course, psychology. Fourth, statistics provides new and useful ways of organizing our thinking. For example, thinking in terms of probability might well change your financial strategy from investing in the lottery to investing in the stock market.

In psychology statistics are used in three ways. First, we use statistics in **understanding research**. Psychology, like any other science, is based on the results of research. This research is reported in journals with the results presented in statistical terms. To understand these first hand reports of research requires a knowledge of statistics. Second, we use statistics in **conducting research**. Nearly all psychologists are required to do research as part of their academic training. And a large percentage of psychologists wind up in jobs in which doing research is at least part of their job duties. Statistical analysis is a key element in the research process. Third, we use statistics in **professional practice**. Statistics are also important in the application of psychology. For example, psychological tests in clinical psychology are interpreted using statistics. In industrial psychology, personnel selection procedures are based on statistical reasoning.

## How to Study Statistics

The way to study statistics is basically the same common sense approach that applies to any course. It all boils down to keeping up. However, keeping up is particularly important in statistics because the material is cumulative. Since new material is based on previous material, learning statistics is like building a brick wall –

you cannot build the eighth layer, or any higher layer, if the seventh layer is missing. So if you get seriously behind, you cannot just jump to the new material. The new stuff is built on the old stuff.

We highly recommend that you follow four common sense rules: (1) attend class *all* of the time; (2) read the book – use class notes and the book together to help each explain the other; (3) keep up with all assignments (work all assigned problems on time and use the feedback to correct your errors); and (4) review frequently; do not wait until the night before the test.

## Three Areas of Statistics

There are three basic categories of statistics (see Table 1-1). The first major area is *descriptive statistics*. The purpose of descriptive statistical techniques is to boil down or distill information from a large set of scores to a small amount of information that summarizes the original set of scores. An unordered set of raw scores (a *raw score* is a score in its original, unaltered form -- such as the number of questions answered correctly on a test) is quite meaningless because we cannot keep all the scores in mind at the same time. Research has shown that human information processing has a bottleneck that allows us to handle only about seven things at a time. So without some technique to summarize them, even a small set of 30 scores on a classroom test overwhelms our ability to handle the information. The set of scores is more meaningful once we know that the class average is 86. Descriptive statistics that summarize the entire set of scores are even more necessary when we deal with very large sets of scores – for example, U.S. census data.

The second major area of statistics is *correlational statistics*. The purpose of correlational statistical techniques is to work with relationships between two sets of scores. In the physical sciences perfect relationships are common. For example, if we were to repeat Galileo's famous experiment by dropping a bowling ball from the Leaning Tower of Pisa, we would find that the relationship between the time the ball travels and the distance it travels is nearly perfect. However, in the behavioral sciences we usually work with imperfect relationships. The prediction of college grade point averages from SAT scores is an example of such an imperfect relationship. When we attempt to predict individual college grade point averages from SAT scores, we will certainly make errors, sometimes large errors. On the other hand, if we were betting with someone who simply guessed each grade point average, we could win most of the time by using SAT scores in making our predictions. Correlational techniques are designed to get the most out of imperfect relationships. There are three main tasks: (1) we can assess the strength of the relationship by computing the correlation coefficient; (2) we can make the best possible predictions by finding the regression line; and (3) we can forecast the typical size of our prediction errors by computing the standard error of estimate.

The third major area of statistics is *inferential statistics*. The purpose of inferential statistical techniques is to draw conclusions about a whole population based on samples taken from the population. The key here is that it can be too costly to get and work with all of the scores in a very large population, but by taking samples we can answer questions about the population almost as accurately as if we had worked with all of the scores. This makes it practical to ask questions about large populations. For example, a political poll sampling only a few thousand voters can give a very accurate picture of the preferences of the entire population of voters in the United States.

Table 1-1
Three Areas of Statistics

| Area | Task Performed | Why We Need It | Example |
|------|----------------|----------------|---------|
| Descriptive statistics | Describing/summarizing sets of scores | Cannot keep track of lots scores at one time | Summarize the performance of a class of 100 students on a history test |
| Correlational statistics | (1) Assess strength of a relationship<br>(2) Generate optimal predictions<br>(3) Forecast size of prediction errors | Work with imperfect relationships between two sets of scores | Relationship between high school grades and college grades |
| Inferential statistics | Make inferences about whole populations from samples drawn from the population | Too costly to get all scores from whole population | Political polls/market research |

## A Brief History of Statistics

It is easy to get the impression that statistical techniques were all developed at the same time and first appeared on Earth on stone tablets. However, statistical techniques are tools that were developed by a number of different people over the course of several hundred years to meet specific needs.

Much of the groundwork for statistics was done by Renaissance mathematicians who developed our idea of probability in order to understand gambling odds. The story is told of Blaise Pascal (1623-1662), a mathematician and religious philosopher, who was seated across from a worldly gambler on a long carriage trip. With time on their hands they began a conversation about the gambler's attempts to improve his outcomes in various games of chance. This stimulated the mathematician in Pascal and he began working on probability as a way to understand the odds of various gambles. One of the tools he developed for dealing with probability, called Pascal's Triangle, will be discussed later in this book.

In the early 1800s Carl Friedrich Gauss (1777-1855) wrote a paper describing the so-called "normal" curve. This bell-shaped curve has been found to characterize the distributions of many features of living organisms – including humans. This normal distribution is a basic idea in statistics and will be encountered many times in this book.

In the late 1800s Francis Galton (1822-1911), a cousin of Charles Darwin, studied human intelligence. Influenced by his cousin, Galton viewed intelligence as an inherited, adaptive trait. His contribution to statistics was his development of techniques to assess the degree of relationship between the intelligence of parents and their children and between different intellectual traits (abilities).

Galton was a wealthy man, and he endowed a chair at the University of London, to be awarded to scholars who would continue to work with his ideas. The first person to hold the Galton Chair was a personal friend, Karl Pearson (1857-1936). In 1886 Pearson developed the Product-Moment Correlation Coefficient, which today is the most commonly used technique for measuring the strength of relationships.

The next holder of the Galton Chair was Sir Ronald Fisher (1890-1962). In the 1920s and 1930s Fisher developed the logic used in inferential statistics and the statistical procedure known as Analysis of Variance. Analysis of variance is the single most popular technique in inferential statistics in use today. Fisher brought these ideas to the United States in the summer of 1937 when he taught at Iowa State University.

Since the 1930s the major developments in statistics have involved dealing with many sets of scores at the same time. Because these multivariate statistical techniques are very complex and the computations are laborious, they became popular only with the availability of computers. These techniques are beyond the scope of an introductory statistics book such as this.

## Measurement and Levels of Measurement

Historically, scientific disciplines such as physics and chemistry have tended to "take off" when they begin to apply measurement to their subject matter. This also has been the case for psychology.

*Measurement* can be defined as the process of assigning numerals to a set of people, objects, or events according to a set of rules.

The great psychologist S. S. Stevens identified four such sets of rules, called *levels (or scales) of measurement* (see Table 1-2). These levels of measurement differ in their sophistication. A *nominal scale* is the least sophisticated level of measurement. The key here is naming. The nominal level of measurement consists of categories or labels that are applied to people to produce a classification system. For example, religious affiliation can be coded by applying the labels "one" to all Catholics, "two" to all Protestants, "three" to all Jews, "four" to all Hindus, etc. The number assigned is merely a label; it has no quantity. So a "four" is not more than a "two." Likewise, blood type is another nominal scale of measurement. Type A blood is different from Type B blood. As this example illustrates, it is not even necessary to use numbers as category labels; letters work just as well. In short, a nominal level of measurement consists of a set of labels that create a classification system. This is a crude, but still powerful, system of measurement.

An *ordinal scale* is a somewhat more sophisticated level of measurement. The key here is a rank ordering; so a higher score represents more of what is being measured. But the numbers do not tell us how much more. There is no guarantee that the steps between numbers represent equal changes in what is being measured. That is, the difference between a rank of three and a rank of four is not necessarily the same as the difference between a rank of one and a rank of two. For example, the Mohs Mineral Hardness Scale is an ordinal scale. It classifies minerals according to which of nine standard minerals (ranked from softest to hardest) is needed to be able to scratch it. Similarly, the outcomes of a county fair baking contest constitute an ordinal scale. The first place recipe is judged as better than the second place recipe, which, in turn, is better than the third place recipe. But, again, we do not know how much better. The first and second place recipes could be excellent, while the third place recipe could be merely good. Like a nominal scale, an ordinal scale of measurement creates a classification system, but this ordinal classification system includes crude information about relative quantity.

An *interval scale of measurement* is still more sophisticated. In an interval scale equal numerical distances represent equal empirical distances. The numbers represent amounts that can meaningfully be added or subtracted. For example, temperature measured on a Fahrenheit scale is an interval scale. The difference between 91 and 92 degrees represents the same amount as the difference between 37 and 38 degrees. However, the weakness of this scale is that it has an arbitrary zero point. Zero degrees Fahrenheit does *not* mean no heat at all. This means that ratios cannot be formed; 100 degrees Fahrenheit is *not* twice as hot as 50 degrees. In sum, an interval scale is like the less sophisticated ordinal scale in that it provides a classification system that includes relative quantity, but now the intervals between numbers are equal.

A *ratio scale of measurement* is the most sophisticated level of measurement. It has all the properties of the previous scales and it has an absolute zero. Therefore, a ratio scale is the only level of measurement for which all the operations of common arithmetic (addition, subtraction, multiplication, and division) can be applied. For example, most of our common physical measurements (height in inches, weight in pounds, temperature on a Kelvin scale) fit this scale. Because there is an absolute zero, we can say that a 40-pound bucket of cement is twice as heavy as a 20-pound bucket.

It is important to know the level of measurement that produced each set of scores with which we work. Each statistical technique is designed to be used with scores produced by specific levels of measurement. Therefore, the level of measurement determines what statistical technique is appropriate. In a similar vein, the level of measurement determines what interpretations can be made about a set of scores. For example, in a survey of the natural hair color of a group of people we might assign the number one to blonde hair, two to red hair, and three to brunette hair. This system is a nominal scale of measurement. For this type of data it makes no sense to summarize our scores by calculating a mean or average. The mean (average) is appropriate only for interval or ratio levels of measurement. So a decision based on an incorrect use of a statistic (in this example, the mean) would be inappropriate and could lead to an inappropriate action.

Table 1-2
Scales of Measurement

| Scale | Description | Mathematical Characteristics | Examples |
|-------|-------------|------------------------------|----------|
| Nominal | A set of labels or categories by which individual cases can be classified -- the size of the category number has no meaning. | $2 \neq 1$ | Blood types<br>Basketball players' numbers<br>Zip codes<br>Religious affiliation |
| Ordinal | A higher number indicates more of the thing being measured but there is no assurance that the steps between numbers represent equal increases in the thing being measured. | $2 \neq 1$<br>$2 > 1$ | Mohs mineral hardness scale<br>Place awarded in a baking contest<br>Class rank |
| Interval | The steps between numbers are equal – numerically equal distances represent empirically equal distances; zero point is arbitrary. | $2 \neq 1$<br>$2 > 1$<br>$10 - 5 = 20 - 15$ | Fahrenheit temperature<br>Centigrade temperature<br>Years on the calendar |
| Ratio | All the properties of ordinary arithmetic hold -- zero really means none of the thing being measured and ratios are meaningful. | $2 \neq 1$<br>$2 > 1$<br>$10 - 5 = 20 - 15$<br>$\dfrac{2}{4} = \dfrac{5}{10}$ | Kelvin temperature<br>Length in inches<br>Weight in pounds |

## Study Questions
*Answers to selected study questions may be found in Appendix A.*

Indicate the appropriate level of measurement for each of the following:
1.  Political affiliation.
2.  Taste preference for five brands of ice cream.
3.  Elapsed time during a foot race.
4.  City of birth.
5.  Number of years it takes Pluto to orbit the sun.
6.  Reaction time.
7.  Socioeconomic class.
8.  Gender.
9.  Temperature (in centigrade) at noon in Salt Lake City.
10. Order of finish in a horse race.
11. College major.
12. Height of radio tower.

# CHAPTER TWO

# Distributions: A Visual Approach

In Chapter One we said that the purpose of descriptive statistical techniques is to boil down the information in a large set of scores to make it meaningful to us with our limited information processing capability. A simple way to do this is to present the summary of the set of scores in a way that is easy to see. That is, we can create a visual presentation of the information.

## Grouped Frequency Distributions

One type of visual presentation of scores is a *grouped frequency distribution*. As an example, a history teacher has given a test to the 30 students in her class. The number of correct answers given by each student is shown in Table 2-1. As the scores appear in Table 2-1, it is very difficult to make much sense of the whole set of scores. It is very difficult to answer such basic questions as: What is a high score? What is a low score? And, what is a typical score?

Table 2-1
Number of Correct Answers Given by Each Student on a History Test

| History Test Scores | | | | | |
|---|---|---|---|---|---|
| 56 | 78 | 62 | 37 | 54 | 39 |
| 28 | 82 | 38 | 72 | 62 | 44 |
| 42 | 55 | 57 | 65 | 68 | 47 |
| 56 | 56 | 55 | 66 | 42 | 52 |
| 47 | 41 | 50 | 52 | 47 | 48 |

One way to answer these sorts of questions is to organize the information in the set of test scores by creating a grouped frequency distribution, as shown in Table 2-2. Now we can quickly and easily make some sense of this set of scores. We can see that a score of about 70 or higher is a high score, because only a few scores are that high. We can also see that a score below about 35 is a low score. And scores between 40 and 60 are quite common; these scores are fairly typical. Notice that these conclusions are easy to make by simply looking at the grouped frequency distribution. The information we wanted almost seems to "jump out" at us.

Our purpose in constructing a grouped frequency distribution is to present the summary of the set of scores as efficiently as possible, so that all users of the grouped frequency distribution can easily understand the information and draw the same conclusions without being misled. In order to do this, we follow a set of conventions whenever we construct a grouped frequency distribution. These conventions are designed to present the information in a format that fits the expectations of the user. Before we can talk about these conventions, however, we must define some terms:

(1) A *class interval* is a range of scores that are grouped together as a single unit. For example, in Table 2-2 one class interval is 55-59. This class interval contains six scores. Another class interval is 40-44.

Table 2-2
Grouped Frequency Distribution for History Test Scores

| History Test Scores | Frequency |
| --- | --- |
| 80 - 84 | 1 |
| 75 - 79 | 1 |
| 70 - 74 | 1 |
| 65 - 69 | 3 |
| 60 - 64 | 2 |
| 55 - 59 | 6 |
| 50 - 54 | 4 |
| 45 - 49 | 4 |
| 40 - 44 | 4 |
| 35 - 39 | 3 |
| 30 - 34 | 0 |
| 25 - 29 | 1 |

(2) The *apparent lower limit* of a class interval is the number written as the lower end of the class interval. For example, the apparent lower limit of the class interval 55-59 is 55.
(3) The *apparent upper limit* of a class interval is the number written as the upper end of the class interval. For the class interval 55-59 the upper apparent limit is 59.
(4) The *real lower limit* of a class interval is the lowest value that would actually cause a case (score) to be placed in that class interval. For example, the class interval 55-59 has a real lower limit of 54.5 because any value between 54.5 and 55 would more reasonably be placed in the class interval 55-59 than in the class interval below it (50-54).
(5) The *real upper limit* of a class interval is the highest value that would actually cause a case (score) to be placed in that class interval. For example, the class interval 55-59 has a real upper limit of 59.5 because any value between 59 and 59.5 would more reasonably be placed in the class interval 55-59 than in the class interval above it (60-64).
(6) The *apparent class interval size* is the difference between the apparent upper limit and the apparent lower limit of the class interval. In our example, the apparent class interval size of the 55-59 class interval is 59 - 55 = 4.
(7) The *real class interval size* is the difference between the real upper limit and the real lower limit of the class interval. In our example, the real class interval size of

the 55-59 class interval is 59.5 - 54.5 = 5. Note that the real class interval is one greater than the apparent class interval size.

Figure 2-1 illustrates the relationships among these components of a grouped frequency distribution.

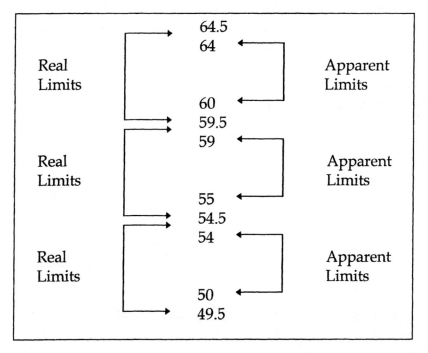

Figure 2-1. The components of a grouped frequency distribution.

*Conventions for constructing grouped frequency distributions.* Now that we have terms to describe the components of grouped frequency distributions, we are able to talk about a set of conventions that are generally used in constructing grouped frequency distributions. These conventions are not merely arbitrary rules, just for the sake of having rules. Rather, they are a set of carefully thought-out guiding principles that help insure that the grouped frequency distribution does its job of condensing and presenting the information as efficiently as possible.

A good grouped frequency distribution should have the following characteristics:
(1) It should contain not less than 10 nor more than 20 class intervals.
(2) The apparent lower limit of the lowest class interval should be an integer multiple of the real class interval size.
(3) Both the highest and the lowest class intervals should contain at least one score.
(4) The real class interval size should be one of the following preferred sizes: 1, 2, 3, 5, 10, 15, 25, 50, 100, or multiples of 100 thereafter.
(5) The lowest class interval should be placed at the bottom of the page and the highest class interval should be placed at the top of the page.

*Step by step procedure for constructing grouped frequency distributions.* These conventions seem reasonable and simple enough to achieve as we discuss them. However, an unsystematic effort to construct a grouped frequency distribution often requires lots of trial and error to produce one that satisfies all of these conventions. Therefore, we recommend the following step by step procedure that will insure that our grouped frequency distribution will satisfy all the conventions on the first try. We will illustrate this procedure using the history test scores from Table 2-1, reproduced here as Table 2-3.

Table 2-3
Number of Correct Answers Given by Each Student on a History Test

| History Test Scores | | | | | |
|---|---|---|---|---|---|
| 56 | 78 | 62 | 37 | 54 | 39 |
| 28 | 82 | 38 | 72 | 62 | 44 |
| 42 | 55 | 57 | 65 | 68 | 47 |
| 56 | 56 | 55 | 66 | 42 | 52 |
| 47 | 41 | 50 | 52 | 47 | 48 |

*Step 1.* Find the range (R). Take the highest score (H) minus the lowest score (L), plus one: (H - L) + 1. In our example, R = (H - L) + 1 = (82 - 28) + 1 = 55.

*Step 2.* Divide this range by 15: $\dfrac{R}{15}$. In our example, $\dfrac{R}{15} = \dfrac{55}{15} = 3.67$.

*Step 3.* Find the first preferred real class interval size that is larger than the value obtained in Step 2. In our example, 5 is the first preferred real class interval size that is larger than 3.67.

*Step 4.* Find the apparent class interval size by subtracting one from the real class interval size (Step 3). In our example, the apparent class interval size is 5 - 1 = 4.

*Step 5.* Find the apparent lower limit of the lowest class interval by taking the value that is the first integer multiple of the real class interval size (from Step 3) that is low enough to include the lowest score. In our example, 5 x 5 = 25 will be our apparent lower limit of the lowest class interval. It is an integer (5) multiple of our real class interval size (5) from Step 3. Note that 4 x 5 = 20 will *not* work, because it will leave an empty interval (20-24) at the bottom of the distribution.

***Step 6.*** Find the apparent upper limit of this lowest class interval by adding the apparent class interval size (Step 4) to the apparent lower limit of the lowest class interval (Step 5). In our example, the apparent upper limit of the lowest class interval is 25 + 4 = 29.

***Step 7.*** Write this lowest class interval at the bottom of the page. In our example, we would write the interval 25-29.

***Step 8.*** Find the next lowest class interval. Add one to the apparent upper limit of the last class interval to get the next apparent lower limit and repeat Step 6 to get the next apparent upper limit. Write this next class interval just above the previous class interval. In our example, the next apparent lower limit is 29 + 1 = 30; the next apparent upper limit is 30 + 4 = 34; so the next class interval is 30-34. Now we put this class interval on the page above the previous class interval:

30 - 34
25 - 29

***Step 9.*** Find the remaining class intervals by repeating Step 8 until the highest interval includes the highest score. In our example, the highest interval is 80-84 that includes the highest score of 82. Thus, so far our grouped frequency distribution should look like this:

80 - 84
78 - 79
. . .
. . .
35 - 39
30 - 34
25 - 29

***Step 10.*** Determine the frequency for each class interval. Make a tally mark beside the class interval in which each score falls. Cross out each score as you make its tally mark. Table 2-4 shows the results of this step for our example.

***Step 11.*** Complete the grouped frequency distribution by placing an Arabic numeral (regular number) beside each class interval, showing how many scores fell into that interval. Table 2-4 shows the completed grouped frequency distribution for our example.

***Step 12.*** Check to make sure that all of the conventions for grouped frequency distributions have been fulfilled. For our example, we check Table 2-4. First, there are 12 class intervals; this satisfies the first convention that there should be from 10 to 20 class intervals. The second convention requires that the apparent lower limit of the lowest class interval should be an integer multiple of the real class interval size: 25 = 5 (an integer) multiplied by 5 (our real class interval size). Third, both the highest class interval (80-84) and the lowest class interval (25-29) each contain one score. Fourth, the real class interval size (5) is one of the preferred sizes. Finally, the lowest class interval (25-29) is at the bottom of the page, and the highest class interval (80-84) is at the top of the page.

Table 2-4
Grouped Frequency Distribution for History Test Scores

| History Test Scores | Tally | Frequency |
|---|---|---|
| 80 - 84 | \| | 1 |
| 75 - 79 | \| | 1 |
| 70 - 74 | \| | 1 |
| 65 - 69 | \|\|\| | 3 |
| 60 - 64 | \|\| | 2 |
| 55 - 59 | \|\|\|\|\|\| | 6 |
| 50 - 54 | \|\|\|\| | 4 |
| 45 - 49 | \|\|\|\| | 4 |
| 40 - 44 | \|\|\|\| | 4 |
| 35 - 39 | \|\|\| | 3 |
| 30 - 34 | | 0 |
| 25 - 29 | \| | 1 |

            ↑                   ↑

        Step 10            Step 11

Now, having completed our grouped frequency distribution, we can begin to make some sense out of our set of raw data. Several things about the set of history test scores are readily apparent. Scores are common in the range from 35 to 69. Scores below 35 and above 69 are rare. There are no scores below 25 nor above 84. Having the data organized in grouped frequency distribution allows us to see all these things at a glance. This organization gives meaning to our scores, which were not meaningful in their raw form. Thus, the grouped frequency distribution goes a long way toward accomplishing the purpose of descriptive statistics; it boils down the data into something compact enough to be successfully handled by our limited information processing capacity.

# Graphs

We can make our summary of the data even clearer by presenting it in a purely visual form called a graph. There are several commonly used graphic techniques. We will discuss three of these ways to graph a set of scores: (1) bar graphs, (2) histograms, and (3) frequency polygons.

***Bar graphs.*** Consider the data in Table 2-5 showing the amount of money generated by various sports at Old Sywash University. A bar graph is appropriate for summarizing this sort of data; we have a nominal scale, consisting of a set of categories (in this case sports), and each category (sport) has some numerical value associated with it (in this case revenue). Figure 2-2 visually summarizes these data in a bar graph.

Table 2-5
Revenue Generated by Sports Programs at Old Sywash University

| Sport | Gross Revenue (x $100,000) |
| --- | --- |
| Baseball | 0.45 |
| Basketball | 6.25 |
| Football | 4.18 |
| Soccer | 0.52 |
| Swimming | 0.15 |
| Track | 0.28 |

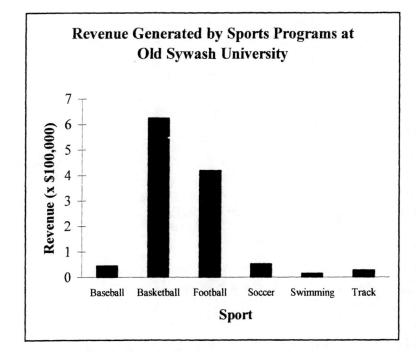

Figure 2-2. Bar graph of the sports revenue data in Table 2-5.

Construction of a bar graph is quite simple. First, make a set of X- and Y-axes, with the Y- (vertical) axis about two-thirds as long as the X- (horizontal) axis. Second, make a numerical scale for the Y-axis with a label (revenue in our example) identifying the scores and numbers ranging from zero to the next round number above the highest score. Third, put the names of the categories (sports in our example) equally spaced along the X-axis and provide a label (e.g., sport) for these categories. Fourth, draw a bar over each category (sport). The height of each bar should reach the value (revenue) for that category (sport). Note that there should be gaps between the bars, indicating that each bar represents a separate category (sport). Finally, put the title of the graph above it.

*Histograms.* A histogram is appropriate when we have a distribution of scores that are of interval level of measurement or higher. This type of graph assumes that these scores have already been organized into a grouped frequency distribution. Figure 2-3 shows a histogram summarizing our distribution of history test scores first presented in Table 2-1 and shown as a grouped frequency distribution in Table 2-2.

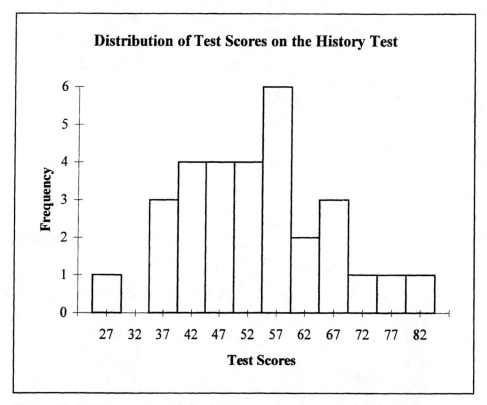

Figure 2-3. Histogram of the history test scores in Table 2-1.

In order to present the information as efficiently as possible, conforming to the expectations of potential users, histograms must follow a set of five conventions or rules:

(1) The Y- (vertical) axis should be 60-75% as long as the X- (horizontal) axis. This relationship is sometimes called the "golden rectangle" because it has been found to be aesthetically pleasing.

(2) The axes should be labeled. The Y-axis should be labeled "Frequency" and a scale of numbers representing the range of frequencies should be provided. The X-axis should have labels for the name of the scores and the midpoint of each class interval.

(3) The histogram should have a title that clearly identifies what scores are represented in the graph.

(4) A bar should be drawn over each class interval, beginning and ending over the real lower and upper limits.

(5) The height of each bar should reach the frequency of that class interval. Note that the bars in a histogram, unlike those in a bar graph, have no gaps between them. This allows us to see the histogram as forming a solid figure that shows the shape of the distribution.

*Frequency polygons.* A frequency polygon is like a histogram in that it creates a solid figure that reflects the shape of the distribution. However, the frequency polygon accomplishes this using a series of connected dots, rather than bars. Figure 2-4 shows a frequency polygon summarizing the same distribution of history test scores first presented in Table 2-1.

As with histograms and other visual display techniques, a frequency polygon is constructed following a set of five conventions designed to ensure that the information is conveyed as effectively as possible:

(1) The "golden rectangle" should be employed, just as with a histogram. The Y-axis should 60-75% as long as the X-axis.

(2) The axes should be labeled. The Y-axis should be labeled "Frequency" and a scale of numbers representing the range of frequencies should be provided. The X-axis should have the name of the scores and the midpoint of each class interval.

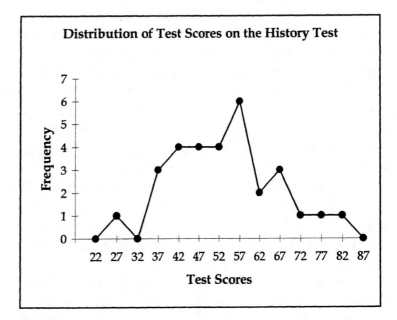

Figure 2-4. Frequency polygon of the history test scores in Table 2-1.

(3) The frequency polygon should have a title that clearly identifies its content.

(4) A dot should be placed over the midpoint of each class interval at a height equal to the frequency of that interval.

(5) One empty class interval should be added to each end of the distribution and the dots connected so that the graph begins and ends on the X-axis, thus forming a closed figure.

## Advantages of Frequency Distributions and Graphs

Frequency distributions and graphs are useful ways of summarizing distributions of scores, because they are so concrete and visual. They are simple to understand, their information can be grasped quickly, and they require no specialized training to understand. For these reasons frequency distributions and/or graphs are very commonly used in professional forums and, especially, in publications intended for the general public, such as newspapers and magazines.

## Limitations of Frequency Distributions and Graphs

Despite their advantages, frequency distributions and graphs have some drawbacks that limit their usefulness in many situations. First, constructing frequency distributions and graphs can be very laborious and time consuming, especially when large sets of scores are involved. Computer generated graphs do not suffer this problem, but may fail to conform to the standard conventions. Second, when the scores are summarized in these visual forms, some of the information is lost. In the frequency distribution of our history test scores shown in Table 2-2, we can see that six scores fall in the interval 55-59, but we no longer know the exact value of each score. Third, and most important, these visual forms are dead end techniques. Once the graph is drawn, no further analysis can be done without retrieving the original scores and starting over. For example, we often want to compare two distributions, but this cannot be done effectively with these visual techniques.

Note that there is a set of purely numerical techniques that avoid these problems. These numerical techniques are very powerful in accomplishing the purpose of descriptive statistics – that of boiling down or summarizing the information in a large set of scores. They are so powerful, in fact, that they can summarize an entire distribution of a million or more scores with only four numbers. With these four numbers the information from the whole distribution would be preserved so well that the entire distribution could be thrown away and, if necessary, the scores could be retrieved with virtually no information lost. Furthermore, if the distribution fits the very common "normal" (bell) shape, only two numbers are needed to summarize and/or reconstruct it. For practical purposes, these two numbers will adequately summarize any distribution that is only approximately normal in shape. In Chapter Three we will present these very powerful numerical techniques.

## Study Questions

*Answers to selected questions may be found in Appendix A*

1. Construct a bar graph for the following data:

Majors of Incoming Freshmen
Old Sywash University 1997

| Major | N |
|-------|-----|
| Business | 408 |
| Communication | 112 |
| Education | 285 |
| Engineering | 218 |
| Fine Arts | 58 |
| Liberal Arts | 362 |
| Science | 157 |

2. Construct a bar graph for the following set of data:

Weekly Sales (in $) for
Employees of Bill's Electronics

| Employee | Sales (in $) |
|----------|-----|
| B. Jones | 985 |
| T. Smith | 808 |
| J. Meyers | 752 |
| M. Wilson | 674 |
| P. Torrance | 560 |

3.  Construct a grouped frequency distribution, a histogram and a frequency polygon for the following set of data.

| Statistics Exam Grades | | | | | |
|---|---|---|---|---|---|
| 58 | 81 | 70 | 68 | 73 | 48 |
| 82 | 75 | 62 | 72 | 84 | 75 |
| 67 | 88 | 74 | 78 | 89 | 79 |
| 91 | 79 | 92 | 71 | 41 | 69 |
| 74 | 77 | 79 | 76 | 81 | 54 |
| 78 | 76 | 96 | 80 | 66 | 84 |

4.  Construct a grouped frequency distribution, a histogram and a frequency polygon for the following set of data.

| Aptitude Test Scores | | | | | |
|---|---|---|---|---|---|
| 18 | 34 | 27 | 26 | 42 | 32 |
| 31 | 42 | 32 | 28 | 22 | 28 |
| 36 | 46 | 29 | 21 | 33 | 26 |
| 22 | 33 | 20 | 31 | 13 | 35 |
| 30 | 37 | 44 | 25 | 36 | 29 |

5.  Construct a bar graph for the following set of data.

Average Birth Weight of Infants Born to
Mothers of Different Socioeconomic Classes

| Socioeconomic Class | Average Birth Weight (in pounds) |
|---|---|
| Low | 6.3 |
| Middle | 7.4 |
| High | 7.9 |

6. Construct a grouped frequency distribution, a histogram and a frequency polygon for the following set of data.

| Supervisor's Ratings of Employee Performance | | | | | | | |
|---|---|---|---|---|---|---|---|
| 56 | 99 | 84 | 69 | 78 | 24 | 101 | 49 |
| 81 | 30 | 42 | 88 | 45 | 107 | 50 | 92 |
| 62 | 79 | 120 | 65 | 99 | 77 | 65 | 111 |
| 72 | 65 | 66 | 41 | 58 | 45 | 39 | 59 |
| 43 | 54 | 104 | 72 | 95 | 114 | 84 | 71 |

# Central Tendency

In Chapter One we said that the purpose of descriptive statistical techniques is to boil down or summarize the information in large sets of scores. In Chapter Two we said that there are numerical techniques that are so efficient that they allow us to summarize the information in large sets of scores, even a set of a million or more scores, using no more than four numbers. These four numbers represent four characteristics of how the scores are distributed relative to each other: central tendency, variability, skewness, and kurtosis.

To illustrate these characteristics of a distribution of scores consider the set of spelling test scores graphed in Figure 3-1. It might be helpful to think of the graph as a brick wall with each brick representing an individual's score. The height of the graph at any one point represents how many bricks must be stacked to represent the number of individuals who earned that score. In Figure 3-1 only some of these individual scores have been illustrated as bricks in the wall.

When we look at the graph, several characteristics of the set of scores are apparent:

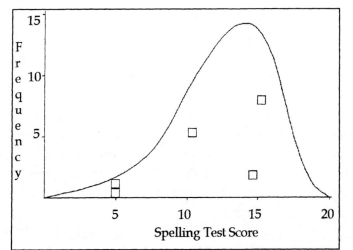

(1) The scores tend to pile up around some central clustering point. This is called *central tendency*.

(2) There is a certain amount of scatter around this central clustering point. This is called *variability*.

(3) The spread of the scores around the central clustering point may not be symmetrical. Instead, there may be more

Figure 3-1. Graph of a distribution of scores on a spelling test.

spread in the scores on one side of the center than on the other side. This is called *skewness*.

(4) The peak of the central clustering point may be steep or gently rounded. This is called *kurtosis*.

If we can express these four characteristics numerically, then we can describe any distribution using just four numbers. In fact, for many distributions only the first two characteristics (central tendency and variability) are needed, so we can describe these distributions with just two numbers. In this chapter and the next chapter we will show how this can be done.

In this chapter we examine the three most common measures of central tendency. These measures are designed to identify, using a single number, the central clustering point of a set of scores.

## The Mode

The mode is the simplest measure of central tendency. On a graph of the distribution it is the highest point or "hump." More formally, the mode is the most frequently occurring score in a distribution of scores.

As an example, consider the following distribution of scores:

3, 5, 1, 4, 7, 5, 2, 4, 5, 8

The mode of this distribution is 5, because there are three 5s and no other score occurs more than twice.

As a second example, consider the following distribution of scores:

3, 5, 2, 2, 7, 5, 2, 4, 5, 8

In this example we have a bimodal distribution. There are three 2s and three 5s; no other score occurs more than once. Therefore, one mode is 2 and the other mode is 5.

All statistical measures have certain advantages and disadvantages associated with their use. There are two advantages and three disadvantages that we should consider when we decide whether to use the mode to measure the central tendency of a distribution of scores.

*Advantages.* (1) One advantage of the mode is that it is very simple to compute. It requires only the ability to count how many times a score occurs. (2) A second advantage is that the mode can be used regardless of the level of measurement of the scores. The mode can be used even when the scores are of nominal level measurement. The mode is the only measure of central tendency that can be used with nominal level data.

*Disadvantages.* (1) One disadvantage of the mode is that it is completely determined by only a few of the scores in the distribution. That is, only the most frequently occurring score influences the mode; all of the remaining scores, no matter how many scores there are, make no contribution to the mode at all. (2) Because the mode is determined by only a few scores and is unaffected by the rest of the scores, it is very unstable in sampling. That is, if, for example, we took several samples of 20 scores from a large distribution of scores, the modes of these samples would be quite different from one another. This a very undesirable characteristic for a statistical measure, because we often want to use the sample-based measure to estimate the value of the measure applied to a whole population. (3) A third disadvantage is that additional, higher level analyses cannot be done using the mode. Thus, the mode is often a dead end.

Because of these disadvantages, the mode is considered to be a rather crude measure of central tendency. Therefore the mode is used much less frequently than other measures of central tendency.

## The Median

The median is the middle score in a distribution. Half of the scores in the distribution will fall above the median, and half of the scores will fall below it. To compute the median we use the following steps:

*Step 1.* Count the scores.
*Step 2.* Arrange the scores in order, from the lowest score to the highest score.
*Step 3.* Count up from the bottom until you have passed half of the scores.
*Step 4.* When the distribution contains an *odd number of scores*, the median will be the score with equal numbers of scores above and below it. When the distribution contains an *even number of scores*, the median will lie halfway between the two middle scores.

As an example, consider the following distribution that contains an *odd* number of scores:

1, 3, 3, 4, 5, 7, 10, 13, 17

The median is 5, because exactly four scores fall above it and exactly four scores fall below it.

As a second example, now consider the following distribution that contains an *even* number of scores:

2, 2, 3, 5, 7, 12

In this case the median is 4, because it lies halfway between the third score (3) and the fourth score (5); these are the two middle scores in the distribution that contains six scores.

Like the other measures of central tendency, there are both advantages and disadvantages associated with the median.

*Advantages.* (1) One advantage of the median is that it is simple to compute. It requires only that the scores be ordered from lowest to highest; then it is a simple matter to count to the middle score. (2) A second advantage is that the median can be used for most (but not all) levels of measurement. Although the median cannot be used when the scores are of nominal level of measurement, it can be used when the scores are of ordinal level of measurement or higher. That is, the median is appropriate for ordinal, interval, or ratio level data. (3) A third advantage is that the median is not excessively influenced by extreme scores. For example, we could used the median to describe the income of American workers. In this case the extremely large incomes of a few very wealthy Americans (such as Bill Gates) would not produce a distorted picture of the income of the typical American worker.

*Disadvantages.* (1) One disadvantage of the median is that it, like the mode, tends to be unstable in sampling. Thus, the median of a sample is a poor estimate of the median of the entire distribution from which the sample was taken. (2) A second disadvantage is that, like the mode, the median cannot be used in many higher level analyses that we often like to do. So the median also can be a dead end. (3) A third disadvantage is that the median gives no extra weight to extreme scores. This is the flip side of the third advantage of the median listed above. In some situations very large or very small scores should receive extra weighting. For example, an elevator with an 800 pound capacity might be described as able to safely carry five persons whose median weight is 150 pounds. However, if one of the persons weighs 450 pounds and the others weigh between 140 and 160, the median weight should not be used to determine the number of people who could safely be carried on the elevator.

## The Mean

The mean is by far the most commonly used measure of central tendency. Its full name is the arithmetic mean, but we usually shorten it to just "the mean." In common language it is generally called the average. The mean represents the centroid, or center of gravity, of the distribution. That is, the mean is the balancing point of any distribution of scores. If we graph the distribution on heavy cardboard, cut it out, and place a pencil under it at the mean, the cardboard cutout will balance on the pencil as shown in Figure 3-2.

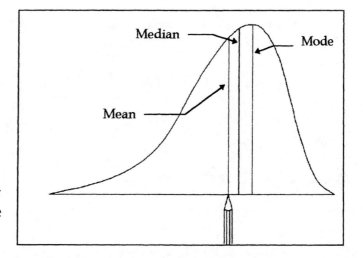

Figure 3-2. The mean is the balancing point of the distribution.

To calculate the mean, we add all the scores in the distribution and divide this total by the number of scores in the distribution. The formula for computing the mean can be written:

$$\overline{X} = \frac{\sum_{i=1}^{N} X_i}{N}$$

In this formula the symbol X represents the scores in the distribution and the symbol $\overline{X}$ represents the mean of the X scores. (We could just as easily use the symbol Y to represent the scores and $\overline{Y}$ to represent the mean.) The symbol $\Sigma$ is the uppercase Greek letter sigma. It is used in mathematics to indicate summation. The notation below it ($i = 1$) tells us with which score to begin adding, and the notion above it (N) tells after which score to stop adding. (N in statistical notation is the number of scores in the distribution.) Thus, the notation $\sum_{i=1}^{N} X_i$ says to begin with the first score and add all of the scores, stopping after the last score. We also can say this using mathematical symbols:

$$\sum_{i=1}^{N} X_i = X_1 + X_2 + X_3 + ... + X_N$$

In statistics when we do a summation, it almost always includes all of the scores in the distribution. So the instructional notion above and below the summation sign ($\Sigma$) and the subscript of the letter representing which distribution of scores is being summed (X in this case) are usually omitted. This system of simplified summation notation is used throughout this book. And the formula for the mean is written:

$$\overline{X} = \frac{\sum X}{N}$$

where $\Sigma$ says to sum all of the scores, X identifies which distribution of scores we are dealing with, and N is the number of scores in the distribution.

As an example, consider the following distribution of scores that we arbitrarily will call the X scores (we could just as easily call them the Y scores):

3, 2, 10, 6, 5, 4

The mean of this distribution of scores is:

$$\overline{X} = \frac{\sum X}{N} = \frac{30}{6} = 5$$

Like the mode and the median, the mean also has its advantages and disadvantages. These are discussed below.

*Advantages.* (1) One advantage of the mean is that it is the measure of central tendency that is most stable in sampling. That is, suppose we took many samples from a single population of scores and calculated the mean of each sample of scores. These sample means would show less chance variation than would either the median or the mode. (2) A second advantage of the mean is that it is the only measure of central tendency that is influenced by the exact value of every score in the distribution. This can be illustrated by looking back at the examples we used earlier to compute the mode and the median. In each example if we increased the value of the last score by 1, then re-computed the mode and the median, we would find that in each case the mode and the median would be unchanged. However, if we made the same change and then re-computed the mean, the resulting value of the mean would be altered. Thus, the mean is the most sensitive measure of central tendency. (3) A third advantage of the mean is that the mean is the basis of many of the higher level analyses that we like to do. So, unlike the mode and median, the mean is not likely to be a dead end. For example, suppose we did an experiment comparing the test scores of students who received computer-assisted training and students who received traditional lecture-based training. We might first calculate the mean test score for each group. Then any higher level statistical technique needed to compare the groups would be based on these means.

*Disadvantages.* (1) One limitation of the mean is that it requires scores that are of either interval or ratio level of measurement. When this requirement is not met we must use another measure of central tendency. (2) A second disadvantage of the mean is that extremely large or extremely small scores can have too much influence on the value of the mean. Since the exact value of every score is added in when we compute the mean, even one very extreme score can cause the mean to be an inaccurate description of the value of a typical score. Thus, when the distribution includes extreme scores, another measure of central tendency may be more appropriate.

## Study Questions
*Answers to selected questions may be found in Appendix A*

For each of the following distributions of scores, determine (a) the mode, (b) the median, and (c) the mean.

1. The following distribution of scores was obtained by introductory statistics students on the first exam.

| Statistics Test Scores | | | | | |
|---|---|---|---|---|---|
| 77 | 86 | 95 | 70 | 81 | 62 |
| 74 | 65 | 79 | 92 | 87 | 75 |
| 68 | 71 | 75 | 91 | 52 | 72 |

2. The following group of scores are the weights of ten college students.

| Weights of Ten College Students (in pounds) | | | | |
|---|---|---|---|---|
| 121 | 181 | 156 | 162 | 142 |
| 156 | 208 | 169 | 127 | 165 |

3. The following group of scores are the heights of nine college students.

| Heights of Nine College Students (in inches) | | |
|---|---|---|
| 64 | 73 | 71 |
| 69 | 75 | 71 |
| 63 | 69 | 66 |

# CHAPTER FOUR
# Variability

In Chapter Three we developed the idea that the graph of a distribution of scores can be thought of as a brick wall, as shown in Figure 4-1. Each individual score is represented by a single brick in the wall. The value of a score is represented by the horizontal position of the brick in the wall.

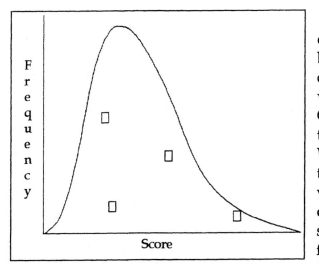

Figure 4-1. Individual scores represented as bricks in a wall.

We also said that the entire distribution can be thoroughly described by computing the numerical value of four characteristics (central tendency, variability, skewness, and kurtosis). In Chapter Three we discussed central tendency, the first of these characteristics. When we compute a value representing the central tendency of a distribution, this value represents a "typical score" in the distribution or the point around which the scores tend to cluster. The mean, the most frequently used measure of central tendency, is illustrated in Figure 4-2.

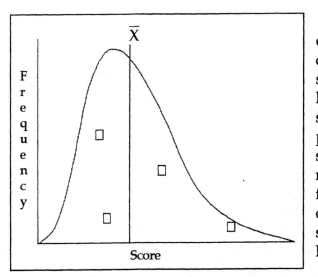

Figure 4-2. The scores clustering around the mean.

When we look at Figure 4-2 it is easy to note that although our measure of central tendency identifies where a typical score lies, the individual scores do not all lie at or even near the mean. Instead, the scores are scattered around this central point of the distribution. Some of the scores are at the mean or very near the mean, but some of the scores are quite far from the mean. Furthermore, the amount of overall scatter around the mean may be small, as in Figure 4-3, or large, as in Figure 4-4.

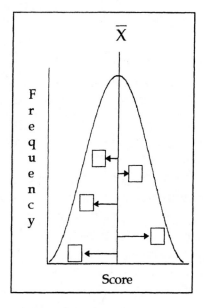

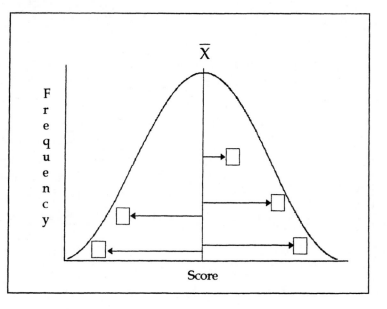

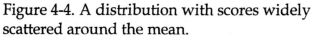

Figure 4-3. A distribution with little scatter around the mean.

Figure 4-4. A distribution with scores widely scattered around the mean.

What we need is a way to numerically summarize the overall amount of scatter (called *variability* or *dispersion* in statistical terminology) around the mean. Several measures of variability have been developed. In this chapter we will discuss two measures of variability: (1) the *range* and (2) the *standard deviation*.

## Range

The *range* is the simplest measure of variability. It can be computed by taking the difference between the highest score and the lowest score and then adding one to this difference. Written as a formula, the range is

$$\text{Range} = (\text{Highest score - Lowest score}) + 1 = (H - L) + 1$$

In effect, we are taking the difference between the real upper limit of the highest score and the real lower limit of the lowest score in the distribution. In a distribution with little scatter this difference between the two most extreme scores should be small. In a distribution with a lot of scatter this difference will be large.

As an example, consider the following distribution of scores:

9, 3, 2, 5, 6, 4

The range of this distribution of scores is

$$
\begin{aligned}
\text{Range} &= (H - L) + 1 \\
&= (9 - 2) + 1 \\
&= (7) + 1 \\
&= 8
\end{aligned}
$$

*Advantages.* The range has two advantages. (1) The first advantage is that the range is simple to understand. (2) The second advantage is that the range is very quick and easy to compute.

*Disadvantages.* However, the range also has two serious disadvantages. (1) First, the range is very unstable from one sample to another sample. This instability across samples is because the range is determined by the two most unusual scores in its distribution. (2) Second, the range is systematically influenced by sample size. Because the range is based on the two most unusual scores in the sample distribution, it tends to be larger when the size of the sample is large. With a large sample there are more chances for a very unusual score to be drawn in the sample.

The range is generally regarded as a rather poor measure of variability because of these disadvantages. Therefore, the range is seldom used. We only use the range when we want a very rough measure of variability that can be computed very quickly and easily.

## Standard Deviation

The *standard deviation* is by far the most commonly used and most useful measure of variability -- almost a universal measure of variability. Furthermore, because statistics can be considered the study of variability, the standard deviation is probably the single most important concept in statistics. Virtually everything that will be covered in the remainder of this book derives in some way from the standard deviation or one of its component parts. It would be impossible to succeed in a statistics course without understanding the concept of standard deviation, knowing how to compute it and its components, and knowing how to use it.

*Basis of standard deviation.* Returning to the idea that the individual scores in a distribution are scattered around the mean, Figure 4-5 shows how some of the scores fall near the mean and other scores fall farther from

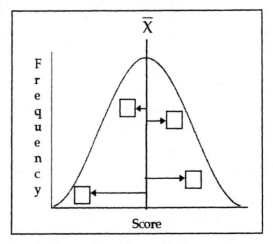

Figure 4-5. Variation of individual scores around the mean.

the mean. What we need is some way to characterize or summarize the overall amount of this variation around the mean.

It might occur to us to try to characterize the overall amount of variation around the mean by calculating an average difference (or deviation) between the individual scores and the mean. However, this idea will not work. When we try to find the sum of the differences between the individual scores and the mean, they will always sum to zero. That is,

$$\Sigma(\text{Individual score - Mean}) = \Sigma(X - \overline{X}) = 0$$

So this idea is thwarted. A measure of variability that always sums to zero is worthless.

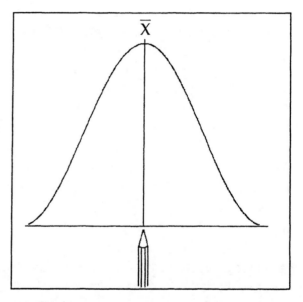

The reason for this goes back to the fact that a cutout of the graph of a distribution will always balance at the mean, as illustrated in Figure 4-6. That is, the mean is the centroid or balance point of the distribution. For this to happen, the sum of the deviations of all the scores that fall below the mean must exactly equal the sum of the deviations of all the scores that fall above the mean. [Note that the deviation of a score from the mean $(X - \overline{X})$ will always be negative if the score is below the mean and positive if the score is above the mean.] Therefore, the positive deviations will be canceled by the negative deviations, so the sum of all the deviations will always be zero.

Figure 4-6. A distribution balanced on a point located at the mean.

***Sum of Squares.*** A better way of representing the total amount of variation around the mean is to square the deviation of each score from the mean and then sum these squared deviations. This procedure avoids the problem of the positive deviations being canceled by the negative deviations, because squaring a number (whether it is negative or positive) always yields a positive number. Furthermore, the sum of these squared deviations of each raw score from the mean (called the ***sum of squares*** in statistical terminology) will be larger when there are many scores that are far from the mean and smaller when there are few scores far from the mean. A comparison of the distributions in Figure 4-7 and Figure 4-8 illustrates this property of the sum of squares. The sum of squares for the distribution in Figure 4-7 should be smaller than the sum of squares for the distribution in Figure 4-8.

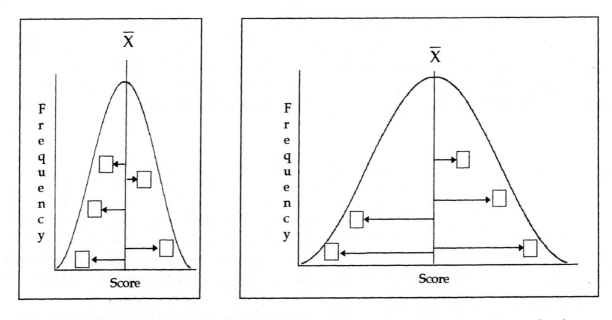

Figure 4-7. A distribution with few scores far from the mean.

Figure 4-8. A distribution with many scores far from the mean.

Written as a mathematical formula, the sum of squares is

$$\text{Sum of squares} = SS = \sum(\text{Individual score} - \text{Mean})^2 = \sum(X - \overline{X})^2$$

***Variance.*** We originally set out to find the average variation around the mean. To do this we must divide the sum of the squared deviations around the mean (the sum of squares) by the number of scores in the distribution. This gives us the mean of the squared deviations. This quantity is known as the ***variance*** or ***mean square.*** Written as a formula, the variance is

$$\text{Variance} = \frac{\text{Sum of squares}}{N} = \frac{\sum(X - \overline{X})^2}{N}$$

***Standard Deviation.*** Remember that we began the process of assessing the variation in a distribution of scores by squaring each deviation of a score from the mean. To get back to the original sized units (rather than squared units) we must take the square root of the variance. This gives us the ***standard deviation.*** Written as a formula, the standard deviation is

$$\text{Standard deviation} = \sqrt{\text{variance}}, \text{ or}$$

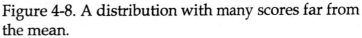

$$\text{Standard deviation} = s = \sqrt{\frac{SS}{N}} = \sqrt{\frac{\sum(\text{individual score} - \text{mean})^2}{N}} = \sqrt{\frac{\sum(X - \overline{X})^2}{N}}$$

The standard deviation tells us the size of a typical (or standard) deviation of a raw score from the mean. The standard deviation also tells us, just for your curiosity, the distance from the mean to the point of inflection in a normal, bell-shaped distribution. The point of inflection is the point on the curve where the slope stops getting steeper as we move away from the mean and begins to get less steep, as shown in Figure 4-9.

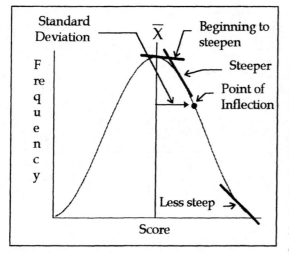

Figure 4-9. The standard deviation as the distance from the mean to the point of inflection.

***Computation of the Standard Deviation.*** Computing the standard deviation involves several steps. Here we present a step-by-step procedure, keeping the results of each step in a simple worksheet. We recommend that you employ this procedure routinely with all of the computational procedures in this course. It is our experience that most computational errors occur when a systematic approach is *not* followed. Therefore, we always systematically break down larger and more complex calculations into a set of simpler ones and keep track of the results obtained in each step using a simple worksheet. So should you.

As an example, consider the following set of scores:   5, 4, 2, 1

***Step 1.*** Set up the column headings for a worksheet and enter the scores in the first column, as shown in Table 4-1.

Table 4-1
Standard Deviation Worksheet

| Score | Score - Mean | (Score - Mean)$^2$ |
|:---:|:---:|:---:|
| X | $X - \overline{X}$ | $(X - \overline{X})^2$ |
| 5 | | |
| 4 | | |
| 2 | | |
| 1 | | |

***Step 2.*** Add the scores in column one of the worksheet and enter this sum of scores at the bottom of column one on the worksheet.

$$\Sigma X = 5 + 4 + 2 + 1 = 12$$

*Step 3.* Calculate the mean.

$$\bar{X} = \frac{\Sigma X}{N} = \frac{12}{4} = 3$$

*Step 4.* Calculate the deviation of each score from the mean and enter these deviations in column two of the worksheet.

$$\text{Score - Mean} = X - \bar{X} = \quad \begin{array}{l} 5 - 3 = 2 \\ 4 - 3 = 1 \\ 2 - 3 = -1 \\ 1 - 3 = -2 \end{array}$$

*Step 5.* Square each deviation calculated in step 2 and enter the squared deviations in column three of the worksheet.

$$(\text{Score - Mean})^2 = (X - \bar{X})^2 = \quad \begin{array}{l} (2)^2 = 4 \\ (1)^2 = 1 \\ (-1)^2 = 1 \\ (-2)^2 = 4 \end{array}$$

*Step 6.* Calculate the sum of squares by adding the squared deviations in column three of the worksheet and enter this value at the bottom of column three in the worksheet. The completed worksheet is shown in Table 4-2.

$$\text{Sum of squares} = SS = \Sigma(X - \bar{X})^2 = 10$$

Table 4-2
Completed Standard Deviation Worksheet

| Score<br>$X$ | Score - Mean<br>$X - \bar{X}$ | (Score - Mean)$^2$<br>$(X - \bar{X})^2$ |
|:---:|:---:|:---:|
| 5 | 2 | 4 |
| 4 | 1 | 1 |
| 2 | -1 | 1 |
| 1 | -2 | 4 |
| $\Sigma X = 12$ | | $SS = \Sigma X - \bar{X})^2 = 10$ |

*Step 7.* Calculate the standard deviation using the sum of squares calculated in step 6.

$$\text{Standard deviation} = s = \sqrt{\frac{\text{sum of squares}}{N}} = \sqrt{\frac{SS}{N}} = \sqrt{\frac{\Sigma(X - \overline{X})^2}{N}} = \sqrt{\frac{10}{4}} = \sqrt{2.50} = 1.58$$

*Note on the term "Sum of Squares."* As we said earlier, the sum of the squares (that is, the sum of the squared deviations of the individual scores from the mean, $\Sigma(X - \overline{X})^2$) is the heart of the standard deviation formula. The sum of squares also figures prominently in many of the other formulae that we will use later in this book. Because of the importance in statistical procedures of squared deviations around the mean, the term "sum of squares" should be reserved for only this meaning. Other quantities, such as $\Sigma X^2$ should be called something else: either the sum of the squared scores or the sum of the squared Xs (pronounced "eckses"). Throughout the book we will symbolize the sum of squares as SS.

*Raw Score Formula for the Standard Deviation.* The formula for the standard deviation that we have presented above is called the *deviation score formula* or the *definitional formula* for the standard deviation. This version of the standard deviation formula is based on calculating the deviations of each raw score from the mean, which constitutes the core definition of the nature of the standard deviation. However, other versions of the formula can be derived that are mathematically equivalent but much less tedious to compute using a hand calculator (especially when the set of scores is large).

The version of the standard deviation formula that we think is most useful is called the *raw score formula*. The raw score formula is calculated directly from the raw scores, and does not require the intermediate steps of calculating the mean and then calculating the deviation of each score from the mean. The raw score formula is written:

$$s = \sqrt{\frac{SS}{N}} = \sqrt{\frac{\Sigma X^2 - \frac{(\Sigma X)^2}{N}}{N}}$$

where $\Sigma X^2$ is the sum of the squared individual scores, or $X_1^2 + X_2^2 + X_3^2 + ... + X_n^2$; and $(\Sigma X)^2$ is the squared sum of the entire set of scores, or $(X_1 + X_2 + X_3 + ... + X_n)^2$.

Now we will provide a step-by-step procedure for computing the standard deviation using the raw score formula. In this example, we will use the same set of scores that we used earlier:

5, 4, 2, 1

*Step 1.* Set up a worksheet with a column for the scores (X) and a column for the squares of the scores (X²); enter the scores in the first column and the squared scores in the second column, as shown in Table 4-3.

Table 4-3
Standard Deviation Worksheet
for the Raw Score Formula

| X | X² |
|---|---|
| 5 | 25 |
| 4 | 16 |
| 2 | 4 |
| 1 | 1 |

*Step 2.* Sum the columns to get the sum of the scores, $\Sigma X$, and the sum of the squared scores, $\Sigma X^2$. Enter these sums at the bottom of the appropriate columns on the worksheet, as shown in Table 4-4.

Table 4-4
Completed Standard Deviation
Worksheet for the Raw Score
Formula

| X | X² |
|---|---|
| 5 | 25 |
| 4 | 16 |
| 2 | 4 |
| 1 | 1 |
| $\Sigma X = 12$ | $\Sigma X^2 = 46$ |

*Step 3.* Apply the raw score formula for the standard deviation:

$$s = \sqrt{\frac{\Sigma X^2 - \frac{(\Sigma X)^2}{N}}{N}} = \sqrt{\frac{46 - \frac{(12)^2}{4}}{4}}$$

$$= \sqrt{\frac{46 - \frac{144}{4}}{4}} = \sqrt{\frac{46 - 36}{4}} = \sqrt{\frac{10}{4}}$$

$$= \sqrt{2.50} = 1.58$$

Our result, s = 1.58, of course is the same as what we obtained using the deviation score version of the formula. Mathematically, the two versions of the standard deviation formula are equivalent; but the raw score version is not so laborious to compute. In fact, with many hand calculators both $\Sigma X$ and $\Sigma X^2$ can be computed in different memories, thereby requiring the raw scores to be entered only once.

*Review and Summary.* We have introduced two versions the standard deviation formula and we have given names to various parts of the formulae. These quantities form the basis for most of what we will do in the rest of this book (and in any more advanced statistics courses you may take). The heart of both versions of the standard deviation is the sum of squares (the sum of the squared deviations of each score from the mean). In each formula we divide the sum of squares by the number of scores to get the variance (which is also called the mean square, because it is the mean of the squared deviations of the individual scores form the mean). We then convert back to our original sized units by taking the square root of the variance. Table 4-5 presents these basic components of the standard deviation in both the deviation score version and raw score version of the formula. We highly recommend that you learn and memorize this table. Just as a soldier practices taking his rifle apart and reassembling it until he can do it automatically, even in the dark and under the most adverse conditions, because it is the key to his survival, you should practice with the components of the standard deviation in both versions, because this level of understanding will be a key to your success in statistics.

Table 4-5
Components of the Standard Deviation

| Component | Symbol | Deviation Score Version | Raw Score Version |
|---|---|---|---|
| Sum of squares | SS | $\sum(X - \overline{X})^2$ | $\sum X^2 - \dfrac{(\sum X)^2}{N}$ |
| Variance | $s^2 = \dfrac{SS}{N}$ | $\dfrac{\sum(X - \overline{X})^2}{N}$ | $\dfrac{\sum X^2 - \dfrac{(\sum X)^2}{N}}{N}$ |
| Standard deviation | $s = \sqrt{s^2} = \sqrt{\dfrac{SS}{N}}$ | $\sqrt{\dfrac{\sum(X - \overline{X})^2}{N}}$ | $\sqrt{\dfrac{\sum X^2 - \dfrac{(\sum X)^2}{N}}{N}}$ |

## Skewness

In Chapter Three we said that a distribution of any number of scores can be completely described by computing four numbers representing each of four characteristics of the distribution. We have now described two of these characteristics -- central tendency and variability (or dispersion). If the distribution is of the so called "normal" or bell-shaped form, we could discard all the raw scores and still rebuild the distribution accurately enough for practical purposes using only the mean and standard deviation. This will be the case, or nearly so, for many of the distributions with which we work in the behavioral sciences. However, when the distribution is not normal in shape, two more characteristics must be considered: skewness and kurtosis.

*Skewness* is defined as the extent to which the distribution departs from symmetry. A distribution is symmetrical when its left and right halves are mirror images of each other. On the other hand, a distribution is asymmetrical when the two sides are dissimilar, giving it an unbalanced appearance. Consider the three distributions graphed in Figure 4 -10 .

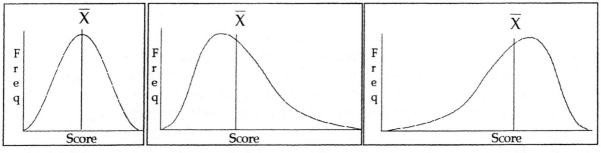

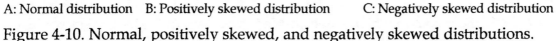

A: Normal distribution    B: Positively skewed distribution    C: Negatively skewed distribution

Figure 4-10. Normal, positively skewed, and negatively skewed distributions.

Distribution A is a normal distribution. Note that its two sides look like mirror reflections of each other. This distribution has a balanced look and the mean splits the distribution into two halves that could be folded on to each other. Distribution B, however, has a long tail pointing to the right, meaning that it has more extreme scores far above the mean (to the right) than it has scores far below the mean (to the left). That is, distribution B has more extremely high scores than extremely low scores. Such a distribution is *positively skewed* (more very high scores). Distribution C has its long tail pointing to the left, indicating the presence of more extremely low scores than extremely high scores. This is a *negatively skewed* distribution.

When we look at a graph of a skewed distribution, it is easy to determine which type of skewness it has. Just remember that the long tail points in the direction of the skewness. If the tail points to the left (downward) toward the lower scores, the distribution is negatively skewed; if it points to the right (upward) toward the higher scores, the distribution is positively skewed.

Another characteristic of a skewed distribution is that the extreme scores pull the mean out toward the long tail, while the median is less affected and the mode is not affected at all by extreme scores. Thus, although the values of the mean, median, and mode are the same when the distribution is symmetrical, when the distribution is skewed the three measures of central tendency are not the same value. This is illustrated in Figure 4-11.

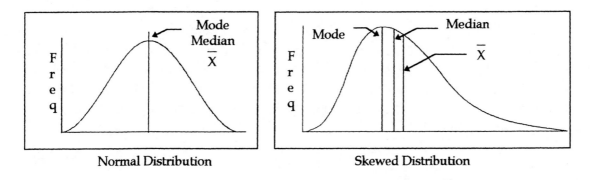

Normal Distribution                    Skewed Distribution

Figure 4-11. Relationship of the mode, median, and mean in symmetrical and skewed distributions.

There are several ways of calculating the skewness of a distribution. One common way is based on the degree to which the mean is pulled away from the peak of the distribution. For our purposes in this book we need not calculate a numerical value for skewness. Instead, it will be sufficient to be able to look at the graph of a markedly skewed distribution and identify the type of skewness (positive or negative).

## Kurtosis

*Kurtosis* is the extent to which a distribution is peaked or flattened relative to the normal distribution. A distribution that has a large number of scores piled up near the mean is called a *leptokurtic* distribution. A distribution that is gently rounded is called a *platykurtic* distribution. The normal distribution, which serves as the standard of comparison, is called *mesokurtic*. These three types of distributions are illustrated in Figure 4-12.

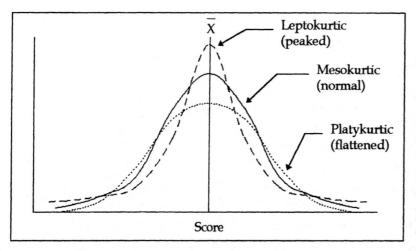

Figure 4-12. Distributions with different types of kurtosis.

Note that kurtosis is not merely a restatement of variability, but rather it tells us where a given amount of variation of scores occurs. All three of the distributions in Figure 4-12 have the same standard deviation (the same overall amount of variability). However, the leptokurtic distribution with the narrow peak has the thickest tails, while the broadly rounded platykurtic distribution has the thinnest tails.

Kurtosis can be calculated using a method based on the fourth power of deviations around the mean. Like skewness, however, for our purposes in this book we need not calculate a numerical value for kurtosis. Instead, it will be sufficient to be able to look at the graph of a distribution and identify the type of kurtosis (leptokurtic, mesokurtic, or platykurtic).

## Study Questions
*Answers to selected questions may be found in Appendix A*

1. Find the range for each of the following distributions of scores.

   a. Distribution of Scores on a Biology Test

   | Biology Test Scores | | | | | |
   |---|---|---|---|---|---|
   | 57 | 89 | 95 | 77 | 82 | 64 |
   | 72 | 62 | 74 | 93 | 86 | 79 |
   | 66 | 78 | 71 | 90 | 55 | 76 |

   b. Distribution of Weights of 10 College Students

   | Weights of Ten College Students (in pounds) | | | | |
   |---|---|---|---|---|
   | 118 | 169 | 133 | 109 | 146 |
   | 140 | 208 | 155 | 122 | 175 |

   c. Distribution of Performance Ratings

   | Supervisor's Ratings of Employee's Performance | | | | | | | |
   |---|---|---|---|---|---|---|---|
   | 81 | 30 | 42 | 88 | 45 | 107 | 50 | 92 |
   | 62 | 79 | 120 | 65 | 99 | 77 | 65 | 111 |
   | 72 | 65 | 66 | 41 | 58 | 45 | 39 | 59 |
   | 43 | 54 | 104 | 72 | 95 | 114 | 84 | 71 |

2. Find the sum of squares, variance, and standard deviation of the following distributions using the deviation score method.

   a. 12, 9, 17, 3, 11, 13, 6, 16, 9, 20

   b. 64, 73, 71, 69, 66

   c. 127, 208, 169, 127, 165

3. Find the sum of squares, variance, and standard deviation of the following distributions using the raw score method.

   a.  8, 11, 5, 1, 6, 7, 2

   b.  56, 76, 64, 32, 44

   c.  3, 2, 7, 1, 5, 14, 11, 2, 3, 7, 2, 12

4. Draw an example of a positively skewed distribution.

5. Draw an example of a leptokurtic distribution.

# CHAPTER FIVE

# The Normal Curve and Standard Scores

We have said several times before that we know a great deal about a distribution of scores if we know just two numbers -- its mean and its standard deviation. We could easily reconstruct a normal distribution of a million scores with no loss of information using only our knowledge of the values of these two measures. Even if the distribution were not perfectly normal, the reconstruction would serve adequately for most practical purposes. Remember that the purpose of descriptive statistical techniques is to boil down the information in a large distribution of scores into a few measures that summarize the entire set of scores. In this chapter we will see how two powerful descriptive statistical techniques -- the mean and standard deviation -- are used to provide very detailed information about a distribution of scores, even in the absence of the original raw scores. This process is particularly accurate when the raw scores form a normal distribution (Remember from Chapter One that Gauss was the first to describe the normal distribution).

The reason that the mean and standard deviation tell us so much about a distribution of scores is that a fixed percentage of the scores in any normal distribution fall within a given number of standard deviations from the mean. For example, we know that approximately 68% of all the scores in a normal distribution will fall within plus or minus one standard deviation of the mean. Similarly, approximately 95% of all the scores will fall within two standard deviations of the mean. Table 5-1 shows the percentages (rounded to the nearest integer) of scores that fall within one, two, or three standard deviations of the mean. Figure 5-1 graphically illustrates this same information.

Table 5-1
Approximate Percentages of Scores Falling Within a Given Number of Standard Deviations of the Mean

| # of Standard Deviations from the Mean | % of Scores this Close or Closer to the Mean |
| --- | --- |
| 1 | 68% |
| 2 | 95% |
| 3 | 99+% |

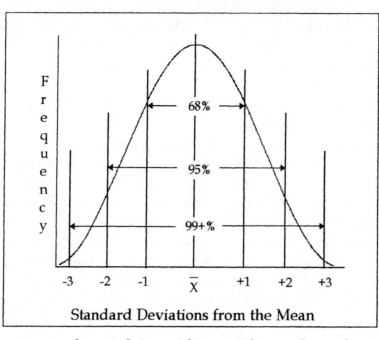

Figure 5-1. Percentages of scores lying within specific numbers of standard deviation units from the mean.

If we know only the mean and standard deviation of a (normal or nearly normal shaped) distribution of scores, we know a lot about the distribution. For example, if we know that the mean of a distribution of history test scores is 51 and the standard deviation is 10, then we also would immediately know that John's history test score of 73 is an extremely high score compared to others in the distribution. John's score is more than two standard deviations above the mean. A score more than three standard deviations above the mean would be very rare, indeed. On the other hand, if Sue scored 56 on the same history test, we would immediately know that her score, which lies within one standard deviation of the mean, is a fairly typical score.

We can easily be much more precise in our interpretation of these test scores. Using a *normal curve table* (Appendix B in this book), we can determine the percentage of scores in the distribution that fall above or below any particular score. Or we could determine the percentage of scores falling between any two scores in the distribution. The normal curve table gives the proportion of scores that lie below (or above) any score; the score itself is expressed in terms of its distance from the mean, in steps of one hundredth of a standard deviation. The tabled values have been graciously prepared for us by mathematicians using calculus. In calculus the process of integration is used to find the area lying below any segment of a curved line (such as the normal curve). Using the normal curve table we can make very precise determinations of the proportion (and, hence, the percentage) of scores that fall above or below any particular score.

## Standard Scores

In order to use the normal curve table we need to know the number of standard deviations that a raw score lies from the mean. The process of determining how many standard deviations a raw score lies from the mean is called converting the raw score to a *standard score*. That is, the standard score associated with any particular raw score tells us how many standard deviations that raw score lies from the mean. The letter "z" is the symbol for a standard score and, therefore, a standard score is often called a *z score*. The standard score or z score for any raw score can be found using the formula:

$$z = \text{standard score} = \frac{\text{\# of standard deviations a}}{\text{raw score lies from the mean}} = \frac{\text{raw score - mean}}{\text{standard deviation}} = \frac{X - \overline{X}}{s}$$

As an example, assume that a psychologist has just administered a test to a client who scored 112. The test manual provides the information that the test has a distribution with a mean of 100 and a standard deviation of 15. To interpret the client's test score, the psychologist needs to know what proportion of all test takers score below the client's score of 112. First, the psychologist determines the number of standard deviations the client's score is from the mean. This is done using the standard score (z score) formula:

$$z = \text{standard score} = \frac{\text{raw score - mean}}{\text{standard deviation}} = \frac{X - \overline{X}}{s} = \frac{112 - 100}{15} = \frac{12}{15} = .80$$

This tells us that the client's score is .80 standard deviations above the mean. Next, we go to the normal curve table (Appendix B) and go down the column headed *z* until we find the value .80. Then we read across to the column headed **Prop. Below** and find the value .7881. This tells us that 78.81% (or 79% rounded to the nearest whole percent) of all scores on this test fall below the client's score of 112.

A similar procedure is the basis for interpreting scores on standardized tests (such as the ACT or SAT). Since the normal curve is a good representation of the distribution of many characteristics of humans and other biological organisms, it is the basis for applications in the social sciences, business, education, and many other fields. In each case we can find the proportion of scores falling above, below, or between any score(s) of interest. All we need to know is the mean and standard deviation of the distribution from which the scores come.

When we solve problems using the normal curve table we recommend using a systematic, step-by-step procedure. Such a systematic procedure will help to clarify our thinking and minimize the chances of making errors. To illustrate the recommended step-by-step procedure consider the following example: On the test described previously, with a mean of 100 and a standard deviation of 15, what proportion of scores would fall above 125?

*Step 1.* Make a small graph with the mean and the raw score of interest drawn in. Shade the area on the graph that represents the proportion we are looking for.

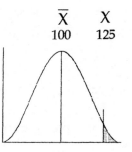

*Step 2.* Plan a strategy to get the proportion we need.

In this case the proportion represented by the shaded portion of the graph can be found in the *Prop. Above* column of the normal curve table in Appendix B.

*Step 3.* Convert the raw score of interest to a standard score (z score).

$$z = \frac{X - \overline{X}}{s} = \frac{125 - 100}{15} = \frac{25}{15} = 1.67$$

*Step 4.* Carry out the strategy planned in Step 2.

In the normal curve table in Appendix B, we go down the first column headed *z* until we reach the standard score we calculated in Step 3 -- in this case 1.67. Then we read across to the third column headed *Prop. Above* and find the value .0475. This tells us that the proportion of people who score above 125 on the test is .0475; or 4.75% of the people score above 125.

Now consider a second example. What percent of scores on this test (mean = 100; standard deviation = 15) will fall between 95 and 110? Again, we will solve this problem using our step-by-step procedure:

***Step 1.*** Make a graph showing the mean and the raw scores of interest. Shade the area of the graph that represents the proportion (or percentage) we need.

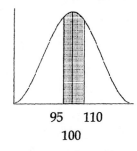

95    110
100

***Step 2.*** Plan a strategy to get the proportion we need.

Since the proportion we are seeking lies above 95, but not above 110, we can find it by subtracting the proportion (B) that lies above 110 from the proportion (A) that lies above 95.

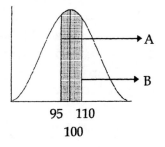

95   110
100

***Step 3.*** Convert the raw scores of interest to standard scores (z scores).

$$z = \frac{X - \overline{X}}{s} = \frac{95 - 100}{15} = \frac{-5}{15} = -.33$$

$$z = \frac{X - \overline{X}}{s} = \frac{110 - 100}{15} = \frac{10}{15} = .67$$

Note that the standard score for the raw score of 95 is negative. (The standard score for any raw score that lies below the mean will always be negative.) Therefore, be sure to use the z value of -.33 (not .33) in the normal curve table.

*Step 4.* Carry out the strategy planned in Step 2.

Go to the normal curve table in Appendix B. First, find -.33 (the standard score for the raw score of 95) in the first column headed $z$; then read across to the third column headed ***Prop. Above*** to get the value .6293 (which represents proportion A). Second, find .67 (the standard score for the raw score of 110) in the first column headed $z$; then read across to the third column headed ***Prop. Above*** to get the value .2514 (which represents proportion B). Now subtract proportion B (the proportion above 110) from proportion A (the proportion above 95):

$$
\begin{array}{r}
.6293 \\
- .2514 \\
\hline
.3779
\end{array}
$$

The proportion of people scoring between 95 and 110 on the test is .3779. That is, 37.79% of the scores on the test lie between 95 and 110.

Note that there are several strategies that will yield the correct result on any problem of the type that we have just been working. The key is to come up with one of the valid strategies in Step 2 when we plan our strategy.

Remember that we had said that the information in a normal distribution of any size -- even if it contains millions of scores -- can be adequately summarized by just two numbers. We have just shown how this is done. We use the mean and standard deviation and a normal curve table. Indeed, the information is preserved so completely that the entire distribution can be reconstructed from just these two numbers and a normal curve table.

## Small Departures from Normality

Fortunately, small or even moderate departures from a normal distribution cause only minor distortions in the proportions of scores that lie within a given number of standard deviations of the mean. A formula known as Tschebycheff's inequality allows us to calculate the minimum proportion of scores falling within any distance of the mean in a distribution of any shape -- even an odd-shaped distribution like that shown in Figure 5-2. The formula for Tschebycheff's inequality is

$$P \geq 1 - \frac{1}{K^2}$$

where P is the minimum proportion of scores guaranteed to lie within K standard deviations of the mean.

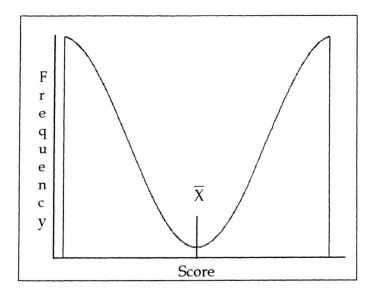

Figure 5-2. A truly bizarre distribution that must nonetheless conform to the rules of Tschebycheff's inequality.

Camp and Meidell modified Tschebycheff's inequality so that it would apply to any distribution that is unimodal and does not have its mode at the end of the distribution. An example of such a distribution is shown in Figure 5-3. Table 5-2 shows the proportions of scores that lie within whole standard deviations of the mean for any normal distribution, for any unimodal distribution (Camp & Meidell), and for any distribution, however bizarre (Tschebycheff).

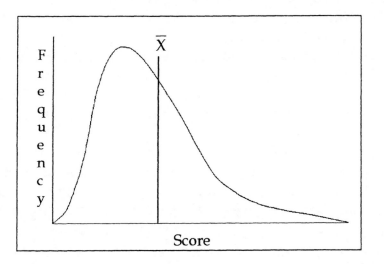

Figure 5-3. A very skewed distribution that must adhere to Camp and Meidell's modification of Tschebycheff's inequality.

Table 5-2

Proportions Guaranteed to Fall Within Several Standard Deviations of the Mean for Distributions of Various Shapes

| Type of Distribution | Number of Standard Deviations | | | |
|---|---|---|---|---|
| | 1 | 2 | 3 | 4 |
| Normal distribution (Gauss) | .6826 | .9544 | .9973 | .9994 |
| Any unimodal distribution (Camp & Meidell) | .5556 | .8889 | .9506 | .9722 |
| Any distribution (Tschebycheff) | 0 | .7500 | .8889 | .9375 |

We can see in Figure 5-3 that the Camp and Meidell model includes distributions that are very unlike the normal distribution. Nevertheless, we can also see in Table 5-2 that even these quite different shaped distributions still produce only modest departures from the proportions associated with the normal curve. This suggests that we can still use the normal curve table in most situations with only negligible distortion of information.

## Percentiles

*Percentile Rank.* A score's *percentile rank* is the percentage (rounded to the nearest whole percent) of the scores in its distribution that fall below that score. So when we find the percentage of scores below a given score, we are in effect finding its percentile rank. Percentile ranks are easily understood and are often used to communicate a person's standing in a distribution.

For example, suppose Joe graduated 30th in his high school class of 200 students. This means that 170 of the 200 students in his graduating class ranked below him. Expressed as a proportion, 170/200 or .85 of the students ranked below him. That is, 85% of the students in Joe's class scored below him. Therefore, Joe's percentile rank in his high school class is 85.

As a second example, suppose Joe also took a test of mathematical ability. This test had a mean of 50 and a standard deviation of 10. Joe's score on the test was 56. To find his percentile rank on this test we can call on our knowledge of the normal curve and use the step-by-step procedure we developed earlier. First, we draw a graph showing the mean and Joe's raw score; then we shade the area we need to find (the area below Joe's score).

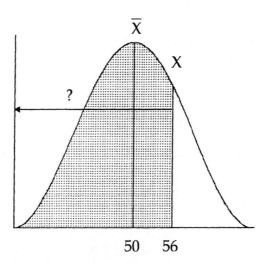

Second, we plan our strategy. We can find the area we need by calculating the z score for Joe's score of 56, finding that z score in the *z* column in the normal curve table, and then reading across to the column headed ***Prop. Below***. Finally, we carry out our strategy:

$$z = \text{standard score} = \frac{X - \overline{X}}{s} = \frac{56 - 50}{10} = \frac{6}{10} = .60$$

In the normal curve table we see that the proportion of scores below a z score of .60 is .7257. This tells us that Joe is at the 73rd percentile on this test. His percentile rank is 73.

    ***Centile Point.*** A centile point (or percentile point) is the opposite side of the coin from a percentile rank. For a percentile rank we started with a raw score and found the percentage of scores in its distribution that fall below that raw score. Sometimes, however, we want to go in the opposite direction. We want to find the raw score below which a particular proportion of the other scores in the distribution will fall. This is called finding the centile point. A given ***centile point*** is the raw score below which that percentage of scores will fall. For example, if we were looking for the 75th centile point in a distribution we would be looking for the score below which 75% of the scores would fall.

    To illustrate the procedure for finding a centile point consider the following example. The Worldwide Widget Company uses a test of widget making ability to select employees from a pool of applicants. The test has a mean of 100 and a standard deviation of 15. The human resources director at Worldwide Widget wants to hire only those people who are in the top 20 percent on widget making ability. That is, she wants to hire only those people who score at the 80th centile point or higher on the test. But what test score is at the 80th centile point? We have a percentage and we need a raw score.

As always, it is useful to make a small graph showing what we know and what we need.

Then we can find any centile point using the normal curve table and the z score formula. However, we need to juggle the formula algebraically to isolate the unknown (the raw score) in the equation:

$$\text{standard score (or z score)} = \frac{\text{raw score} - \text{mean}}{\text{standard deviation}}$$

$$\text{or,} \quad z = \frac{X - \overline{X}}{s}$$

$$z(s) = X - \overline{X}$$

$$z(s) + \overline{X} = X$$

$$X = z(s) + \overline{X}$$

Since we know the mean and standard deviation of the test, we can find the z score for our centile point by using the normal curve table. We begin in the *Prop. Below* column and find the proportion (or the closest value to it) that must lie below the score we are looking for. In this example the value closest to .80 is .7995. Next, we read across to the left to the z column to get the z score corresponding to this proportion below. In our example the z score is .84. Finally, we plug the three values (mean = 100, standard deviation = 15, and z = .84) into the juggled z score formula to get the centile point:

$$X = z(s) + \overline{X}$$

$$X = (.84)(15) + 100$$

$$X = 12.60 + 100$$

$$X = 112.60$$

Since test scores are reported only as integers, we round the centile point to 113. The 80th centile point on this test is 113. This tells us that if Worldwide Widget hires only people who score 113 or above on the test of widget making ability, the company will be getting workers who are in the top 20 percent on the test.

## Study Questions
*Answers to selected questions may be found in Appendix A*

1.  The following raw scores are taken from a distribution with a mean of 60 and a standard deviation of 8. Convert each raw score to a z score.

    a. 48                          b. 62
    c. 70                          d. 55
    e. 60                          f. 52

2.  For a distribution of IQ scores with a mean of 100 and a standard deviation of 16:

    a. What percentage of scores is above 104?
    b. What percentage of scores is above 88?
    c. What percentage of scores is below 92?
    d. What percentage of scores is between 85 and 120?
    e. What percentage of scores is between 105 and 115?

3.  Determine the percentile ranks for the following raw scores from a distribution with a mean of 50 and a standard deviation of 10:

    a. 46                          b. 62
    c. 38                          d. 55
    e. 51                          f. 42

4.  Determine the raw scores corresponding to the following centile points from a distribution with a mean of 500 and a standard deviation of 100:

a. 25th                              b. 67th
c. 76th                              d. 84th
e. 99th                              f. 40th

# CHAPTER SIX

# Probability

In nearly every aspect of life we are faced with uncertainty. Will it rain on the day of our picnic? Will my car start tomorrow morning when I leave for work? Will I get an A on my next statistics test? Will the flu shot I plan to get cause an allergic reaction? It would be nice to be able to know in advance the correct yes or no answers to these and other similar questions. That is, it would be nice to be able to eliminate uncertainty. Then it would be easy to make decisions.

However, in most situations we cannot eliminate uncertainty. Instead, we attempt to deal with uncertainty by understanding the principles by which it operates, which allows us to measure uncertainty. We estimate the likelihood of a desired outcome and make our decision based on whether the outcome is likely enough. For example, if 97 out of every 100 people who receive flu shots do not suffer allergic reactions, should I be willing to get a flu shot?

## Basic Definition of Probability

The formal system developed by mathematicians and statisticians to deal with uncertainty is called *probability theory*. The area of statistics called inferential statistics applies probability theory to help us make decisions involving uncertainty.

A useful definition of *probability* holds that the probability of a favored event is equal to the number of possible outcomes resulting in the favored event divided by the total number of possible outcomes, when each possible outcome has an equal opportunity to occur. Thus, probability is the relative frequency of the favored outcomes in the population of possible outcomes. Probability is expressed as a proportion that can range from zero (the favored event cannot occur) to one (the favored event is certain to occur).

The basic formula for probability can be written:

$$p(\text{favored event}) = \frac{\text{number of possible outcomes resulting in the favored event}}{\text{total number of possible outcomes}}$$

or, if we call the favored event A:

$$p(A) = \frac{\text{\# of outcomes resulting in event A}}{\text{\# of possible outcomes}}$$

As an example of a simple application of the formula, suppose we had a jar containing 10 blue marbles, 30 red marbles and 60 green marbles. If we thoroughly mixed the marbles in the jar and then asked a blind-folded volunteer to draw a single marble from the jar, what is the probability of drawing a blue marble? The question can be answered using our probability formula:

$$p(\text{blue marble}) = \frac{10 \text{ blue marbles}}{100 \text{ total marbles}} = \frac{10}{100} = .10$$

Similarly, the probability of drawing a green marble is:

$$p(\text{green marble}) = \frac{60 \text{ green marbles}}{100 \text{ total marbles}} = \frac{60}{100} = .60$$

Clearly, if we had to bet on the color of a marble to be drawn, we would prefer to bet on a green marble. This is not because there is anything special about green marbles. Indeed, each of the 100 marbles in the jar has an equal chance of being drawn. Rather, there are simply more chances of drawing a green one.

Many games of chance involve throwing a pair of dice. As a second example, consider the case where we will throw a single die. The possible outcomes are a 1, 2, 3, 4, 5, or 6. Thus, the probability of throwing a 5 would be 1/6, since one of the six possible outcomes constitutes the favored outcome (5). The probability of throwing an even number (2, 4, or 6) would be 3/6 = ½ , since three of the six possible outcomes are favored outcomes.

## Probability of A "and" B (Multiplication Rule)

One situation that we commonly must assess involves the probability of two outcomes both occurring. If event I and event II are independent, the joint probability of outcome A and outcome B is equal to the probability of A multiplied by the probability of B. That is,

$$p(A \text{ and } B) = p(A)p(B)$$

Note that the two events are independent when the outcome of one event has no effect on the outcome of the other event.

As an example, consider the situation in which we are throwing a pair of dice. In this case the two events (throwing die I and throwing die II) are independent because the outcome on die I has no effect on the outcome on die II. The probability of throwing an odd number first on die I and then a 4 on die II is:

$$p(\text{odd and } 4) = p(\text{odd})p(4) = (3/6)(1/6) = 3/36 = 1/12$$

since the probability of an odd number on die I is 3/6, and the probability of a 4 on die II is 1/6. Note that each of these two component probabilities comes directly from our basic definition of probability:

$$p(\text{favored event}) = \frac{\text{number of possible outcomes resulting in the favored event}}{\text{total number of possible outcomes}}$$

## Probability of A "or" B (Addition Rule)

Another situation we often must assess is the probability that one or the other of two outcomes will occur. In the most general case, the probability of outcome A or outcome B is equal to the probability of A plus the probability of B minus the probability of A and B. Note that we must subtract the probability of A and B because it is included in both the probability of A and the probability of B (we counted it twice, so we must subtract it once). That is,

$$p(A \text{ or } B) = p(A) + p(B) - p(A \text{ and } B)$$

or, since $p(A \text{ and } B)$ is equal to $p(A)p(B)$,

$$p(A \text{ or } B) = p(A) + p(B) - p(A)p(B)$$

As an example, what is the probability of throwing two dice and obtaining an odd number on die I or a number larger than 4 on die II? To answer this question we apply our formula and find that:

$$p(\text{odd or larger than 4}) = p(\text{odd}) + p(\text{larger than 4}) - p(\text{odd})p(\text{larger than 4})$$

$$= 3/6 + 2/6 - (3/6)(2/6)$$

$$= 3/6 + 2/6 - 6/36$$

$$= 3/6 + 2/6 - 1/6$$

$$= 4/6$$

$$= .67$$

since the probability of an odd number on die I is 3/6, the probability of a number larger than 4 on die II is 2/6, and the probability of both an odd number on die I and a number larger than 4 on die II is 1/6.

Sometimes we work with *mutually exclusive* outcomes. Two outcomes are mutually exclusive when they cannot both occur at the same time. If outcomes A and B are mutually exclusive, then the probability of A and B is zero (they cannot both occur) and the formula simplifies to:

p(A or B) = p(A) + p(B)

As an example, suppose we draw a single card from a well-shuffled deck of cards. What is the probability that it will be an ace or a king? It is impossible for a card to be both an ace and a king, so these outcomes are mutually exclusive and p(Ace and King) = 0. Therefore, the probability of an ace or a king is:

$$p(\text{Ace or King}) = p(\text{Ace}) + p(\text{King})$$

$$= 4/52 + 4/52$$

$$= 8/52$$

$$= .15$$

since there are 4 aces in a deck of 52 cards and 4 kings in a deck of 52 cards.

## Conditional Probability (Probability of B given A)

Conditional probability is the probability of one outcome given that another specific outcome has already occurred. Using the following formula, we can compute the conditional probability of outcome B given that outcome A has occurred:

$$\text{Probability of B given A} = \frac{p(A \text{ and } B)}{p(A)}$$

or, we can write this as

$$p(B|A) = \frac{p(A \text{ and } B)}{p(A)}$$

As an example, suppose that we conduct a study for the Post Office, investigating the common belief that a barking dog that wags its tail will not bite, but a barking dog that does not wag its tail will bite. We observe many encounters between mail carriers and barking dogs, and determine the probabilities of the various types of outcomes as shown in Table 5-1.

Table 5-1
Probabilities of Tail Wagging and/or Biting by Dogs

|  | B (Bites) | $\overline{B}$ (Does Not Bite) |  |
|---|---|---|---|
| A (Wags Tail) | .05 | .35 | p(A) = .40 |
| $\overline{A}$ (Does Not Wag Tail) | .20 | .40 | p($\overline{A}$) = .60 |
|  | p(B) = .25 | p($\overline{B}$) = .75 |  |

At the upper right margin of the table, we can see that, overall, the probability that a dog will wag its tail is p(A) = .40. The upper left entry in the table shows that the probability that a dog will wag its tail and bite is p(A and B) = .05. The probability that a dog will bite given that it wags its tail can be found by plugging these values into our formula:

$$p(B|A) = \frac{p(A \text{ and } B)}{p(A)}$$

$$p(\text{Bites}|\text{Wags its Tail}) = \frac{p(\text{Wags its Tails and Bites})}{p(\text{Wags its Tail})}$$

$$= .05/.40 = .13$$

Similarly, we can find the probability that a dog will bite given that it does not wag its tail. First, we note at the bottom right of Table 5-1 that the overall probability that a dog will not wag its tail is p($\overline{A}$) = .60. The top entry in the second column of the table gives the probability that a dog will not wag its tail and will bite, p($\overline{A}$ and B) = .20. When we adapt our conditional probability formula for this question, we get

$$p(B|\overline{A}) = \frac{p(\overline{A} \text{ and } B)}{p(\overline{A})}$$

$$p(\text{Bites}|\text{Does not Wag its Tail}) = \frac{p(\text{Does not Wag its Tail and Bites})}{p(\text{Does not Wag its Tail})}$$

$$= .20/.60 = .33$$

From these calculations we can conclude that a dog that wags its tail is considerably less likely to bite (p = .13) than a dog that does not wag its tail (p = .33). However, a mail carrier cannot be certain that a dog will not bite, even if it wags its tail. Furthermore, even if it does not wag its tail, a dog is still less likely to bite than it is to not bite.

## Multiplication Rule for Dependent Events

Events are *dependent* when the outcome of one event affects the probability of the outcome of a second event. This commonly happens when we are sampling without replacement. For example, what is the probability of drawing two kings in successive draws from a well-shuffled deck of cards? Since the first card drawn is not replaced in the deck before the second card is drawn, this is an example of drawing two samples (of one card each) from the deck without replacement. Thus, the outcome of the first draw affects the probability of the favored outcome on the second draw.

For this sort of problem the appropriate formula is:

$$p(A \text{ and } B) = p(A)p(B|A)$$

Applying this formula to find the probability of drawing two kings in successive draws from a deck of cards requires that we first find the component probabilities. Since there are four kings in a deck of 52 cards, the probability of drawing a king on the first draw is:

$$p(King) = 4/52 = 1/13$$

Given that a king was drawn on the first draw, three of the remaining 51 cards are kings, so:

$$p(King|King) = 3/51$$

Now we can plug these values into the formula to get the probability of drawing two kings in succession:

$$p(King \text{ and } King) = p(King) \, p(King|King)$$

$$= (1/13)(3/51)$$

$$= 3/663 = .0045$$

## Summary of Basic Probability

We have discussed a number of applications of the basic probability formula. These applications are summarized in Table 5-2.

Table 5-2
Summary of Applications of Basic Probability

| | Application | Formula | Example |
|---|---|---|---|
| I. | Basic Probability | $p = \dfrac{\#\ \text{favored events}}{\#\ \text{possible events}}$ | Marbles: probability of drawing a red marble from a jar containing 10 red and 90 blue marbles |
| II. | Probability of A and B (Multiplication Rule) | | |
| | A. Independent Events | $p(A \text{ and } B) = p(A)p(B)$ | Dice: probability of throwing a 4 on die I and an odd number on die II |
| | B. Dependent Events | $p(A \text{ and } B) = p(A)p(B|A)$ | Cards: probability of drawing 2 kings in succession from a deck of cards |
| III. | Probability of A or B (Addition Rule) | | |
| | A. Non-mutually Exclusive Events | $p(A \text{ or } B) = p(A) + p(B) - p(A \text{ and } B)$ | Die: probability of throwing an odd number or a number larger than 4 |
| | B. Mutually Exclusive Events | $p(A \text{ or } B) = p(A) + p(B)$ | Cards: probability of drawing an Ace or a King from a deck of cards |
| IV. | Probability of B given A (Conditional Probability) | $p(B|A) = \dfrac{P(A \text{ and } B)}{P(A)}$ | Dogs: probability that a dog will bite given that the dog wags its tail |

# Counting Rules

As we have noted earlier, the basic probability formula is simple. However, often it is difficult to identify and count how many favored outcomes and how many total outcomes are possible. To help us get these values to plug into the probability equation, we can use a set of formulae called counting rules.

The key component in all of these counting rule formulae is the *factorial*, symbolized by "!". The factorial of a number, N, is written "N!" and is read "N factorial." To calculate the factorial of a number, that number is multiplied by all of the integers between that number and one. Expressed in mathematical notion,

$$N! = N(N-1)(N-2) \ldots (1)$$

For example, four factorial is found by:

$$4! = 4(3)(2)(1) = 24$$

Note that there are two special cases of factorials:

$$0! = 1$$
$$1! = 1$$

## Permutations

Often we are interested in the number of different arrangements that can be made of a given set of events or objects. The arrangements are called *permutations*. For example, in a psychology experiment we intend to test the effects of three different treatments: treatment A, treatment B, and treatment C. We suspect that the order of presentation of the three treatments may influence their effects. Therefore, we would like to employ all possible orders. The question is, how many possible orders are there? With only three treatments it is easy to list all the possible orders and then count them. The possible orders are:

ABC
ACB
BAC
BCA
CAB
CBA

Note that if there were many more than three treatments, it would be very laborious to list each possible order. Indeed, the number of possible permutations (orders) increases very rapidly with an increase in the number of events or objects to be ordered.

As a second example, consider a memory experiment in which subjects will be asked to memorize a set of five words. Because the order of the words might make the list easier or harder to learn, the experimenter would like to cancel this effect by presenting all possible orders of words. Again, the question is how many possible orders are there?

Questions like these are easily answered by using the general formula for permutations. The number of permutations of N things is equal to N factorial, which can be written:

$$P_N = N!$$

In our example, the number of different orders of the five words in our list is:

$$P_5 = 5!$$

$$= 5(4)(3)(2)(1)$$

$$= 120$$

There are 120 different orders of the five words. Note that 120 orders are a lot to list and count. Most of us would prefer to use the permutation formula.

## Permutations of N things taken r at a time

Sometimes we are interested in the number of permutations (orders) that can be made of a given number of things when not all of the things are used in each arrangement. For example, I am planning a dinner party. I have six friends, but I can afford to invite only four of them. How many seating arrangements of four guests can I make of my six friends? This sort of problem asks for the number of permutations of N things taken r at a time. It can be solved by using the general formula:

$$_NP_r = \frac{N!}{(N-r)!}$$

where N is the total number of things available and r is the number of things to be used in each arrangement.

In this case I want to find the number of permutations of six friends taken four at a time. Plugging this information into our general formula, we get:

$$_NP_r = \frac{N!}{(N-r)!}$$

$$_6P_4 = \frac{6!}{(6-4)!}$$

$$= \frac{6!}{2!}$$

$$= \frac{(6)(5)(4)(3)(2)(1)}{(2)(1)}$$

$$= (6)(5)(4)(3)$$

$$= 360$$

There are 360 possible seating arrangements. Even if several of my friends hate each other, I should be able to find a seating arrangement in which no one has to sit next to someone she does not like.

## Combinations of N things taken r at a time

Sometimes we are not interested in the arrangements of things, but rather we are interested only in what things are grouped together. These groupings are called *combinations*. For example, [A,B] and [B,A] are two permutations of the letters A and B, but only one combination, because order does not matter for combinations.

We can compute the number of combinations of N things taken r at a time using the formula:

$$_NC_r = \frac{N!}{(N-r)!r!}$$

where N is the total number of things available and r is the number of things to be used in each grouping.

As an example, consider the dilemma of a high school track coach. She has seven girls on her track squad and must form a four-person relay team. How many different relay teams are possible? To answer this question we see that N represents the seven girls available and r represents the four girls required to form a relay team. Plugging these values into our formula gives:

$$_NC_r = \frac{N!}{(N-r)!r!}$$

$$_7C_4 = \frac{7!}{(7-4)!4!}$$

$$= \frac{7!}{3!4!}$$

$$= \frac{(7)(\cancel{6})^2(5)(\cancel{4})(\cancel{3})(\cancel{2})(\cancel{1})}{(\cancel{3})(2)(1)(\cancel{4})(\cancel{3})(\cancel{2})(\cancel{1})}$$

$$= \frac{(7)(\cancel{2})(5)}{\cancel{2}}$$

$$= (7)(5)$$

$$= 35$$

This leaves the coach with a large number of choices. She could form any of 35 possible relay teams.

## The Binomial Distribution

As we have noted repeatedly, the basic probability formula is simple, consisting of the frequency of favored outcomes relative to the total number of possible outcomes. One interesting and important application of probability occurs when we deal with an event, such as a coin toss, which has only two possible outcomes. Each possible outcome has a fixed probability of occurring. One of the outcomes (e.g., heads) is considered a "success" and the other outcome (e.g., tails) is a "failure." Each event of this type, taken by itself, is a very simple application of probability. However, we are usually interested in a more complex application in which we want to determine the probability of a given number of successes in a sequence of trials. For example, what is the probability of getting eight or more heads in 10 coin tosses? Each of these individual trials (coin tosses) is called a *Bernoulli trial*. The distribution of probabilities of all possible numbers of successes in a series of Bernoulli trials is called a *binomial distribution*.

If we tossed four coins, we could get 0 heads, 1 head, 2 heads, 3 heads, or all 4 could be heads. There is only one way to get 0 heads; all four coins must be tails. However, there are four ways to get 1 head. The first coin could be the head and the remaining coins tails, or the second coin could be the head and all others tails, etc. Table 5-3 lists the number of ways in which each possible number of heads could be obtained. We can see from the table that there are 16 possible outcomes when we toss four coins. Each of these outcomes is equally likely. The corresponding probabilities of the various numbers of heads are computed by dividing the number of ways of obtaining them by the total number of possible ways, using our basic probability formula:

$$p(r \text{ heads}) = \frac{\text{number of outcomes yielding r heads}}{\text{total number of possible outcomes}}$$

where r is equal to the number of heads in which we are interested. These probabilities are listed in the bottom row of Table 5-3.

Table 5-3
Ways of Obtaining Difference Numbers of Heads in Four Coin Tosses

|  | 0 Heads | 1 Head | 2 Heads | 3 Heads | 4 Heads |  |
|---|---|---|---|---|---|---|
|  | TTTT | HTTT | HHTT | HHHT | HHHH |  |
|  |  | THTT | HTHT | HHTH |  |  |
|  |  | TTHT | HTTH | HTHH |  |  |
|  |  | TTTH | THHT | THHH |  |  |
|  |  |  | THTH |  |  |  |
|  |  |  | TTHH |  |  |  |
| Total # of ways | 1 | 4 | 6 | 4 | 1 | Grand Total 16 |
| Probability | 1/16 | 4/16 | 6/16 | 4/16 | 1/16 |  |

## Pascal's Triangle

If there are very many Bernoulli trials (e.g., coin tosses) in the sequence, it becomes very difficult to list and count all the possible outcomes (ways of getting each number of heads). One clever way to determine "the count," that is, the numbers of outcomes associated with various numbers of successes, is to use a simple device known as

*Pascal's Triangle.* A Pascal's Triangle, named after its inventor Renaissance mathematician Blaise Pascal, is shown in Table 5-4.

Table 5-4
Pascal's Triangle

| # of Bernoulli trials (N) | | # of possible outcomes ($2^N$) |
|---|---|---|
| 0 | 1 | 1 |
| 1 | 1  1 | 2 |
| 2 | 1  2  1 | 4 |
| 3 | 1  3  3  1 | 8 |
| 4 | 1  4  6  4  1 | 16 |
| 5 | 1  5  10  10  5  1 | 32 |
| 6 | 1  6  15  20  15  6  1 | 64 |
| 7 | 1  7  21  35  35  21  7  1 | 128 |
| 8 | 1  8  28  56  70  56  28  8  1 | 256 |

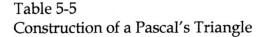

No Successes            All Successes

A Pascal's triangle can be constructed by following four rules: First, begin with a 1 in the top row, at the top of the triangle. Second, every row has one more element than the row above it. Third, every row begins and ends with a 1. Fourth, every element of a row, except the first and last elements, is the sum of the two elements diagonally above it. Table 5-5 illustrates the construction of a Pascal's Triangle.

Table 5-5
Construction of a Pascal's Triangle

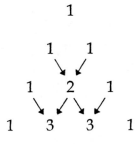

We use Pascal's Triangle to get "the count" of the number of favored outcomes and the total number of possible outcomes in a given number of Bernoulli trials in the following way. First, choose the row corresponding to the number of Bernoulli trials in the sequence; in Table 5-4 the left column identifies the number of trials that corresponds to each row. Second, get the total number of possible outcomes corresponding to the number of Bernoulli trials in the sequence; this can be done by reading across to the right column. Third, get "the count" of the number of favored outcomes by selecting the element in the chosen row of the triangle that corresponds to the number of successes of interest. The first element in the row is the number of outcomes yielding no successes; the second element in the row is the number of outcomes yielding one success, etc. The last element in the row is the number of outcomes yielding successes on all trials. Note that the sum of all the elements in a row is equal to the total number of outcomes, which is also listed in the right column.

As an example, we can use Pascal's Triangle to find the number of ways we could get 0, 1, 2, 3, or 4 heads in four coin tosses, without having to list and count all the possible outcomes as we did in Table 5-3. Using Pascal's Triangle (Table 5-4), we first go down the left column to find the row corresponding to four Bernoulli trials (i.e., four coin tosses). Reading across to the right column, we see that there are a total of 16 possible outcomes. Finally, the first element in the chosen row of the triangle tells us that there is only 1 outcome yielding 0 successes (heads). The second element tells us that there are 4 outcomes yielding 1 success (head). The third element indicates that there are 6 ways to get 2 successes (heads). The fourth element indicates that there are 4 ways to get 3 successes (heads). The final element indicates that only 1 outcome yields all 4 successes (heads). The probabilities of getting each number of successes (heads) can be calculated by dividing each of these values by the total of 16 possible outcomes, just as in Table 5-3.

## Direct calculation of binomial probabilities

Pascal's Triangle is handy when we have relatively few Bernoulli trials, but it becomes unwieldy as the number of trials increases. In addition, when the probability of a success is not equal to the probability of a failure on each trial, Pascal's Triangle does not provide all the information needed to calculate the probabilities of the various numbers of successes.

However, there is a procedure that can be used to directly calculate any binomial probability. The probability of any number of successes in a given number of trials can be found using the following formula:

p(r successes in N trials) = (# of ways to get r successes)(probability of each way)

$$= {}_NC_r p^r q^{N-r}$$

$$= \frac{N!}{(N-r)!r!}\, p^r q^{N-r}$$

where p is the probability of a success on an individual trial, q is the probability of a failure on an individual trial, N is the number of trials in the series, and r is the number of successes with which we are concerned. Note that the first part of the formula, ${}_NC_r$, is "the count" of the number of ways of getting the desired number of successes, which can be gotten from Pascal's Triangle. The second part of the formula is the probability of each way that the desired number of successes can be obtained.

As an example, we can directly calculate the probabilities of all possible numbers of heads (successes) in six coin tosses (Bernoulli trials). Our formula for directly calculating binomial probabilities is:

p(r Heads in N tosses) $= {}_NC_r p^r q^{N-r}$

$$= \frac{N!}{(N-r)!r!}\, p^r q^{N-r}$$

Since the probability of a success (p) is 1/2 and the probability of a failure (q) is 1/2 on a single coin toss, and we are making a series of 6 coin tosses (N), the probability of 0 heads (r) is

$$p(0 \text{ Heads in 6 tosses}) = \frac{6!}{(6-0)!0!}\,(1/2)^0\,(1/2)^{6-0}$$

$$= \frac{6!}{6!0!}\,(1/2)^0\,(1/2)^6$$

$$= (1)(1)(1/64)$$

$$= 1/64 = .016$$

Continuing this procedure for the remaining possible numbers of heads, we get:

$$p(1 \text{ Head}) \;=\; \frac{6!}{(6-1)!1!}\,(1/2)^1(1/2)^{6-1}$$

$$=\; \frac{6!}{5!1!}\,(1/2)(1/2)^5$$

$$=\; 6(1/2)(1/32)$$

$$=\; 6(1/64) \;=\; 6/64 \;=\; .094$$

$$p(2 \text{ Heads}) \;=\; \frac{6!}{(6-2)!2!}\,(1/2)^2(1/2)^{6-2}$$

$$=\; \frac{6!}{4!2!}\,(1/2)^2(1/2)^4$$

$$=\; 15(1/4)(1/16) \;=\; 15/64 \;=\; .234$$

$$p(3 \text{ Heads}) \;=\; \frac{6!}{(6-3)!3!}\,(1/2)^3(1/2)^{6-3}$$

$$=\; \frac{6!}{3!3!}\,(1/2)^3(1/2)^3$$

$$=\; 20(1/8)(1/8) \;=\; 20/64 \;=\; .313$$

$$p(4 \text{ Heads}) \;=\; \frac{6!}{(6-4)!4!}\,(1/2)^4(1/2)^{6-4}$$

$$=\; \frac{6!}{2!4!}\,(1/2)^4(1/2)^2$$

$$=\; 15(1/16)(1/4) \;=\; 15/64 \;=\; .234$$

$$p(5 \text{ Heads}) = \frac{6!}{(6-5)!5!} (1/2)^5 (1/2)^{6-5}$$

$$= \frac{6!}{1!5!} (1/2)^5 (1/2)^1$$

$$= 6(1/32)(1/2) = 6/64 = .094$$

$$p(6 \text{ Heads}) = \frac{6!}{(6-6)!6!} (1/2)^6 (1/2)^{6-6}$$

$$= \frac{6!}{0!6!} (1/2)^6 (1/2)^0$$

$$= 1(1/64)(1) = 1/64 = .016$$

The beauty of this direct procedure for calculating binomial probabilities is that it works equally well in cases where the probability of a success (p) on a single trial is not equal to the probability of a failure (q). For example, on a 10-item multiple choice history quiz with four alternatives per item, the probability of guessing correctly on a single item (p) is 1/4, since only one of the four alternatives is correct. The probability of guessing incorrectly on a single item (q) is 3/4, since three of the four alternatives are incorrect. Using our direct procedure, we can calculate the probability of obtaining each possible score on the quiz, simply by guessing. Our formula for directly calculating binomial probabilities is:

$$p(\text{guessing r items correctly in N items}) = {_N}C_r p^r q^{N-r} = \frac{N!}{(N-r)!r!} p^r q^{N-r}$$

Since the probability of a success (p) is 1/4 and the probability of a failure (q) is 3/4 on a single item, and we have a total of 10 items (N), the probability of guessing correctly on zero (r) items is:

$$p(0 \text{ correct in 10 items}) = \frac{10!}{(10-0)!0!} (1/4)^0 (3/4)^{10}$$

$$= (1)(1)(3/4)^{10} = 59049/1048576 = .056$$

Continuing this process for the remaining numbers of correct guesses, we get:

$$p(1 \text{ correct}) = \frac{10!}{(10-1)!1!} (1/4)^1 (3/4)^9$$

$$= (10)(1/4)(19683/262144) = 10(19683/1048576) = .187$$

$$p(2 \text{ correct}) = \frac{10!}{(10-2)!2!} (1/4)^2 (3/4)^8$$

$$= (45)(1/16)(6561/65536) = 45(6561/1048576) = .282$$

$$p(3 \text{ correct}) = \frac{10!}{(10-3)!3!} (1/4)^3 (3/4)^7$$

$$= (120)(1/64)(2187/16384) = 120(2187/1048576) = .251$$

$$p(4 \text{ correct}) = \frac{10!}{(10-4)!4!} (1/4)^4 (3/4)^6 = 210(729/1048576) = .146$$

$$p(5 \text{ correct}) = \frac{10!}{(10-5)!5!} (1/4)^5 (3/4)^5 = 252(243/1048576) = .059$$

$$p(6 \text{ correct}) = \frac{10!}{(10-6)!6!} (1/4)^6 (3/4)^4 = 210(81/1048576) = .016$$

$$p(7 \text{ correct}) = \frac{10!}{(10-7)!7!} (1/4)^7 (3/4)^3 = 120(27/1048576) = .003$$

$$p(8 \text{ correct}) = \frac{10!}{(10-8)!8!} (1/4)^8 (3/4)^2 = 45(9/1048576) = .000$$

$$p(9 \text{ correct}) = \frac{10!}{(10-9)!9!} (1/4)^9 (3/4)^1 = 10(3/1048576) = .000$$

$$p(10 \text{ correct}) = \frac{10!}{(10-10)!10!} (1/4)^{10} (3/4)^0 = 1(1/1048576)(1) = .000$$

## Characteristics of the binomial distribution

In the last two examples, calculating the probabilities of getting various numbers of heads in six coin tosses and calculating the probabilities of guessing correctly on various numbers of items on a 10-item history quiz, we have found all the terms for two binomial probability distributions. Figures 5-1 and 5-2 show the graphs of these two binomial distributions.

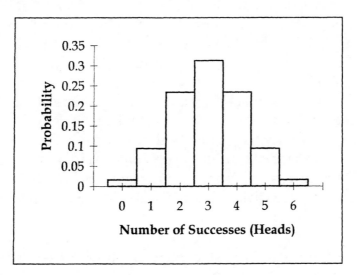

Figure 5-1. Binomial distribution showing the probabilities of various numbers of heads in six coin tosses.

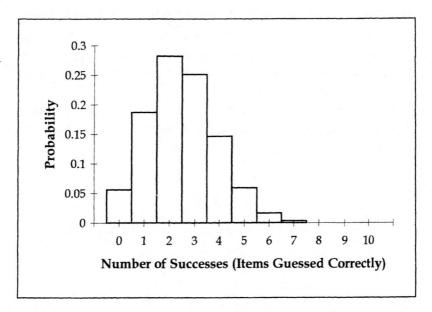

Figure 5-2. Binomial distribution showing the probabilities of guessing correctly on various numbers of 4-alternative multiple choice items on a 10-item history quiz.

Binomial distributions such as these are relatively simple examples of sampling distributions. A *sampling distribution* links every possible value of a variable with an associated probability. For example, every possible score on the 10-item multiple choice quiz has an associated probability, as shown in Figure 5-2.

There are two basic principles that govern the shape of the binomial distribution. First, the binomial distribution is symmetrical when p (the probability of a success on a given trial) is equal to q (the probability of a failure on a given trial). This can be seen in Figure 5-1 which shows a binomial distribution for coin tosses, where p = q = .5. Conversely, the binomial distribution is skewed when p is not equal to q. This can be seen in Figure 5-2 which shows a binomial distribution for a multiple choice quiz, where p = .25 and q = .75.

Second, the binomial distribution approaches the shape of the normal distribution as N (the number of trials) increases. In fact, when N is infinitely large, the binomial and normal distributions are identical. Fortunately, the binomial's approximation of the normal distribution occurs quite rapidly as N increases. This approximation of the normal distribution occurs regardless of whether or not p and q are equal; but it requires more trials (a larger N) as p and q become more unequal.

## Using the Normal Curve to Approximate Binomial Probabilities

When we have a long string of Bernoulli trials (approximately 20 or more), calculating binomial probabilities is very laborious. Fortunately, because the binomial distribution approximates the normal distribution quite quickly as the number of trials increases, we can use our knowledge of the normal curve to estimate binomial probabilities. As a rule of thumb, if $Npq \geq 4$ (where N is the number of Bernoulli trials, p is the probability of a success on a given trial, and q is the probability of a failure on a given trial) the normal approximation of the binomial will produce only negligible errors in probability estimates.

To use the normal curve table (see Appendix B) we need to know the mean and standard deviation of the binomial distribution with which we are working. For any binomial distribution the mean is

$$\overline{X} = Np$$

In addition, the standard deviation of any binomial distribution is

$$s = \sqrt{Npq}$$

As an example, what is the probability of correctly guessing on at least 30 items on a 50-item true-false geography quiz (and, therefore, getting a passing grade without studying)? To find this probability using the normal approximation of the binomial we use the following step-by-step procedure:

**Step 1.** Determine whether the normal approximation of the binomial can be used to solve this problem. N, the number of trials (items on the quiz), is 50; p, the probability of a success on a given trial (correctly guessing on an item), is .5; and q, the probability of a failure on a given trial (incorrectly guessing on an item), is .5; so

$$Npq = 50(.5)(.5) = 12.5$$

Since Npq = 12.5 is greater than 4, according to our rule of thumb, we *can* use the normal approximation of the binomial to solve our problem.

**Step 2.** Find the mean of this binomial distribution.

$$\overline{X} = Np = 50(.5) = 25$$

**Step 3.** Find the standard deviation of this binomial distribution.

$$s = \sqrt{Npq} = \sqrt{50(.5)(.5)} = \sqrt{12.5} = 3.54$$

**Step 4.** Draw a graph of the distribution showing the mean and the area of interest (Figure 5-3).

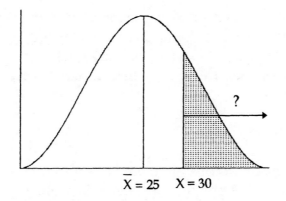

$\overline{X} = 25 \quad X = 30$

Figure 5-3. Graph of binomial distribution showing the mean and the area of interest.

*Step 5.* Find the z-score corresponding to the minimum number of successes of interest (i.e., the minimum number of items to be guessed correctly).

$$z = \frac{X - \overline{X}}{s} = \frac{30 - 25}{3.54} = \frac{5}{3.54} = 1.41$$

since X, the minimum number of items to be guessed correctly, is 30, $\overline{X}$, the mean of the binomial distribution, is 25, and s, the standard deviation of the binomial distribution, is 3.54.

*Step 6.* Find the probability of guessing correctly on at least 30 items. Using the normal curve table in Appendix B, we see that the proportion of scores falling above our z of 1.41 is .0793. Thus, the probability of passing the quiz is very low (.0793); perhaps it would be best to study.

Now consider a second example, in which p and q are not equal. In this example, assume that Norbert has done quite well in his introductory physics course. Now that the course is almost over, he has determined that to earn an A in the course he needs only 35 correct answers on the 100-item final exam, which will have a multiple-choice format with 4 alternatives per item. Norbert is not doing as well in his other classes. He is considering skipping all of his physics classes and not studying physics at all, so that he can spend that additional time working to bring up his grades in his other classes. What is the probability that he can still get an A in physics if he simply guesses on the final exam?

To answer Norbert's question we would like to use the normal approximation of the binomial. We follow the same steps as in our first example.

*Step 1.* Check to see if we can use the normal approximation of the binomial for this problem. N, the number of trials (items on the final exam), is 100; p, the probability of a success on a given trial (correctly guessing on an item), is .25; and q, the probability of a failure on a given trial (incorrectly guessing on an item), is .75. So,

$$Npq = 100(.25)(.75) = 18.75$$

Since Npq is greater than 4, according to our rule of thumb, we can use the normal approximation of the binomial to solve this problem.

*Step 2.* Find the mean of the binomial distribution.

$$\overline{X} = Np = 100(.25) = 25$$

*Step 3.* Find the standard deviation of the binomial distribution.

$$s = \sqrt{Npq} = \sqrt{100(.25)(.75)} = \sqrt{18.75} = 4.33$$

*Step 4.* Draw a graph of the distribution showing the mean and the area of interest (Figure 5-4).

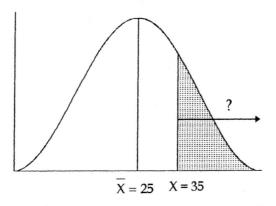

$$\overline{X} = 25 \quad X = 35$$

Figure 5-4. Graph of the binomial distribution showing the mean and the area of interest.

*Step 5.* Find the z-score for the minimum number of items Norbert must guess correctly.

$$z = \frac{X - \overline{X}}{s} = \frac{35 - 25}{4.33} = \frac{10}{4.33} = 2.31$$

*Step 6.* Find the probability of guessing correctly on at least 35 items. Using the normal curve table in Appendix B, we see that the proportion of scores falling above our z of 2.31 is .0104. Thus, the probability that Norbert could get his A in the physics course without studying for the final exam is very low (.0104); he had better study physics.

Note that in these cases we were *not* interested in the probability of getting *exactly* 30 successes (guessing correctly on exactly 30 items) and *exactly* 35 successes (guessing correctly on exactly 35 items). Rather, we were interested in the probability of 30 *or more* successes and the probability of 35 *or more* successes. This is usually the case when we find probabilities based on sampling distributions. When we use probabilities in inferential statistics in the following chapters, the typical question concerns the probability of obtaining a value of *at least* a given size, simply by chance. In particular, we are interested in whether that chance probability is very low.

## Study Questions
*Answers to selected questions may be found in Appendix A*

1.  A jar contains 10 red marbles, 25 green marbles, 30 blue marbles and 35 white marbles. What is the probability of randomly selecting:
    a.  a red marble?
    b.  a green marble?
    c.  a white marble?

2.  A card is drawn at random from a well-shuffled deck of 52 playing cards. What is the probability that the card will be:
    a.  the Jack of hearts?
    b.  a face card?
    c.  a heart or a face card?

3.  Two cards are drawn at random without replacement from a well-shuffled deck of 52 cards. What is the probability that:
    a.  both cards will be spades?
    b.  neither card will be a spade?
    c.  both cards will be aces?

4.  List all possible outcomes of a coin that is tossed five times. Calculate the probability of:
    a.  four heads.
    b.  three heads and two tails.
    c.  at least two heads.

5.  What is the number of possible arrangements of a list of:
    a.  6 words?
    b.  10 words?
    c.  12 words?

6.  How many different 5-member basketball teams are possible when a coach has:
    a.  6 players?
    b.  8 players?
    c.  9 players?

7.  A coin is tossed 8 times. What is the probability of:
    a.  getting exactly 2 heads?
    b.  getting exactly 6 heads?
    c.  getting exactly 0 heads?

8.  What is the probability of correctly guessing on at least 60 items on a 100-item true-false statistics exam?

9.  What is the probability of correctly guessing on at least 30 items on a 100-item multiple choice exam that has 4 alternatives per item?

10. What is the probability of correctly guessing on at least 20 items on a 50-item multiple choice exam that has 4 alternatives per item?

11. A social psychologist interested in social interactions among college students collected the data below. Given that a particular student knows another student, what is the probability that he also knows her roommate?

Probabilities of Knowing a Student and/or Knowing Her Roommate

|  | B (Knows Roommate) | $\overline{B}$ (Does Not Know Roommate) |  |
|---|---|---|---|
| A (Knows Student) | .28 | .22 | p(A) = .50 |
| $\overline{A}$ (Does Not Know Student) | .21 | .29 | p($\overline{A}$) = .50 |
|  | p(B) = .49 | p($\overline{B}$) = .51 |  |

12. A traffic safety engineer investigated the incidence of fatal injuries in drivers that either did or did not wear their seatbelts. Given that a driver was not wearing his or her seatbelt, what is the probability that he or she suffered a fatal injury?

Probabilities of Wearing a Seatbelt and/or Having a Fatal Injury

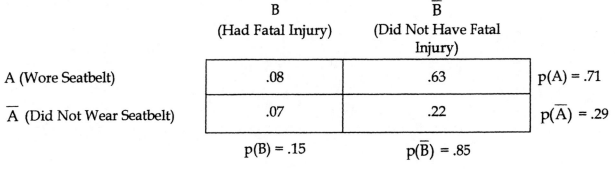

|  | B (Had Fatal Injury) | $\overline{B}$ (Did Not Have Fatal Injury) |  |
|---|---|---|---|
| A (Wore Seatbelt) | .08 | .63 | p(A) = .71 |
| $\overline{A}$ (Did Not Wear Seatbelt) | .07 | .22 | p($\overline{A}$) = .29 |
|  | p(B) = .15 | p($\overline{B}$) = .85 |  |

# CHAPTER SEVEN

# Correlation: Measuring the Strength of a Relationship

In Chapter One we said that there are three basic categories of statistics (descriptive statistics, correlational statistics, and inferential statistics). In our first five chapters we discussed descriptive statistics, which are used to summarize a set of scores. Now we turn to the second category of statistics -- correlational statistics. Correlational statistics were created to work with the relationship between two sets of scores or, in other words, the relationship between two variables.

## A Variable

A *variable* is any characteristic of a set of people or things that can vary from one individual case to the next case. For example, suppose the students in a history class took a test and each received a history test score. Test score is a variable, and the scores on this variable are shown in Table 7-1.

Table 7-1
Scores on the Variable "History Test Score"

| Student | History Test Score | |
|---------|--------------------|---|
| | | Variable name |
| John | 74 | |
| Darla | 88 | |
| Jennifer | 82 | Individual cases |
| Bill | 91 | |
| Ryan | 79 | |

Other examples of variables might be age, weight, and IQ score. As noted in Chapter Three, when we work with a set of scores we often identify the set as the "X scores." This means that we are talking about the scores on variable X. Similarly, if we have a set of scores on a second variable we could call these the "Y scores," or the scores on variable Y.

## Pairs of Variables

So far in this book we have been working with distributions of scores on one variable at a time. In this chapter we will work with the relationship between pairs of variables. As a matter of fact, in science a great deal of time is devoted to investigating the relationships between pairs of variables. We might even say that this is the main purpose of science.

In the physical sciences many of these relationships between variables are virtually perfect. For example, suppose we decide to replicate Galileo's famous experiment in the field of physics. If we drop weights off the Leaning Tower of Pisa and keep very careful measurements of time (variable X) and distance traveled (variable Y), we would find that the relationship between the two variables can be described almost perfectly by the following equation

$$Y = 16X^2 \qquad \text{or} \qquad \text{Distance traveled} = 16(\text{time})^2$$

when distance is measured in feet and time is measured in seconds.

If all relationships were this precise, we would have no need for correlational statistics. However, in the behavioral sciences and in many other areas of human endeavor we usually work with imperfect relationships, and often these relationships cannot even be detected without using statistical methods. Nonetheless, these imperfect relationships are strong enough to be useful. We can use our knowledge of these relationships to make predictions that are much better than mere guesses. For example, the imperfect relationship between high school grades and college grades, between test scores and work performance, or between educational level and income can be used to make predictions that have practical applications.

## Three Tasks of Correlational Statistics

Correlational statistical techniques are used to perform three tasks that could not be done efficiently without them. The first task is to determine whether a relationship exists between two variables and, if so, to *measure the strength of the relationship*. This is accomplished by *computing the correlation coefficient*.

The second task is to *make the best possible predictions* of one variable from the other, based on our knowledge of the relationship between them. This is accomplished by *finding the regression line*.

The third task is to *forecast (in advance) the size of a typical prediction error*. This is accomplished by *calculating the standard error of estimate*.

The remainder of this chapter is devoted to the first task, that of measuring the strength of the relationship between two variables. We will deal with the other tasks in Chapters Eight and Nine.

## Measuring the Strength of the Relationship: A Visual Approach

Suppose that we are interested in the relationship between high school grades and college grades. We have followed 10 students through high school and college and have calculated their grade point averages (GPAs). Our results are shown in Table 7-2.

Table 7-2
High School and College Grade Point Averages for Ten Students

| Student # | X<br>High School GPA | Y<br>College GPA |
|:---:|:---:|:---:|
| 1 | 3.7 | 3.0 |
| 2 | 2.5 | 2.1 |
| 3 | 3.5 | 3.3 |
| 4 | 2.8 | 2.7 |
| 5 | 3.2 | 3.3 |
| 6 | 2.6 | 1.8 |
| 7 | 3.6 | 2.9 |
| 8 | 2.9 | 2.5 |
| 9 | 3.4 | 3.2 |
| 10 | 2.2 | 1.1 |

*The scattergram.* In Chapter Two we presented graphic techniques for describing a set of scores representing a single variable. In this chapter we present a similar graphic technique for illustrating the relationship between two variables. The technique, developed in the late 1800s by Francis Galton, is called a *scattergram* (or *scatterplot*).

*Conventions for constructing a scattergram.* Remember that in Chapter Two we had conventions for making graphs to ensure that these visual displays presented the information as efficiently as possible. We also have conventions for constructing a scattergram. A good scattergram should have the following characteristics:

(1) The variable to be used as a predictor (e.g., high school GPA) should be placed on the horizontal or X-axis, with an axis label and a numerical scale.
(2) The variable to be used as the criterion (the one you wish to predict) should be placed on the vertical or Y-axis, with an axis label and a numerical scale.
(3) The horizontal and vertical axes should be of equal length, using equal-sized intervals if possible.
(4) Each subject (student) should be represented on the scattergram by a dot at the intersection of his scores on the two variables.

*Interpreting a scattergram.* Figure 7-1 is a scattergram of the high school GPA and college GPA pairs for 10 students shown in Table 7-2. We can easily see in this scattergram that high school GPA and college GPA are strongly related, because the points representing the students seem to string out along a line.

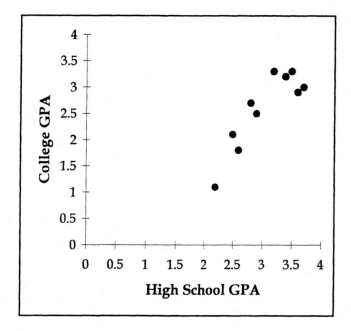

Figure 7-1. Scattergram for high school and college GPA data.

In the scattergram in Figure 7-2 we have roughly estimated and drawn in a line that minimizes the errors around itself (that is, we have drawn a line that minimizes the vertical distances of each point from the line). This line can be used to make rough predictions of college GPA from high school GPA. For example, suppose we know that Ryan's high school GPA is 3.5. To predict his college GPA we locate 3.5 on the horizontal axis in Figure 7-2; then we determine the vertical distance from this point on the horizontal axis to the line. This vertical distance is the predicted college GPA, for someone with a high school GPA of 3.5.

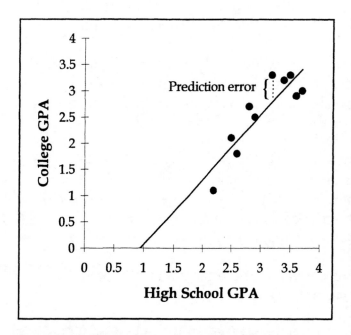

Figure 7-2. Scattergram for high school and college data with prediction (regression) line.

Note that while the line in Figure 7-2 represents predicted college GPAs, the dots represent the actual college GPAs. So when the dots string out closely along the line, the predictions are more accurate than when the dots are more widely scattered around the line. In fact, this is how we can visually determine the strength of a relationship. In a ***strong relationship*** the dots of the scattergram string out closely along a line; in a ***weak relationship*** the dots are scattered widely around a line. When there is ***no relationship*** the dots form a random pattern and no good prediction line can be found. Figure 7-3 shows several scattergrams illustrating different degrees of relationship.

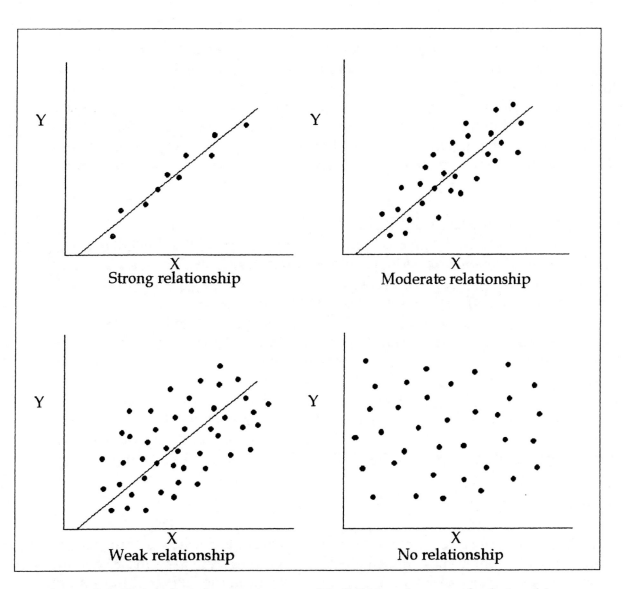

Figure 7-3. Examples of scattergrams with different degrees of relationship.

***Advantages and limitations of scattergrams.*** This graphic method provides a good, but rough, visual illustration of an imperfect relationship between a pair of variables. A scattergram summarizes the nature of the relationship, this information can be grasped quickly by someone without specialized training, and the very rough predictions made from the scattergram are better than simply guessing. On the other hand, there are also some serious drawbacks associated with scattergrams that limit their usefulness. First, constructing a scattergram can be very laborious and time consuming, especially when a large number of pairs of scores are involved. Second, a scattergram is imprecise. The assessment of the strength of the relationship can only be a rough estimate. Likewise, the location and angle of the prediction line can only be roughly approximated on a scattergram -- each person would draw a different prediction line. Third, a scattergram is a dead end technique. Once the scattergram is drawn, no further analysis is possible without retrieving the original pairs of scores and starting over.

For these reasons scattergrams are considered useful primarily for rough visual illustrations of relationships. Fortunately, much more precise numerical techniques are available for measuring the strength of a relationship and for making predictions based on the relationship. In practice these numerical techniques are used almost exclusively.

## Measuring the Strength of the Relationship: The Pearson r

The most widely used numerical procedure for measuring the strength of a relationship is the *Pearson product-moment correlation coefficient*. Karl Pearson, the protégé of Francis Galton, created this correlation coefficient in 1886. Since *r* is the symbol used for this coefficient, it is usually called the *Pearson r*.

Like the standard deviation (and almost everything else in statistics), the Pearson r is based on deviations of scores around the mean. However, in the case of a correlation we are working with a *bivariate distribution*. That is, now we are working with a distribution of two variables, rather than with a *univariate distribution* (which involves only a single variable) as we have in the past. The key for the correlation is how the scores on two variables vary together. And we can get a handle on how this works by comparing the univariate case with the bivariate case. In the univariate case we sum the squared deviations of the scores from the mean to get the sum of squares:

$$\text{Sum of squares} = \Sigma\left(X - \overline{X}\right)^2 = \Sigma\left[\left(X - \overline{X}\right)\left(X - \overline{X}\right)\right]$$

Similarly, in the bivariate case we can sum the products of the deviations of the scores on the first variable from its mean (deviations of the X scores from the X mean) and the deviations of the scores on the second variable from its mean (deviations of the Y scores from the Y mean) to get the *cross product*:

$$\text{Cross product} = \Sigma\left[\left(X - \overline{X}\right)\left(Y - \overline{Y}\right)\right]$$

Next, we average these values. In the univariate case we divide by N (the number of scores) to get the variance:

$$\text{Variance} = \frac{\Sigma\left(X - \overline{X}\right)^2}{N} = \frac{\Sigma\left[\left(X - \overline{X}\right)\left(X - \overline{X}\right)\right]}{N}$$

Similarly, in the bivariate case we divide by N (the number of pairs of scores) to get the *covariance*:

$$\text{Covariance} = \frac{\sum[(X - \bar{X})(Y - \bar{Y})]}{N}$$

While the variance gives us a measure of variation in a single variable, the covariance shows how much variation is shared by the two variables. Now we can compare this measure of the shared variance with the variances of the two individual variables by dividing the covariance by the standard deviations of the two variables. This value is the correlation coefficient:

$$r = \text{correlation coefficient} = \frac{\text{covariance}}{s_X s_Y} = \frac{\sum[(X - \bar{X})(Y - \bar{Y})]}{N s_X s_Y}$$

In effect, by dividing by the standard deviations of the individual variables we have standardized the scores. Remember that the deviation of a raw score from the mean, divided by the standard deviation is how we find a standard (z) score. So our correlation formula reduces to

$$r = \frac{\sum z_X z_Y}{N} = \frac{\sum(\text{standard score for X})(\text{standard score for Y})}{N}$$

So it turns out that our measure of correlation is simply the average of the products of the X scores expressed as z scores and the Y scores expressed as z scores.

This *standard score formula* for the correlation coefficient is simple to understand, but laborious to calculate. Therefore we prefer to use the following *raw score formula* that is much easier to compute using a hand calculator (even though it looks more complex):

$$r = \frac{\sum XY - \frac{\sum X \sum Y}{N}}{\sqrt{\left[\sum X^2 - \frac{(\sum X)^2}{N}\right]\left[\sum Y^2 - \frac{(\sum Y)^2}{N}\right]}}$$

where $\sum X$ is the sum of the X scores, $\sum Y$ is the sum of the Y scores, $\sum X^2$ is the sum of the squared X scores, $\sum Y^2$ is the sum of the squared Y scores, $\sum XY$ is the sum of the products of each pair of X and Y scores, and N is the number of pairs of scores. In this book we will use the raw score formula whenever we calculate the Pearson r correlation coefficient.

*Interpreting correlations.* The possible values of the correlation coefficient range from negative one to zero to positive one. A correlation of zero indicates no relationship between the two variables. A correlation of negative one or positive one indicates a perfect relationship in which variable Y can be predicted without error from variable X. A *positive correlation* indicates that as X increases, Y tends to increase also; a *negative correlation* indicates that as X increases, Y tends to decrease. To summarize, we can say that the absolute value of a correlation coefficient indicates the strength of the relationship and its sign tells us the direction of the relationship.

Table 7-3 provides some general rules of thumb for interpreting correlations of various sizes. Later we will develop a more sophisticated system for interpreting correlations, but for now this table can serve as our interpretation guide.

Table 7-3
Rules of Thumb for Interpreting Correlations of Various Sizes

| Correlation Coefficient | Strength of Relationship | Accuracy of Prediction |
| --- | --- | --- |
| .00 - .29 | Nonexistent or weak | Poor |
| .30 - .59 | Moderate | Fairly good classification into rough group (e.g., low versus high scores) |
| .60 - .89 | Strong | Few large prediction errors |
| .90 - 1.00 | Very strong | Very accurate predictions |

Figures 7-4 through 7-8 show scattergrams of correlations of various sizes. Note that the scattergram in Figure 7-8 shows a negative correlation. This negative correlation is easily distinguished by the fact that as X increases, Y decreases (the scattergram slopes down from left to right), while the remaining figures illustrate positive relationships in which X and Y tend to increase together (and the scattergrams slope up from left to right).

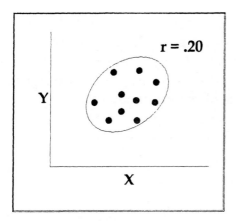

Figure 7-4. Scattergram for a weak relationship.

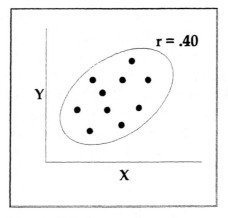

Figure 7-5. Scattergram for a moderate relationship.

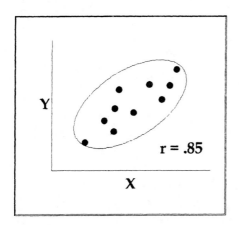

Figure 7-6. Scattergram for a strong relationship.

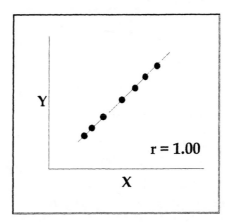

Figure 7-7. Scattergram for a perfect relationship.

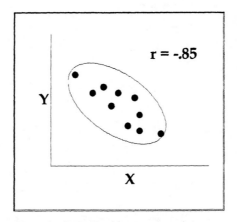

Figure 7-8. Scattergram for a strong negative relationship.

*Computing the Pearson r.* To illustrate the calculation of the Pearson r consider the following problem. A fast food company has had problems with high turnover among its employees. We are developing a test to help select employees who will be successful and remain on the job for a longer time. We give the test to some applicants, hire them all without looking at their test scores, and see how long they remain with the company. (Note that in practice we would want to use a large number of employees, but in this example we will use only five employees to keep our calculations simple.) The scores for our five employees are shown in Table 7-4.

Table 7-4
Test Scores and Length of Employment for Five Fast Food Company Employees

| Employee | Test Score (X) | Months Employed (Y) |
|---|---|---|
| 1 | 5 | 7 |
| 2 | 7 | 5 |
| 3 | 3 | 2 |
| 4 | 1 | 3 |
| 5 | 9 | 7 |

To determine the strength of the relationship between test score and months employed we use the raw score formula for the Pearson r correlation coefficient. Remember that the raw score formula for the Pearson r is

$$r = \frac{\sum XY - \dfrac{\sum X \sum Y}{N}}{\sqrt{\left[\sum X^2 - \dfrac{(\sum X)^2}{N}\right]\left[\sum Y^2 - \dfrac{(\sum Y)^2}{N}\right]}}$$

First, we make a worksheet and calculate the quantities we will need to plug into the formula, as shown in Table 7-5.

Table 7-5
Worksheet for Calculating the Quantities Needed for Computing the Pearson r

| Employee | X (Test Score) | $X^2$ | Y (Months Employed) | $Y^2$ | XY |
|----------|---------------|-------|--------------------|-------|-----|
| 1 | 5 | 25 | 7 | 49 | 35 |
| 2 | 7 | 49 | 5 | 25 | 35 |
| 3 | 3 | 9 | 2 | 4 | 6 |
| 4 | 1 | 1 | 3 | 9 | 3 |
| 5 | 9 | 81 | 7 | 49 | 63 |
| | $\sum X=25$ | $\sum X^2=165$ | $\sum Y=24$ | $\sum Y^2=136$ | $\sum XY=142$ |

Now we can plug the needed values into the formula and compute the Pearson r:

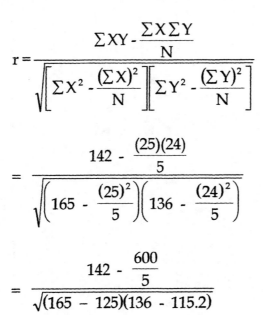

$$r = \frac{\sum XY - \dfrac{\sum X \sum Y}{N}}{\sqrt{\left[\sum X^2 - \dfrac{(\sum X)^2}{N}\right]\left[\sum Y^2 - \dfrac{(\sum Y)^2}{N}\right]}}$$

$$= \frac{142 - \dfrac{(25)(24)}{5}}{\sqrt{\left(165 - \dfrac{(25)^2}{5}\right)\left(136 - \dfrac{(24)^2}{5}\right)}}$$

$$= \frac{142 - \dfrac{600}{5}}{\sqrt{(165 - 125)(136 - 115.2)}}$$

$$= \frac{142 - 120}{\sqrt{(40)(20.8)}}$$

$$= \frac{22}{\sqrt{832}}$$

$$= \frac{22}{28.84} = .76$$

Our correlation of r = .76 tells us that there is a strong relationship (see Table 7-3) between the test score and how long employees last on the job. This should enable us to predict how long new applicants would stay on the job much better than if we had to guess; our predictions should seldom produce large errors. Therefore, if the company decided to use this test to select applicants it should be considerably more efficient.

Figure 7-9 shows a scattergram constructed from our test score/months on the job data in Table 7-4. Looking at the scattergram of the relationship, we can easily see that the employees with higher scores on X (test score) also tend to have higher scores on Y (months on the job). Furthermore, this tendency is rather pronounced. Of course, this visual representation of the relationship is what we expected based on our correlation coefficient of .76.

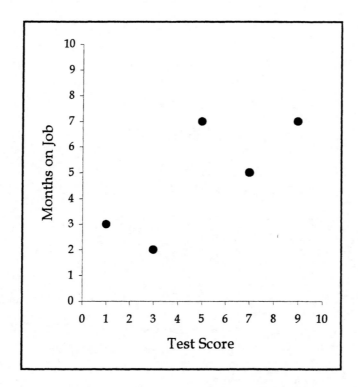

Figure 7-9. Scattergram of test score and months employees stay on the job.

## Study Questions
*Answers to selected questions may be found in Appendix A*

1. A clinical researcher has devised a measure of test anxiety and given it to 10 college students. She also recorded their GPAs. The data are shown in the table below. Construct a scattergram and visually estimate the strength of the relationship as weak, moderate, strong, or very strong. If you calculated the correlation coefficient, would it be positive or negative?

| Student | Test Anxiety Score | GPA |
|---------|---------|---------|
| 1 | 8 | 1.64 |
| 2 | 4 | 2.65 |
| 3 | 1 | 3.78 |
| 4 | 2 | 3.95 |
| 5 | 4 | 3.10 |
| 6 | 6 | 2.25 |
| 7 | 2 | 3.42 |
| 8 | 3 | 2.95 |
| 9 | 5 | 2.18 |
| 10 | 1 | 3.23 |

2. A social scientist wonders if height is related to income. He obtains height and salary information for ten executives. Calculate the Pearson r for this set of data and interpret the correlation coefficient in terms of the strength and direction of the relationship.

| Executive | Height (in inches) | Salary (in thousands of dollars) |
|---------|---------|---------|
| 1 | 77 | 46.5 |
| 2 | 64 | 33.1 |
| 3 | 68 | 36.5 |
| 4 | 70 | 38.3 |
| 5 | 63 | 33.1 |
| 6 | 60 | 33.0 |
| 7 | 67 | 42.1 |
| 8 | 69 | 45.2 |
| 9 | 72 | 46.1 |
| 10 | 67 | 37.2 |

3. An elementary school teacher is interested in whether there is a relationship between scores on a reading readiness test administered to preschool children and how well those children perform on spelling tests during the first year of school. She obtains the reading readiness scores and spelling grades for a group of 8 children. Calculate the Pearson r for this set of data and interpret the correlation coefficient in terms of the strength and direction of the relationship.

| Child | Reading Readiness Score | Spelling Grade |
|-------|-------------------------|----------------|
| 1 | 22 | 94 |
| 2 | 16 | 90 |
| 3 | 9 | 74 |
| 4 | 12 | 82 |
| 5 | 5 | 70 |
| 6 | 18 | 89 |
| 7 | 15 | 86 |
| 8 | 13 | 79 |

# Regression: Making the Best Possible Predictions

In Chapter One and again in Chapter Seven we said that there are three tasks that we hope to accomplish using correlational techniques. The first task is to determine the strength of the relationship between two variables. This is done by computing the correlation coefficient, which was the subject of Chapter Seven. The second task is to make the best possible prediction of one variable from the other, and is the subject of this chapter. The third task, to forecast the size of the prediction errors, will be discussed in the next chapter.

We accomplish the task of making optimal predictions of one variable from another by finding the equation of a line called the *regression line*. The reason for this rather strange sounding name is a historical accident. You may recall that Francis Galton invented the scattergram and did much of the early work on correlational techniques. When Galton was examining the relationship between the height of fathers and their sons, he noticed that the heights of the sons of the tallest fathers tended to also be above average, but not as much as their extremely tall fathers. That is, the heights of sons of very tall fathers tended to "regress" or fall back toward the mean. Therefore he called the line that described this phenomenon a regression line. He could have more simply called it a prediction line, because that is what it is. The regression line is the line that generates the best predictions of one variable from the other.

To illustrate the regression line, consider the example from Chapter Seven of a fast food company developing a test to predict the length of time employees will stay on the job. The data from this example are reproduced here in Table 8-1, and Figure 8-1 shows a scattergram based on the data. Remember that in Chapter Seven we found that the correlation between test score and months on the job was r = .76. According to our interpretation chart (Table 7-3), this is a strong correlation and should allow us to make predictions of months on the job with few large errors.

Table 8-1
Test Scores and Length of Employment for Five Fast Food Company Employees

| Employee | Test Score (X) | Months Employed (Y) |
|----------|----------------|---------------------|
| 1 | 5 | 7 |
| 2 | 7 | 5 |
| 3 | 3 | 2 |
| 4 | 1 | 3 |
| 5 | 9 | 7 |

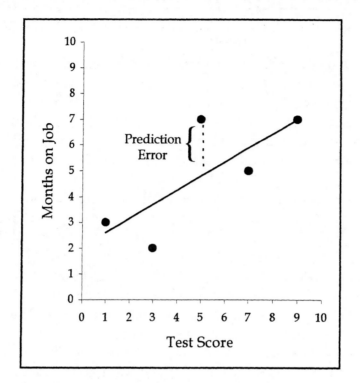

Figure 8-1. Scattergram with regression line.

In the scattergram in Figure 8-1 the solid line passing through the set of points is the regression (or prediction) line. The vertical distance between each point and the regression line (represented for one case by a dotted line) is the prediction error for that employee. The best possible regression line is the line that will minimize the sum of the squared prediction errors (around the line). So, here we have another version of a sum of squares (which we first talked about in Chapter Four). We could graphically estimate the regression line as in Figure 8-1 by attempting to draw a line through the middle of the points, but this estimate would be inexact and could be quite inaccurate. Instead, we would like to find the exact equation of the ideal regression line.

To create the ideal regression (prediction) line, we must find the equation of the straight line that will produce the minimum sum of squared errors around itself. This equation is called a least squares solution (it minimizes the sum of the squared errors). Mathematically, finding this equation is a classical minimization problem requiring calculus. Fortunately, mathematicians love to do this sort of thing, and they have graciously solved our problem for us. We have only to employ their solution. However, before we can do this, we need to be familiar with the analytical geometry of a straight line.

## The Analytical Geometry of a Straight Line

If we look at the graph of a straight line (for example, consider the line shown in Figure 8-2), two characteristics of the line turn out to be critical. First, the line has a *slope*, or a certain amount of steepness. The slope can range from steep to flat. Figure 8-3 shows a set of lines with different slopes.

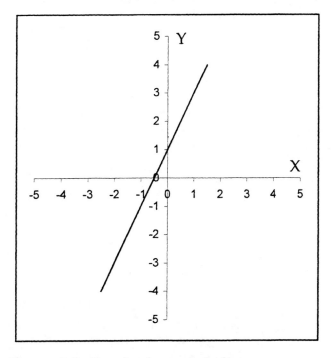

Figure 8-2. Graph of a straight line.

Slope is defined mathematically as the amount of change in Y relative to the amount of change in X for any particular line:

$$\text{Slope} = \frac{\text{Change in Y}}{\text{Change in X}}$$

In mathematics the Greek letter delta ($\Delta$) is often used to denote change, so we can rewrite our equation using this symbol:

$$\text{Slope} = \frac{\Delta Y}{\Delta X}$$

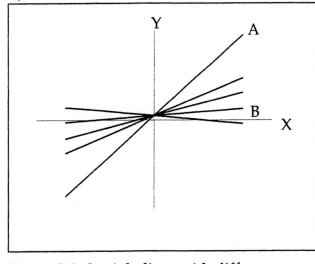

Figure 8-3. Straight lines with different slopes.

Note that for line A in Figure 8-3 a small change in X produces a large change in Y, because the slope of line A is steep. On the other hand, for line B the same amount of change in X produces only a small change in Y, because the slope of line B is relatively flat.

The second characteristic of a straight line is that at some point it crosses the Y-axis. The value of Y at the point where the line crosses the Y-axis (where X = 0) is called the *Y intercept*. Figure 8-4 shows a set of lines all of which have the same slope, but different Y intercepts.

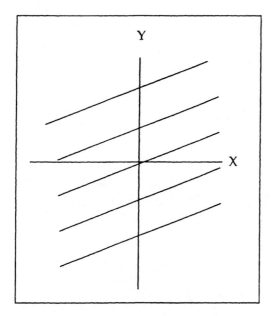

Figure 8-4. Straight lines with different Y intercepts.

The combination of its slope and Y intercept uniquely defines any straight line. That is, for any particular combination of slope and Y intercept there will be only one straight line that is described by that combination. Once we know the slope and the Y intercept of a line, we can write the equation of that line. The equation of any straight line is of the following form:

$$Y = \text{slope}(X) + Y\text{ intercept}$$

Or, if we let *b* represent the slope and *a* represent the Y intercept, the equation for a straight line can be written:

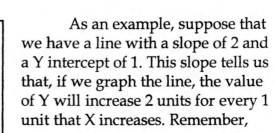

$$Y = bX + a$$

Slope ⟋ ⟍ Y intercept

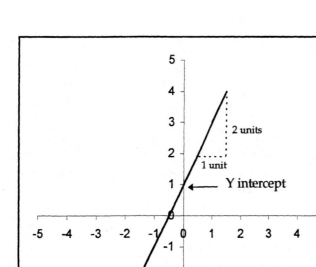

Figure 8-5. Graph of the equation Y = 2X +1.

As an example, suppose that we have a line with a slope of 2 and a Y intercept of 1. This slope tells us that, if we graph the line, the value of Y will increase 2 units for every 1 unit that X increases. Remember,

$$\text{Slope} = \frac{\text{Change in Y}}{\text{Change in X}} = \frac{\Delta Y}{\Delta X}$$

And the Y intercept of 1 tells us that the line will cross the Y-axis where Y = 1. Since the equation for any straight line is of the form
Y = slope (X) + Y intercept
or Y = bX + a, the equation for the line in our example is Y = 2X +1. Figure 8-5 shows the graph of this line.

## Finding the Equation for the Regression Line

Returning to our search for the best regression (or prediction) line, we need to find only the slope and Y intercept of our regression line to uniquely define it. As mentioned earlier, the best regression line is the line that minimizes the sum of the squared prediction errors around it. So we need to find the slope and Y intercept of the line that meets this requirement. Mathematicians, using calculus, have done the hard work for us and we have only to apply their results. It turns out that we can find the slope and Y intercept of the regression line using many of the same quantities that we used in computing the correlation coefficient (Chapter Seven). First, we find the slope using the formula:

$$b = \text{slope} = \frac{\text{Change in Y}}{\text{Change in X}} = \frac{\Delta Y}{\Delta X} = \frac{\Sigma XY - \dfrac{\Sigma X \Sigma Y}{N}}{\Sigma X^2 - \dfrac{(\Sigma X)^2}{N}}$$

where $\Sigma X$ is the sum of the X scores, $\Sigma Y$ is the sum of the Y scores, $\Sigma X^2$ is the sum of the squared X scores, $\Sigma XY$ is the sum of the products of X multiplied by Y for each XY pair of scores, and N is the number of pairs of scores.

Second, we find the Y intercept using the formula:

$$a = \text{Y intercept} = \overline{Y} - b\overline{X}$$

where $\overline{Y}$ is the mean of the Y scores, b is the slope that we just found in the previous step, and $\overline{X}$ is the mean of the X scores.

The form of the equation for a regression line is nearly identical to the form of the equation for any straight line. However, note that we use Y' as the symbol representing the predicted value of Y in our regression equation to distinguish it from the actual value of Y (which will almost always be somewhat different). Thus, the equation for a regression line will be of the form

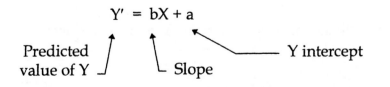

$$Y' = bX + a$$

Predicted value of Y    Slope    Y intercept

Our final step in finding the regression line is to plug the values for the slope and Y intercept into this general equation for a regression line.

# Finding the Equation of a Regression Line: An example

To illustrate the computations involved in finding the equation of a regression line, consider our example data on a test for predicting how long fast food employees will remain on the job. Table 8-2 shows these data (reproduced from Table 8-1) in the form of a worksheet with some necessary quantities also provided.

Table 8-2
Test Scores and Length of Employment for Five Fast Food Company Employees

| Employee | X (Test Score) | X² | Y (Months Employed) | XY |
|----------|----------------|-----|----------------------|-----|
| 1 | 5 | 25 | 7 | 35 |
| 2 | 7 | 49 | 5 | 35 |
| 3 | 3 | 9 | 2 | 6 |
| 4 | 1 | 1 | 3 | 3 |
| 5 | 9 | 81 | 7 | 63 |
| | $\Sigma X=25$ | $\Sigma X^2=165$ | $\Sigma Y=24$ | $\Sigma XY=142$ |

$$\overline{X}=\frac{\Sigma X}{N}=\frac{25}{5}=5 \qquad \overline{Y}=\frac{\Sigma Y}{N}=\frac{24}{5}=4.80$$

The first step is to calculate the slope of the regression line:

$$b=slope=\frac{\Sigma XY-\dfrac{\Sigma X \Sigma Y}{N}}{\Sigma X^2-\dfrac{(\Sigma X)^2}{N}}=\frac{142-\dfrac{(25)(24)}{5}}{165-\dfrac{(25)^2}{5}}=\frac{142-120}{165-125}=\frac{22}{40}=.55$$

Second, we calculate the Y intercept, which requires that we plug in the value we just obtained for the slope ($b = .55$):

$$a = Y \text{ intercept} = \overline{Y} - b\overline{X} = 4.80 - (.55)(5) = 4.80 - 2.75 = 2.05$$

Finally, we must plug these values for the slope and Y intercept into the equation for the regression line:

Predicted value of Y  =  (slope) X + Y intercept

$$Y' = bX + a$$

$$Y' = .55X + 2.05$$

## Using the Regression Equation to Make Predictions

So far, we have generated the equation for the regression line that will have a smaller sum of squared errors around it than any other possible straight line would have. This equation can be written in several ways:

$$Y' = .55X + 2.05 \qquad \text{or} \qquad \text{Predicted value of Y} = (.55)(\text{value of X}) + 2.05$$

Or, in our specific case relating test scores to how long fast food employees remain on the job:

$$\text{Predicted number of months on the job} = (.55)(\text{test score}) + 2.05$$

We can look at the regression equation as a rule that specifies the relationship between test score and months on the job for any specific test score. This allows us to make the best possible prediction of how long a person with any possible test score will stay on the job. As an example, consider Joe, an applicant who scored 6 on the test. What is our best possible prediction of how long Joe will stay on the job? To answer this question we plug Joe's test score into our regression equation and solve for Y' (the predicted value of Y).

$$\text{Predicted value of Y} = .55(\text{test score}) + 2.05$$

$$Y' = .55X + 2.05$$

$$Y' = .55(6) + 2.05$$

$$Y' = 3.30 + 2.05$$

$$Y' = 5.35$$

Our best possible prediction is that Joe will stay on the job for 5.35 months. The mean length of stay on the job is 4.80 months (see Table 8-2). Therefore we would probably want to hire Joe, because he appears to be likely to stay on the job longer than the average.

If we look again at our example data (Table 8-3) and the scattergram with the regression line (Figure 8-6), we see that the regression line is indeed an ideal fit to the data. Note also that the prediction errors are rather small (as our correlation coefficient of $r = .76$ indicated they would be).

Table 8-3
Test Scores and Length of Employment for Five Fast Food Company Employees

| Employee | Test Score (X) | Months Employed (Y) |
|:---:|:---:|:---:|
| 1 | 5 | 7 |
| 2 | 7 | 5 |
| 3 | 3 | 2 |
| 4 | 1 | 3 |
| 5 | 9 | 7 |

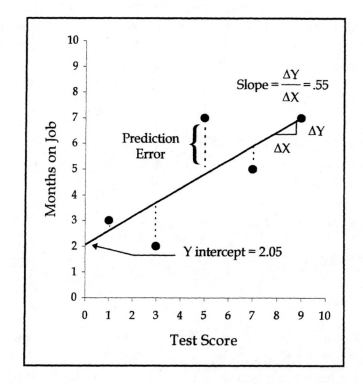

Figure 8-6. Scattergram of fast food example data with regression line.

## Study Questions
*Answers to selected questions may be found in Appendix A*

1.  In the study questions for Chapter 7, data were presented on the relationship between a person's score on a measure of test anxiety and his or her GPA. The data set is reproduced below. Determine the equation for the regression line and predict the GPA for an individual that scores 7 on the test anxiety measure.

| Student | Test Anxiety Score | GPA |
|---------|--------------------|-----|
| 1 | 8 | 1.64 |
| 2 | 4 | 2.65 |
| 3 | 1 | 3.78 |
| 4 | 2 | 3.95 |
| 5 | 4 | 3.10 |
| 6 | 6 | 2.25 |
| 7 | 2 | 3.42 |
| 8 | 3 | 2.95 |
| 9 | 5 | 2.18 |
| 10 | 1 | 3.23 |

2.  A human resources manager has devised an aptitude test that he wants to use for hiring decisions. He has given the test to 12 employees and tracked their productivity in terms of the average number of units produced per day. These data are shown in the table below. Determine the equation for the regression line and predict the average number of units produced per day for an individual that scores 20 on the aptitude test.

| Employee | Aptitude Test Score | Avg. No. of Units Produced/day |
|----------|---------------------|-------------------------------|
| 1 | 12 | 25 |
| 2 | 25 | 57 |
| 3 | 16 | 38 |
| 4 | 19 | 44 |
| 5 | 22 | 45 |
| 6 | 18 | 49 |
| 7 | 17 | 42 |
| 8 | 21 | 54 |
| 9 | 15 | 35 |
| 10 | 18 | 38 |
| 11 | 21 | 42 |
| 12 | 14 | 33 |

3. A field biologist is interested in whether the water temperature can be used to predict the number of mating calls by a particular species of frog. For 10 days she measures the temperature of a pond at dusk and monitors the average number of mating calls per hour made over a 12 hour period roughly from dusk to dawn. Her data are shown in the table below. Determine the equation for the regression line and predict the number of mating calls expected if the water temperature is 19.2°C.

| Day | Water Temperature (°C) | Avg. No. of Mating Calls/Hr. |
|-----|------------------------|------------------------------|
| 1 | 16.4 | 5 |
| 2 | 14.8 | 7 |
| 3 | 18.2 | 10 |
| 4 | 19.8 | 12 |
| 5 | 18.7 | 10 |
| 6 | 20.5 | 15 |
| 7 | 19.9 | 16 |
| 8 | 17.5 | 13 |
| 9 | 17.9 | 15 |
| 10 | 18.4 | 15 |

# Forecasting Error in Prediction

One more time, recall that there are three tasks associated with correlational statistics. First, we measure the strength of the relationship between two variables by computing the correlation coefficient. This was the subject of Chapter Seven. Second, we make optimal predictions of one variable from the other. We do this by finding the equation of the regression line. This was the subject of Chapter Eight. The third task is to forecast the size of a typical prediction error. This task is the subject of the present chapter. Once we understand the concept of forecasting the size of prediction errors, we will also be able to develop a more sophisticated system of interpreting a correlation than the crude one we presented in Chapter Seven.

## Forecasting Prediction Error
When we make predictions of one variable from another using the equation of the regression line, our predictions will be the best that we can make, but they will still not be perfectly accurate. Therefore, it would be very useful to us to be able to know in advance how large a typical prediction error would be. As an example, consider the set of data (from Chapters Seven and Eight) in Table 9-1 relating test scores to how long applicants stay on the job at a fast food chain. Figure 9-1 shows the scattergram of the data from Table 9-1, including the regression (prediction) line and prediction errors around the regression line.

Table 9-1
Test Scores and Length of Employment for Five Fast Food Company Employees

| Employee | Test Score (X) | Months Employed (Y) |
|:--------:|:--------------:|:-------------------:|
| 1 | 5 | 7 |
| 2 | 7 | 5 |
| 3 | 3 | 2 |
| 4 | 1 | 3 |
| 5 | 9 | 7 |

The prediction error for each subject (employee) is the difference between her actual time on the job (Y) and the time on the job predicted by our regression equation (Y'). That is,

Prediction error $= (Y - Y') =$ (actual value of Y - predicted value of Y)

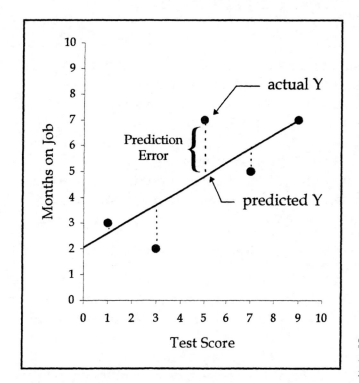

Figure 9-1. Fast food prediction data with prediction errors.

Graphically, the prediction error is the vertical distance from the actual value of Y (for a given subject) to the regression line. These prediction errors for each of the five subjects in our example are drawn on the scattergram in Figure 9-1.

To calculate the standard deviation of these prediction errors we can use the old, familiar standard deviation formula from Chapter Four:

$$\text{Standard deviation} = \sqrt{\frac{\Sigma(\text{score} - \text{mean})^2}{N}}$$

Since the "score" in this case is a prediction error, our formula becomes

$$\text{Standard deviation of prediction errors} = \sqrt{\frac{\Sigma(\text{error} - \text{mean error})^2}{N}}$$

Note, however, that the mean prediction error around the regression line will always be zero. This is an inherent characteristic of a regression line, since it runs through the "middle" of the set of points. We can see and intuitively understand this by looking at Figure 9-1. About half the points are above the regression line (and represent positive errors) and half are below (and represent negative errors). Thus, these positive and negative differences between the points and the regression line will cancel each other and average out to zero. So our formula becomes

$$\text{Standard deviation of prediction errors} = \sqrt{\frac{\Sigma(\text{error} - \text{mean error})^2}{N}}$$

$$= \sqrt{\frac{\Sigma(\text{error} - 0)^2}{N}}$$

$$= \sqrt{\frac{\Sigma(\text{error})^2}{N}}$$

This quantity is a special kind of standard deviation and is called the ***standard error of estimate.*** The notation $s_{est}$ is commonly used to represent the standard error of estimate. So,

$$s_{est} = \text{standard error of estimate}$$

$$= \text{standard deviation of prediction errors around the regression line}$$

$$= \sqrt{\frac{\Sigma(\text{prediction errors})^2}{N}}$$

$$= \sqrt{\frac{\Sigma(\text{actual value of Y - predicted value of Y})^2}{N}}$$

$$= \sqrt{\frac{\Sigma(Y - Y')^2}{N}}$$

Once we know the standard error of estimate we actually know quite a lot, because the standard error of estimate is a standard deviation and because prediction errors are normally distributed. That is, now we can apply our knowledge of the normal curve and use our normal curve tables to tell us how many errors of any given size we would make if we used the regression equation to make predictions of Y. This is almost magic! Remember from Chapter Five that in a normal distribution the number of cases falling within any given distance of the mean is easily found; we just have to express the distance in standard deviation (or z-score) units.

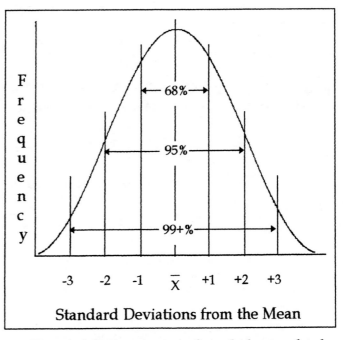

Figure 9-2. Percentages for whole standard deviation units under the normal curve.

Figure 9-2 summarizes this information by showing the percentages of scores falling within 1, 2, or 3 standard deviations of the mean.

Our regression line can be thought of as a sliding mean and the standard error of estimate is the standard deviation of errors around it. This is illustrated in Figure 9-3.

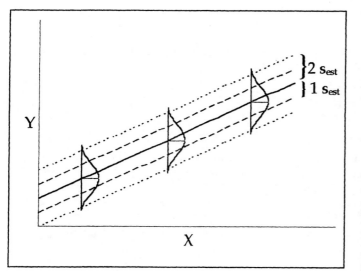

Figure 9-3. Normal distribution of errors around the regression line.

A critic might protest that this is not very useful because we must already have made our predictions and computed the prediction errors (Y - Y′) before we can calculate their standard deviation. (Remember, we want to be able to forecast the size of the standard deviation of prediction errors). So this is somewhat like locking the barn after the horse has been stolen. Fortunately, there is another way to calculate the standard error of estimate that does not require that we first make each prediction and then compute each prediction error. That is, we can *forecast* what the standard error of estimate will be if we know the correlation between the two variables. Thus, the formula used to forecast the standard error of estimate is

$s_{est}$ = standard error of estimate

= standard deviation of prediction errors

= standard deviation of Y $\sqrt{1 - (\text{correlation})^2}$

= $s_Y \sqrt{1 - r^2}$

And, in summary

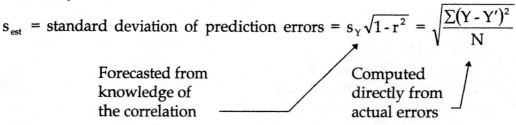

$$s_{est} = \text{standard deviation of prediction errors} = s_Y \sqrt{1 - r^2} = \sqrt{\frac{\Sigma(Y - Y')^2}{N}}$$

Forecasted from
knowledge of
the correlation

Computed
directly from
actual errors

The truly obstinate critic might still protest that our formula for forecasting the standard error of estimate from knowledge of the correlation still requires us to know the standard deviation of Y. However, this is not much of a problem because the standard deviation of Y (the criterion variable) is usually known, can be readily obtained from past data, or at the very least, can be estimated from the sample data in our study.

## Computing the Standard Error of Estimate

To illustrate the computation of the standard error of estimate, consider our example in which we want to predict how long employees will stay on the job in a fast food restaurant. Fast food restaurants have been around for many years; and this particular fast food restaurant has probably also been in operation for at least a few years. So we know from past experience how long employees tend to stay on the job. What we want to know now is: If we use this test as a predictor, how well will we be able to predict the length of time individuals will stay on the job?

The standard error of estimate provides us with the answer to this question. Because we have already (in Chapter Seven) calculated the correlation between test score and months on the job ($r = .76$), we can use it to forecast the value of the standard error of estimate. First, we calculate the standard deviation of the Y scores (months on the job) using the data from Table 9-1 (reproduced here as Table 9-2):

Table 9-2
Test Scores and Length of Employment for Five Fast Food Company Employees

| Employee | Test Score (X) | Months Employed (Y) |
|----------|----------------|---------------------|
| 1 | 5 | 7 |
| 2 | 7 | 5 |
| 3 | 3 | 2 |
| 4 | 1 | 3 |
| 5 | 9 | 7 |
| | | $\sum Y = 24$ |
| | | $\sum Y^2 = 136$ |

Using our old raw score formula for the standard deviation (from Chapter Four), but using Y instead of X as the variable in the formula, we calculate the standard deviation as follows:

$$s_Y = \text{standard deviation of } Y = \sqrt{\frac{\sum Y^2 - \frac{(\sum Y)^2}{N}}{N}} = \sqrt{\frac{136 - \frac{(24)^2}{5}}{5}}$$

$$= \sqrt{\frac{136 - 115.2}{5}} = \sqrt{\frac{20.8}{5}} = \sqrt{4.16} = 2.04$$

Now we can forecast the standard deviation of our prediction errors. That is, now we calculate the standard error of estimate:

$s_{est}$ = standard error of estimate = standard deviation of prediction errors

$$= \text{standard deviation of } Y \sqrt{1 - (\text{correlation})^2}$$

$$= s_Y \sqrt{1 - r^2}$$

$$= 2.04 \sqrt{1 - (.76)^2}$$

$$= 2.04 \sqrt{1 - .58}$$

$$= 2.04 \sqrt{.42}$$

$$= 2.04(.65)$$

$$= 1.33$$

As a check, we can make actual predictions, calculate the prediction errors, and compute the standard deviation of these prediction errors. For this example, we can use the equation for the regression line (which we computed in Chapter Eight) to make a prediction for every fast food employee in our study. Then we can compare each prediction ($Y'$) to that employee's actual length of employment ($Y$) to get each prediction error. Finally, we can calculate the standard deviation of these prediction errors. It should be the same value as we forecasted (1.33). This check is shown below.

Recall from Chapter Eight that our regression equation for this fast food company example data is

$$Y' = .55X + 2.05 \qquad \text{or}$$

Predicted length of employment = .55(test score) + 2.05

Using our example data in Table 9-2, we substitute each employee's test score for X in the regression equation to get a predicted number of months of employment (Y') for each employee:

$$Y'_{employee\ 1} = .55(5) + 2.05 = 4.80$$
$$Y'_{employee\ 2} = .55(7) + 2.05 = 5.90$$
$$Y'_{employee\ 3} = .55(3) + 2.05 = 3.70$$
$$Y'_{employee\ 4} = .55(1) + 2.05 = 2.60$$
$$Y'_{employee\ 5} = .55(9) + 2.05 = 7.00$$

Now we compute our prediction errors (Y - Y') and find the standard deviation of these prediction errors (the standard error of estimate) as shown in Table 9-3.

Table 9-3
Test Scores and Length of Employment for Five Fast Food Company Employees:
Computation of Standard Error of Estimate

| Employee | X<br>Test<br>Score | Y<br>Actual # of<br>Months Employed | Y'<br>Predicted # of<br>Months Employed | Y - Y'<br>Prediction<br>Error | (Y - Y')²<br>Squared<br>Prediction Error |
|---|---|---|---|---|---|
| 1 | 5 | 7 | 4.80 | 2.20 | 4.84 |
| 2 | 7 | 5 | 5.90 | -0.90 | 0.81 |
| 3 | 3 | 2 | 3.70 | -1.70 | 2.89 |
| 4 | 1 | 3 | 2.60 | 0.40 | 0.16 |
| 5 | 9 | 7 | 7.00 | 0.00 | 0.00 |
| | | | | | $\Sigma(Y-Y')^2 = 8.70$ |

$S_{est}$ = standard error of estimate

= standard deviation of prediction errors

$$= \sqrt{\frac{\Sigma(Y-Y')^2}{N}}$$

$$= \sqrt{\frac{8.70}{5}}$$

$$= \sqrt{1.74} = 1.32$$

113

This value of the standard error of estimate (1.32) calculated directly from actual prediction errors is within rounding error of the value of the standard error of estimate (1.33) that we forecasted using our knowledge of the correlation. So our check indicates that our method of forecasting the standard error of estimate really does work (and it is easier than having to make actual predictions and calculate the prediction errors first)!

## Interpreting Correlations Revisited

In Chapter Seven we presented a table (Table 7-3) that provided rules of thumb for making rough interpretations of correlation coefficients of various sizes. Now, armed with an understanding of the standard error of estimate, we are in position to develop a much more sophisticated system for interpreting correlations. This system is based on a comparison of prediction error and guessing error.

*Guessing error.* Assume that in our fast food company example we had no knowledge of X (the test scores) and therefore could only guess at Y (number of months the newly hired employees would remain on the job). It turns out that our best guessing strategy would be to always guess the mean of Y. The reason for this is that the sum of squares (and, hence, the standard deviation) around the mean is smaller than it would be around any other value. Table 9-4 shows our best guess (the mean) for each fast food employee in our example and the guessing error.

Table 9-4
Best Guesses (the Mean) and Actual Months of Employment for Five Fast Food Company Employees

| Employee | $Y$ <br> Actual # of Months Employed | $\bar{Y}$ <br> Best Guess | $Y - \bar{Y}$ <br> Guessing Error | $(Y - \bar{Y})^2$ <br> Squared Guessing Error |
|---|---|---|---|---|
| 1 | 7 | 4.80 | 2.20 | 4.84 |
| 2 | 5 | 4.80 | 0.20 | 0.04 |
| 3 | 2 | 4.80 | -2.80 | 7.84 |
| 4 | 3 | 4.80 | -1.80 | 3.24 |
| 5 | 7 | 4.80 | 2.20 | 4.84 |

$\Sigma Y = 24$ $\qquad$ $\Sigma(Y - \bar{Y}) = 0$ $\quad$ $\Sigma(Y - \bar{Y})^2 = 20.80$

$$\bar{Y} = \frac{\Sigma Y}{N} = \frac{24}{5} = 4.80$$

Note that when we guess the mean, the sum of the guessing errors will always be zero. So the average guessing error will zero and the sum of squares for guessing error will be

$$\sum(\text{Guessing error} - \text{Mean guessing error})^2 = \sum[(Y - \overline{Y}) - 0]^2 = \sum(Y - \overline{Y})^2$$

This is nothing other than the sum of the squared guessing errors, or deviations around the mean of Y. So the standard deviation of our guessing errors (when we employ the best guessing strategy by always guessing the Y mean) will always be the plain old standard deviation of Y. In Chapter Four we presented the deviation score formula for calculating the standard deviation. Now we use this deviation score formula in terms of Y (instead of X as we usually see it) to calculate the standard deviation of guessing errors:

Standard deviation of guessing errors = standard deviation of Y when we use the best guessing strategy (always guessing the Y mean)

$$= \sqrt{\frac{\sum(Y - \overline{Y})^2}{N}}$$

$$= \sqrt{\frac{20.80}{5}}$$

$$= \sqrt{4.16}$$

$$= 2.04$$

***Prediction error versus guessing error.*** Now we can compare our overall prediction error with our overall guessing error. Remember that our measure of the overall prediction error is the standard error of estimate (the standard deviation of the prediction errors), and our measure of the overall guessing error is the standard deviation of Y (the standard deviation of guessing errors).

$s_{est}$ = standard error of estimate = standard deviation of prediction errors = 1.32

and

$s_Y$ = standard deviation of Y = standard deviation of guessing errors = 2.04

Notice that the standard deviation of our prediction errors around the regression line (the standard error of estimate) is less than the standard deviation of Y (the standard deviation of guessing errors). This tells us that when we use our regression equation (that is, when we use our knowledge of the relationship between X and Y) to predict Y, our errors in prediction will be smaller than the errors we would make if we had to guess. In fact, if a correlation exists between X and Y, it will always be true that the prediction errors will be smaller than the guessing errors. Furthermore, when the correlation between X and Y is stronger, the disparity between the size of the guessing error and the size of the prediction error will be larger.

Now we can directly compare the prediction error to the guessing error for our fast food example by forming a ratio:

$$\frac{\text{Standard deviation of prediction errors}}{\text{Standard deviation of guessing errors}} = \frac{\text{Standard error of the estimate}}{\text{Standard deviation of Y}} = \frac{s_{est}}{s_Y} = \frac{1.32}{2.04} = .65$$

Our ability to interpret the fast food correlation rests on this ratio. It tells us that our overall prediction error is only 65% as large as our overall error if we guess. Figure 9-4 shows a scattergram of both our prediction errors around the regression line and our guessing errors around the mean. In Figure 9-4 we can easily see that, overall, the prediction errors are smaller.

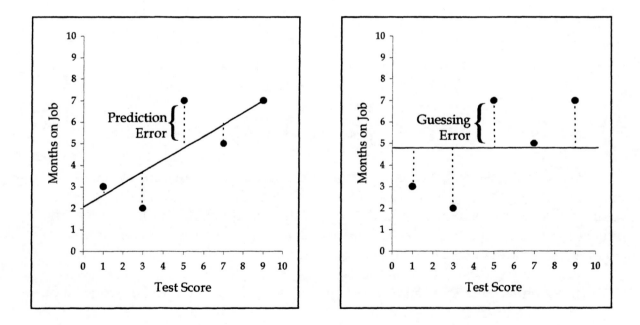

Figure 9-4. Prediction errors versus guessing errors for fast food study data.

*Quantitative interpretation of correlation.* We are now in position to develop a sophisticated quantitative system of interpretation for the Pearson r correlation coefficient. We simply take the relationships, formulae, and definitions that we have developed so far in this chapter and combine them, using a little bit of simple algebra and a dollop of logic.

We begin with our formula for forecasting the standard error of estimate from our knowledge of the correlation:

$$\text{standard error of estimate} = \text{standard deviation of Y} \sqrt{1 - (\text{correlation})^2}$$

$$s_{est} = s_Y \sqrt{1 - r^2}$$

If we divide both sides of the equation by $s_Y$, we get

$$\frac{s_{est}}{s_Y} = \sqrt{1 - r^2}$$

Recall that the standard error of estimate ($s_{est}$) is the standard deviation of prediction errors and that the standard deviation of Y ($s_Y$) is the standard deviation of guessing errors. So we can plug these definitions into the equation:

$$\frac{\text{Standard deviation of prediction errors}}{\text{Standard deviation of guessing errors}} = \sqrt{1 - r^2}$$

Now we can simplify the equation by noting that the ratio on the left of the equation is a proportion -- the proportion of guessing error still remaining when we predict using the regression line instead. So the equation can be rewritten as

$$\text{Proportion of guessing error remaining in our predictions} = \sqrt{1 - r^2}$$

This quantity, which is frequently used in the interpretation of correlations, is called the *coefficient of alienation* and represented by the symbol *k*.

$$k = \text{coefficient of alienation}$$

$$= \text{proportion of guessing error remaining in our predictions}$$

$$= \sqrt{1 - r^2}$$

However, often what we are interested in is not how much guessing error is left in our predictions, but rather what proportion of guessing error we are able to eliminate by making predictions using our regression equation. Once we know the coefficient of alienation, it is easy to get this new information. We know that

| Amount of error eliminated by making predictions | = | Total amount of guessing error | - | Amount of guessing error remaining in our predictions |

Expressing this as a proportion of the total of guessing error, we get

| Proportion of guessing error eliminated by making predictions | = | 1 | - | Proportion of guessing error remaining in our predictions |

or

| Proportion of guessing error eliminated by making predictions | = | 1 | - | Coefficient of alienation |

$$= 1 - k$$

$$= 1 - \sqrt{1 - r^2}$$

This quantity, which is also frequently used in the interpretation of correlations, is called the *index of forecasting efficiency*. The symbol for the index of forecasting efficiency is *E*. Thus,

$$E = \text{Index of forecasting efficiency} = \text{Proportion of guessing error eliminated by making predictions} = 1 - k = 1 - \sqrt{1 - r^2}$$

These two quantities (E and k) allow us to interpret the strength of correlations in terms of a standard deviation (of guessing errors). They tell us the proportion by which the standard deviation of guessing errors is reduced by making predictions (in the case of E -- the index of forecasting efficiency), or the proportion of the standard deviation of guessing errors still remaining in our predictions (in the case of k -- the coefficient of alienation).

However, sometimes we find it useful to interpret the strength of correlations in terms of a variance, rather than a standard deviation. To do this, we return to our basic standard error of estimate formula

$$s_{est} = s_Y \sqrt{1 - r^2}$$

If we divide both sides of the equation by $s_Y$, we get

$$\frac{s_{est}}{s_Y} = \sqrt{1 - r^2}$$

Next, if we square both sides of the equation, we get

$$\frac{s_{est}^2}{s_Y^2} = 1 - r^2$$

Looking at the left side of the equation, since $s_{est}$ is the standard deviation of prediction errors, then $s_{est}^2$ is the variance of prediction errors. Similarly, since $s_Y$ is the standard deviation of Y, then $s_Y^2$ is the variance of Y. Using these definitions, our equation becomes

$$\frac{\text{Variance of errors remaining when predicting Y from X}}{\text{Variance of Y}} = 1 - r^2$$

or, expressing this as a proportion we get

Proportion of variance of Y not accounted for by a knowledge of $X = 1 - r^2$

This is another quantity that is frequently used for interpreting correlations. It is known as the *coefficient of non-determination.* So we can summarize:

Coefficient of non-determination $=$ Proportion of the variance of Y not accounted for by a knowledge of X $= 1 - r^2$

The coefficient of non-determination provides useful information, but what we *really* want to know is what proportion of the variance of Y *is* accounted for if we know X. Now we can easily find this quantity:

Proportion of the variance of Y accounted for by a knowledge of X $=$ All of the variance of Y $-$ Proportion of the variance of Y not accounted for by a knowledge of X

or

Proportion of the variance of Y accounted for by a knowledge of X $=$ 1 - (Coefficient of non-determination)

so

Proportion of the variance of Y accounted for by a knowledge of X $=$ $1 - (1 - r^2)$

and, by simple algebra:

Proportion of the variance
of Y accounted for by a $\qquad = \qquad \cancel{Y} - \cancel{Y} + r^2 = r^2$
knowledge of X

This quantity is called the ***coefficient of determination*** and is the most frequently used quantity for interpreting correlations. To summarize,

$r^2$ = Coefficient of determination = Proportion of the variance of Y accounted for by our knowledge of X

Another useful way to look at the coefficient of determination is to say that it tells us the proportion of one variable's variance that is shared by the two variables (X and Y). This can be illustrated by a Venn Diagram (shown in Figure 9-5) in which the variances of variable X and variable Y are represented by circles:

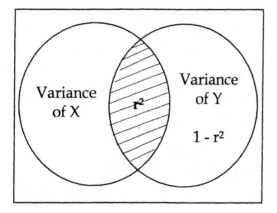

Figure 9-5. Shared and non-shared proportions of variance indicated by a correlation.

The overlapping or shared portion of the variance of a variable is equal to the square of the correlation coefficient, which is the coefficient of determination. The non-overlapping, or unique portion of the variance of a variable is the coefficient of non-determination, or $1 - r^2$.

To give a concrete example, suppose we have two variables with a correlation of r = .50. The coefficient of determination, $r^2$, is $(.50)^2$ = .25. This tells us that 25% of one variable's variance is shared with the other variable, and the remaining $1 - r^2$ of the variance, or 75% is not shared.

***Summary.*** The four quantities that we have just developed constitute a sophisticated and very useful system for interpreting correlation coefficients. This system replaces the crude, rule of thumb system that we presented in Chapter Seven. Table 9-5 summarizes our new, quantitative system for interpreting correlations.

Table 9-5
Summary of Quantities used in Interpreting Correlations

| Name | Formula | Information Provided |
|---|---|---|
| Coefficient of Alienation | $k = \sqrt{1 - r^2}$ | Proportion of guessing error remaining when we make predictions based on our knowledge of the relationship between X and Y |
| Index of Forecasting Efficiency | $E = 1 - \sqrt{1 - r^2}$ | Proportion of guessing error eliminated by making predictions, rather than guessing |
| Coefficient of Determination | $r^2$ | Proportion of the variance of Y that is accounted for by a knowledge of X |
| Coefficient of Non-determination | $1 - r^2$ | Proportion of the variance of Y that is *not* accounted for by a knowledge of X |

To illustrate the use of these quantities, consider the correlation we obtained in our fast food company example. Recall that in this example the correlation between test score (X) and months on the job (Y) was r = .76. Given our knowledge of this correlation coefficient, we could make the following four conclusions (without ever making any specific predictions):

(1) The proportion of guessing error left in our predictions will be

$$k = \text{Coefficient of alienation} = \sqrt{1 - r^2} = \sqrt{1 - .76^2} = \sqrt{1 - .58} = \sqrt{.42} = .65$$

This tells us that the standard deviation of our prediction errors when we predict how many months employees will stay on the job from their test scores (the standard error of estimate) will be 65% as large as the standard deviation of guessing errors (the standard deviation of months on the job).

(2) The proportion of guessing error we can eliminate by making predictions will be

$$E = \text{Index of forecasting efficiency} = 1 - \sqrt{1 - r^2} = 1 - \sqrt{1 - .76^2} = 1 - \sqrt{1 - .58}$$

$$= 1 - \sqrt{.42} = 1 - .65 = .35$$

This tells us that by using the test to predict how long applicants will stay on the job, we can reduce the standard deviation of our errors by 35% over what it would be if we merely guessed.

(3) The proportion of the variance of months employees remain on the job that can be accounted for by their test scores is

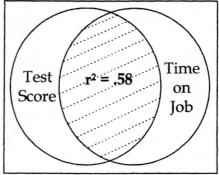

$$\text{Coefficient of determination} = r^2$$
$$= (.76)^2 = .58$$

Figure 9-6. Proportion of shared variance of test score and time on job in the fast food study.

This tells us that 58% of the variance in the months employees remain on the job can be accounted for (or is shared ) by test scores. This relationship is illustrated in Figure 9-6.

(4) The proportion of the variance of months employees remain on the job that cannot be accounted for by their test scores is

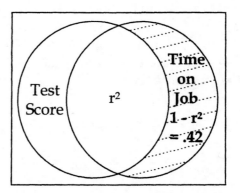

$$\text{Coefficient of non-determination} = 1 - r^2$$
$$= 1 - (.76)^2 = 1 - .58 = .42$$

This tells us that 42% of the variance of months employees remain on the job cannot be accounted for (or is not shared) by their test scores and, thus, remains entirely unexplained with our current knowledge. This relationship is illustrated in Figure 9-7.

Figure 9-7. Proportion of variance in time on the job *not* shared with test score in the fast food study.

## Graphing the Index of Forecasting Efficiency

Table 9-6 shows the value of the index of forecasting efficiency for various values of correlation. In Figure 9-8 we have graphed this relationship between correlation and index of forecasting efficiency. Note that the graph forms a distinctive pattern -- a curved line, rather than a straight line.

Table 9-6
Values of the Correlation Coefficient and Corresponding Values of the Index of
Forecasting Efficiency

| Correlation Coefficient (r) | Index of Forecasting Efficiency $\left( E = 1 - \sqrt{1 - r^2} \right)$ |
|:---:|:---:|
| .00 | .000 |
| .10 | .005 |
| .20 | .020 |
| .30 | .050 |
| .40 | .080 |
| .50 | .130 |
| .60 | .200 |
| .70 | .290 |
| .80 | .400 |
| .90 | .560 |
| .95 | .690 |
| .98 | .800 |
| 1.00 | 1.000 |

On the graph we can clearly see that the relationship between correlation (r) and index of forecasting efficiency (E) is not a straight line. Rather, as the correlation rises, forecasting efficiency rises very slowly at first, but very rapidly once the correlation becomes large. Hence, the gain in forecasting efficiency is much greater as the correlation rises from .80 to .90 than when the correlation rises from .20 to .30.

This brings us to an important point -- since the Pearson r ranges in absolute value from 0 to 1, it is tempting to think of it as a percent of something. This is *not* so and constitutes a serious error. The

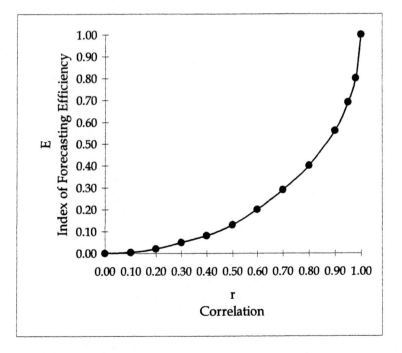

Figure 9-8. Graph of correlation and index of forecasting efficiency.

*only* way that a correlation coefficient can be interpreted in terms of percentages (or proportions) is to transform it into one of the four quantities discussed above -- coefficient of alienation, index of forecasting efficiency, coefficient of determination, or coefficient of non-determination.

## Study Questions
*Answers to selected questions may be found in Appendix A*

For each of the following correlation coefficients, compute each of the four quantities described in Table 9-5 (i.e., the coefficient of alienation, the index of forecasting efficiency, the coefficient of determination, and the coefficient of non-determination) and explain what this tells us in each case.

1. r = .42
2. r = -.86
3. r = .27
4. r = .70
5. r = .64

# CHAPTER TEN

# Assumptions of the Pearson r and Alternative Measures of Correlation

During the era of Enlightenment, the philosopher Voltaire wrote the book *Candide*. The main characters in the book are Candide, an idealistic young man, and his sidekick, a philosopher named Pangloss (said to be patterned after the real philosopher Leibnitz, the co-discoverer of calculus). The two men travel the world in an effort to understand and better it. Pangloss, in particular, is full of high flown theories that tend to justify the unjustifiable, excuse the inexcusable, and lead to disaster whenever an effort is made to apply them. After several years of nearly unrelenting troubles brought on by their own efforts, Candide and Pangloss decide that the secret of successful living is simplicity. They settle down on a small country place and become subsistence farmers. They have one cardinal rule of conduct: no discussion of philosophy is allowed. However, one day as they are blissfully hoeing the potatoes, a weighty philosophical question occurs to Pangloss. He says "You know, I wonder if ...." Without pausing or looking up, Candide interrupts, saying "Shut up and hoe the potatoes."

In this book we have tried very hard to stick closely to the hoeing in the interest of simplicity. But there are some issues of a theoretical or even philosophical nature with which we must occasionally deal. These issues must be considered in order to most effectively use our statistical methods and to appreciate how they function as tools in the broader human endeavor of science.

## Platonic Idealism

The ancient Greek philosopher Plato believed that there existed two distinct, but related worlds. One was the *sensory world* -- what we might call the world of everyday experience or the material world -- where we perceive the things around us through our senses. We see tables, mountains, animals and the other objects in the world around us. The other world was the *ideal world*, a non-material world of ideas. The two worlds are related in that the things in the sensory world are imperfect copies of the ideas in the ideal world. For example, we see tables in the everyday or sensory world. The idea of "tableness" exists in the ideal world. My dining table is an imperfect copy of the idea of tableness (my dining table has some scuffs and scratches in the varnish and a gouge on one leg).

Plato developed this idea in his allegory of the cave. He said that we live our lives like prisoners in a cave, tied up in such a way that we can only see the wall in front of us. The only source of light is a fire behind us. The real action of the world takes place between the fire and us. Thus, what we see are the shadows of that reality cast on the wall in front of us. The shadow images derive from and do resemble the real action taking place behind us, but they are dark, shimmering, imperfect copies of it.

By now, if you are a "normal" person, you are wondering why we are so far off the track of statistics. This philosophy stuff seems to border on the downright wacky.

The example of "tableness" seems strained and artificial. It is unclear how any of this relates to statistics. You might even think that the authors, after a shaky start, have finally lost it altogether.

Perhaps we should look at some other examples. Consider the definition of a line. A line is perfectly straight; it has no width; and it extends forever. If we attempt to draw a line (as in Figure 10-1) on a piece of paper, a blackboard, or any other surface, it will not be possible to make it perfectly straight, without width, and infinitely long. We might, however, make it fairly straight, very thin, and somewhat long. Similarly, a point is said to have position, but not extension. That is, it does not take up any space. Again, any attempt to draw a point (as in Figure 10-1) will fall short, because it will actually occupy some space.

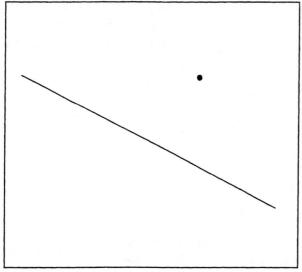

Figure 10-1. A doomed, futile, and sadly inadequate attempt at drawing a straight line and a point.

Clearly, "lineness" and "pointness" exist only in the perfect world of ideas. Yet, our admittedly imperfect applications of them in the everyday, sensory world are extraordinarily useful when we do things like survey land for a highway or navigate a ship at sea. In fact, the field of mathematics is filled with these sorts of imperfect applications of perfect ideas. Infinite sets of numbers, instantaneous slopes of curved lines, and shapes sliced into pieces so thin that there are an infinite number of them are all ideas that cannot be perfectly produced in the everyday world. But applications of these ideas are very useful in creating the comfortable and prosperous everyday world we inhabit today.

## Scientific Theory and Idealization

Modern scientific theories work largely by this process of idealization. They consist of a set of ideas that create a "model" that represents some process in the natural world. We may never find the ideas exactly duplicated in the everyday world. However, if the theory is a useful one, the duplication is close enough that successful predictions can be made from the model and an improved understanding of the material world can be achieved. For example, Isaac Newton's First Law of Motion states that an object in motion tends to remain in motion. Did you ever see an object in motion that actually remained in motion? All the objects that we have ever seen have tended to stop -- usually pretty quickly. Even the motion of the planets is slowing perceptibly.

Nevertheless, the principles of Newton's physics have served us very well. They allow us to predict the positions of the planets years in advance, to hit a target with artillery from miles away, and to send a space vehicle to the moon or Mars.

## Statistical Models

When we work with statistical methods we also employ this process of idealization and modeling. We have a set of ideas that we use to describe some process or thing. These ideas create a model that helps us to better conceive of, understand, and work with that thing.

For example, earlier in this book we worked with percentages under the normal curve for tests of intellectual ability. In this case we used the normal curve as a model for the nature of human intellectual performance, and we assumed that our test scores are of an appropriate level of measurement (the levels of measurement discussed in Chapter One are models of measurement that form the basis for this sort of modeling). Almost certainly our models are not perfect. The distribution of human intellectual performance is probably not a perfect normal distribution. Likewise, our measurement of human intellectual performance is probably not a truly interval level of measurement. But we come close enough to fulfilling these idealized assumptions that our work is useful in both a practical and a theoretical sense.

To summarize this discussion we can say that behind any theoretical model or prediction system is a set of assumptions. These assumptions will probably not be met perfectly and the model will probably not perfectly describe the material world. However, it is important that we know what our assumptions are, that we have a carefully considered idea of how accurate these assumptions are, and that we take this into account when deciding to apply our statistical model.

## Application to Correlation

The Pearson product-moment correlation coefficient, like any other statistical procedure, makes certain assumptions about the data being examined. The accuracy of everything we have said in the last three chapters (about strength of the relationship, ability to make predictions, and forecasting prediction error) depends on the degree to which the scores fit the model created by these assumptions. While the assumptions will rarely be met perfectly, more extreme violations of the assumptions will produce more serious errors in the conclusions we draw from the results of our calculations. For this reason we must always be aware of the assumptions behind our procedures and be sensitive to the appropriateness of our data for the statistical method we use.

## Assumptions of the Pearson r

Four assumptions underlie the Pearson r. These assumptions are listed and explained below.

*Assumption 1: Both variables to be correlated are continuous variables.* A *continuous variable* has an infinite number of possible values arranged in infinitely small steps. An example of a continuous variable is weight (measured in pounds). There are an infinite number of weights a person might have and there is no minimum difference between weights that could not be further reduced. One person might weigh 155 pounds and another might weigh 154 pounds. A third person could weigh 154.9 pounds or 154.97 pounds. For any score we might choose, however close to 155, there can always be another even closer to 155. Thus, there is no limit on closeness between two scores. This is in contrast to the other major type of variable -- a *discrete variable*. A discrete variable usually (but not always) has a finite set of possible values that are arranged in a step-like manner (always), so that we must go all the way from one value to the next value as if each value were a step on a ladder. An example of a discrete variable would be the score obtained when tossing a die (singular of dice). The lowest score we could get would be a 1. The next lowest score would be a 2. We could not get a 1.2 or 1.78, as would be possible with a continuous variable; and there are only six possible outcomes, 1 through 6. A *dichotomous variable* is a special kind of discrete variable. A dichotomous variable has only two possible outcomes. For example, the answer to a question could be scored as either correct or incorrect. Or a switch could be either on or off.

*Assumption 2: Both variables are of interval level of measurement or ratio level of measurement.* Recall from Chapter One that in an interval scale of measurement (and in a ratio scale of measurement) equal sized intervals between scores represent equal sized differences in the variable being measured. That is, the 10 degree difference between 35 degrees Fahrenheit and 45 degrees Fahrenheit represents the same difference in temperature as the 10 degree difference between 85 degrees Fahrenheit and 95 degrees Fahrenheit.

*Assumption 3: The relationship between the two variables is linear.* This assumption states that the relationship between the two variables is best described by a straight line (rather than a curved line). The scattergram of a linear relationship between two variables shown in Figure 10-2 illustrates a case in which Assumption 3 is met. In contrast, Figure 10-3 shows the scattergram of a non-linear relationship between two variables -- a case in which Assumption 3 is not met.

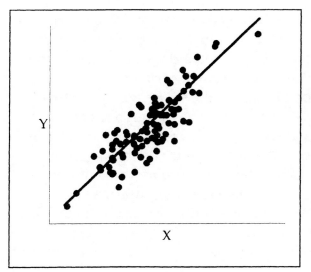

Figure 10-2. A linear relationship.

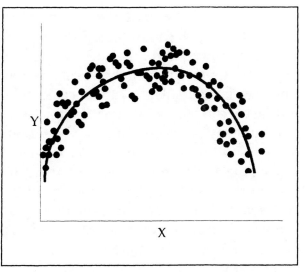

Figure 10-3. A non-linear relationship.

The Pearson r measures the prediction efficiency of the best straight line that can be fit to the data. A Pearson r computed on the data in Figure 10-3 would yield a correlation coefficient of just about zero. This would lead to the erroneous conclusion that there is no relationship between the two variables. Actually, however, we can see that there is a quite strong relationship between the variables; it is just not a **linear** relationship.

*Assumption 4: The relationship between the variables is characterized by the property of homoscedasticity.* In a homoscedastic relationship the variance around the regression line remains the same throughout the range of the two variables. This characteristic is what produces the smooth elliptical shape of a scattergram, as shown in Figure 10-4. On the other hand, the scattergram of a heteroscedastic relationship may have irregular lumps or bulges along its length, such as is shown in Figure 10-5.

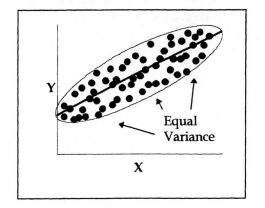

Figure 10-4. Homoscedastic distribution.

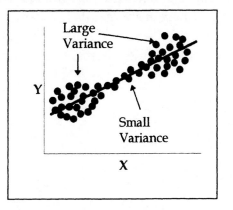

Figure 10-5. Heteroscedastic distribution.

*How do you know if assumptions have been seriously violated?* Although there is no guaranteed, cut-and-dried method, it is usually possible to determine whether or not the assumptions of the Pearson r have been seriously violated. Visual inspection of the scattergram will usually reveal a serious departure from linearity or homoscedasticity. And a careful consideration of the way the scores were generated will usually tell us something about how well we have met the assumptions of continuously scored variables and interval or ratio level measurement of the variables.

*What if assumptions have been seriously violated?* If our variables do seriously violate the assumptions of the Pearson r, then it is clearly inappropriate to employ this procedure. However, it is not the end of the world. There are other measures of correlation that require different assumptions and/or less stringent assumptions. We can usually find one of these other measures of correlation that is appropriate for our data. As an example, in the next section we will consider one of these alternate forms of correlation.

## Spearman's rho

Spearman's rho is made for situations in which our data are in the form of ranks. (Ranking represents an ordinal level of measurement; thus, the Pearson r assumption of interval or ratio levels of measurement is not met). Informally, Spearman's rho is sometimes called a rank-order correlation coefficient.

The computation of Spearman's rho is based on the squared differences between ranks for each pair of observations on our two variables. Since this squared difference is the only thing that must be calculated from the data, computation of Spearman's rho is much simpler than the computation of the Pearson r.

As an example, suppose we conducted a study attempting to assess the effectiveness of the interview as a selection technique for hiring new employees for our company. In particular, we wish to determine the reliability of our interview process. That is, to what extent do the interviews produce consistent results? (An interview cannot yield accurate results if it cannot produce consistent results.) We ask two interviewers to independently interview five applicants for the same job and to rank the applicants on their perceived suitability for the job. These rankings are given in Table 10-1.

Table 10-1
Ranks Assigned to Five Job Applicants by Two Interviewers

| Applicant | Rank Assigned by Interviewer #1 | Rank Assigned by Interviewer #2 |
|-----------|--------------------------------|--------------------------------|
| 1 | 2 | 3 |
| 2 | 4 | 1 |
| 3 | 5 | 4 |
| 4 | 1 | 2 |
| 5 | 3 | 5 |

As we mentioned previously, the computation of Spearman's rho is based on the sum of squared differences between ranks on the two variables (in this case the two interviewers) for each subject (in this case each applicant). If the differences tend to be small, the correlation will be high. If the differences tend to be large, the correlation will be low.

The formula for Spearman's rho is

$$rho = 1 - \left[ \frac{6 \sum D^2}{N(N^2 - 1)} \right]$$

where D is the difference in ranks on the two variables for one subject, and N is the number of subjects or cases in the study.

Now we can use this formula to calculate rho for our interviewing study. Table 10-2 shows the necessary quantities and the calculations for rho.

Table 10-2
Ranks Assigned to Five Job Applicants by Two Interviewers: Calculation of rho

| Applicant | Rank Interviewer #1 | Rank Interviewer #2 | D Difference | D² (Difference)² |
|-----------|---------------------|---------------------|--------------|------------------|
| 1 | 2 | 3 | -1 | 1 |
| 2 | 4 | 1 | 3 | 9 |
| 3 | 5 | 4 | 1 | 1 |
| 4 | 1 | 2 | -1 | 1 |
| 5 | 3 | 5 | -2 | 4 |
| | | | | $\sum D^2 = 16$ |

$$rho = 1 - \left[\frac{6\sum D^2}{N(N^2 - 1)}\right] = 1 - \left[\frac{6(16)}{5(5^2 - 1)}\right] = 1 - \left[\frac{96}{5(24)}\right] = 1 - \left[\frac{96}{120}\right] = 1 - .80 = .20$$

Based on the value of our correlation coefficient, rho = .20, we would conclude that our interviewers were not in very close agreement on their rankings of the job applicants. Perhaps we should change our interviewing process.

## Additional Issues Regarding Correlation

In this section we discuss two issues that frequently are associated with errors in the interpretation of correlations. The first issue arises when we have several correlation coefficients (for example, from several different studies) and we want to calculate an average correlation. In this case we must take into account the fact that correlations do not constitute an interval scale of measurement; we cannot simply add the correlations and divide by the number of correlations. The second issue stems from the fact that if one thing causes something else, then the two things must be correlated. However, if two things are correlated, it does not necessarily mean that one causes the other. Each of these issues is discussed in more detail below.

*Averaging correlations.* As we saw in Chapter Nine (see Table 9-6), the error eliminated (measured by the index of forecasting efficiency) as correlations increase grows faster when correlations are large than when they are small. That is, the difference in explanatory power between correlations of .30 and .40 is much less than that between correlations of .80 and .90. Because of this, it is inappropriate to average correlations in their raw form. Fortunately, the great statistician Ronald Fisher created a transformation (now commonly called Fisher's z -- not to be confused with the standard score or z-score that we introduced in Chapter 5) that gets around this problem. Appendix D contains the table for the Fisher's z transformation. Note that in Appendix D each value of r has an associated value of z , and the values of z increase slowly when r is low and increase more rapidly when r is large.

As an example, suppose that we have created a test to predict the widget making ability of applicants for jobs in the widget industry. Furthermore, we have done a study of the test's ability to predict widget output of workers at four widget plants. The correlations are .87, .27, .55, and .96. We wish to report the average correlation for the study. As we stated earlier, it is *not appropriate* to simply add the four raw correlations and then divide by four to get an average correlation of .66. Instead, the proper way to find the average correlation is to use Fisher's z transformation in Appendix D according to the following step-by-step procedure:

*Step 1.* Convert each correlation to its associated z value, using the Fisher's z table in Appendix D:

| Correlation | Fisher's z |
|:---:|:---:|
| r | $z_r$ |
| .87 | 1.333 |
| .23 | .234 |
| .55 | .618 |
| .96 | 1.946 |
| | $\sum z_r = 4.131$ |

*Step 2.* Find the mean of the $z_r$ values:

$$\bar{z}_r = \frac{\sum z_r}{N} = \frac{4.131}{4} = 1.033$$

*Step 3.* Return to the Fisher's z table in Appendix D and read down the $z_r$ column (*not* the r column) until we find the value closest to our computed mean of 1.033. In this case this value is $z_r = 1.045$.

*Step 4.* Read one column to the left (the r column) to find the value of r associated with the $z_r$ that we just found. In this case the value is r = .78. Thus, the value of the average correlation (rounded to two places) is r = .78.

*Correlation and causation.* It is widely and erroneously believed that if two things are correlated, one must cause the other. Newspapers and popular magazines frequently print articles that make this (incorrect) leap from correlation to causation. In these cases, it is also amusing that the authors of these articles appear to be certain that they can identify which variable is the cause and which variable is the effect.

As an example, suppose we know that having taken Latin in high school is correlated with good grades in college. The error is to conclude that taking Latin in high school *causes* good grades in college. And this error is compounded when we then suggest that all students should be required to take Latin in high school, because this will make them all good students.

If you learn nothing else from this book than that correlation does not imply causation, then you have probably gotten your money's worth. At best, a causal relationship is very difficult to establish; it requires many controlled, experimental studies (like those discussed later in this book), rather than a single correlational study.

For the purpose of illustration, consider this laughably simple example. Suppose that we go to a grade school, measure the length of the pant legs for all the boys, and give all boys a spelling test. We would almost certainly find a high correlation between pant leg length and spelling test score. Are we to conclude that long pant legs cause boys to become good spellers? Are we then to translate this into action by buying longer pants for our boys (and letting the boys walk on the cuffs) in hopes of making the boys better spellers? Certainly not. In this case the explanation is that older boys generally have longer legs (which require longer pants). Also, older boys are more mature intellectually, and they have been in school longer. Thus, increasing age causes both longer pant legs and better spelling scores.

Of course this is a simple, even silly, example. But if you keep your eyes open, it should not be long before you encounter proposals almost this silly in newspapers and magazines, in advertising, and in political speeches.

## Study Questions
*Answers to selected questions may be found in Appendix A*

1. Which of the following violates one or more of the assumptions of the Pearson r? What are the violations?

   a.                                                      b.

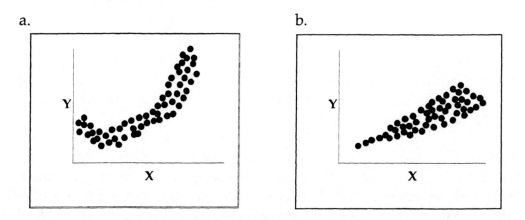

   c. A correlation between the verbal and math SAT scores made by a class of incoming freshmen.

   d. A correlation between two sets of ranks given to five different beverages by two participants in a "taste test survey."

   e. A correlation between average daily rainfall and the growth rate of St. Augustine grass.

2. How well do these two book critics agree?

| Book | Critic #1 Rank | Critic #2 Rank |
|---|---|---|
| Gone with the Wind | 8 | 10 |
| Catcher in the Rye | 2 | 3 |
| For Whom the Bell Tolls | 6 | 6 |
| The Turn of the Screw | 7 | 5 |
| Portrait of the Artist as Young Man | 9 | 7 |
| Slaughterhouse Five | 1 | 1 |
| The Naked Lunch | 10 | 2 |
| The Unbearable Lightness of Being | 4 | 4 |
| The Great Gatsby | 5 | 9 |
| The Color Purple | 3 | 8 |

3. How well do these two supervisors agree?

| Employee | Supervisor #1 Rank | Supervisor #2 Rank |
|---|---|---|
| J. Phillips | 3 | 1 |
| S. Monroe | 9 | 7 |
| B. Manning | 2 | 6 |
| D. King | 4 | 5 |
| S. Smith | 1 | 3 |
| L. Wilson | 5 | 4 |
| A. Franklin | 8 | 8 |
| R. Robertson | 7 | 9 |
| C. Williams | 6 | 2 |

4. Average each of the following sets of correlation coefficients.

a. .45, .33, .76, .51
b. .68, .40, .71, .36
c. .19, .34, .94, .61

CHAPTER ELEVEN
# Sampling Distributions and the Standard Error of the Mean

In Chapter One we stated that there are three basic categories of statistics. The first major area is *descriptive statistics.* The purpose of descriptive statistics is to describe the distribution of scores of a single variable. We want to boil down the information in a large number of scores to make it meaningful to us. We can accomplish this by using a variety of descriptive techniques, the most common of which are the *mean* and the *standard deviation*. The use of descriptive statistics was discussed in Chapters Two through Five.

The second major area of statistics is *correlational statistics.* The purpose of correlational statistics is to work with (imperfect) relationships between pairs of variables. The techniques used in correlational statistics include: (1) the *correlation coefficient,* which measures the strength of the relationship between two variables, (2) the *regression line*, which allows us to make the best possible predictions of one variable from the other variable, and (3) the *standard error of estimate,* which allows us to forecast (in advance) the size of the typical prediction error and, thereby, allows us to create a sophisticated system for interpreting correlational data. The use of correlational techniques was discussed in Chapters Seven through Ten.

The third major area of statistics is *inferential statistics.* The purpose of inferential statistics is to draw conclusions about a whole population, based on samples that constitute only a small proportion of the population. The inferential statistical techniques that we employ to accomplish this purpose will be discussed in the remaining chapters of this book.

## Purpose of Inferential Statistics

The reason that we often use samples to make inferences about whole populations is that in many cases it would not be feasible to obtain scores from every member of the population. For example, we might need to make decisions about a population consisting of millions of members; in this case we might be able to afford the cost of measuring only a few hundred or, at most, a few thousand members. By using inferential statistics we can use samples that comprise only a small proportion of the population to make decisions about the characteristics of the entire population. And our decisions will be almost as accurate as if we had measured all the members of the population. Thus, while it would be impractical because of time and expense to measure an entire population, we can easily measure a sample of members from the population and draw quite accurate inferences from these sample scores.

This procedure of using samples to make inferences about whole populations is quite common. As examples, consider how samples are used to draw inferences about the populations in opinion polling, market research, and product testing. An opinion poll might be conducted to determine what percentage of the voters support a particular presidential candidate. There are well over one hundred million eligible voters in the United States. To poll each one of these potential voters would be nearly impossible -- it would be extremely time-consuming and costly. However, it would be relatively easy to poll a few hundred potential voters and, if done properly, this sample could tell (within a few percentage points) what percentage of the population of voters favors this candidate.

A similar approach might be used in market research. When a company introduces a new product, often the product is first sold in a few test markets. Then, based on these test market sales, the product is either discontinued or made available nationwide. The test market is a sample of the national market and provides a relatively inexpensive opportunity to determine how well the product will sell.

As a final example, consider how a pharmaceutical company might test a new product -- a drug that is designed to cure the common cold. It would be impossible to administer this drug to the entire population of cold sufferers. However, we could test the drug against an inert "placebo" drug in a relatively small study of only a few hundred cold sufferers. That is, we could administer the new drug to a sample of 250 people and the placebo drug (a sugar pill) to another sample of 250 people. Then we would compare the amounts of time required to recover from the colds. Note that this third example is particularly important because it illustrates how an empirical test can be conducted economically any time we have a new medical treatment that promises improved results, a new manufacturing process that promises better products, or a new scientific theory that purports to give a better explanation of a principle of nature.

## Basic Approach

To illustrate the logic of inferential statistics consider the following example. Suppose that a paper company suspects that people might be able to read faster when the text is printed on green paper (since it is less prone to glare) rather than on traditional white paper. The company decides to do an experiment to test this idea. While we discuss this experiment, we can also look at the basic structure of any scientific experiment. In this example experiment, paper color serves as the *independent variable*. To be a variable, paper color must have at least two values so that it can vary. In our experiment these values are green paper and white paper. Our two values or levels of the independent variable are often called the *experimental group*, where some new procedure or treatment is used (green paper), and the *control group*, which consists of the "old" procedure or no treatment (white paper). The name independent variable comes from the fact that the experimenter actively manipulates its values. For example, in this experiment the experimenter chooses green paper and white paper as the values of the independent variable. Then half of the subjects are randomly assigned to each of the two treatment groups.

Each subject reads the same material printed on his assigned paper color and his reading score is obtained. Reading speed is called the *dependent variable*, because each subject's reading speed depends on the value of the independent variable (paper color) to which she is assigned. That is, the scores on the dependent variable are affected by the assigned values of the independent variable.

If the independent variable and the dependent variable are related, this will be revealed by the fact that the mean score on the dependent variable (reading speed) will be different for the two values (or levels) of the independent variable (paper color). Figure 11-1 illustrates the case where the independent variable and the dependent variable are related. Figure 11-2 illustrates the case where the independent and dependent variables are not related.

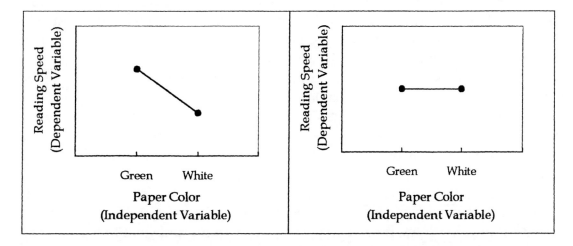

Figure 11-1. An experimental result where the independent and dependent variables are found to be related.

Figure 11-2. An experimental result where the independent and dependent variables are found to be unrelated.

It may seem strange that a relationship between two variables shows up as a difference. However, it simply reflects the fact that if the two variables are related, then when the independent variable varies (green versus white paper) the dependent variable must also vary (faster versus slower reading speeds).

An experiment may have more than two values (or levels) of the independent variable, and it may have more than one independent variable; but to be an experiment it must have least one independent variable that must have at least two values (or levels).

In our paper company's experiment, 100 subjects are randomly assigned to read a passage printed on green paper (the experimental group) and another 100 subjects are randomly assigned to read the same passage printed on white paper (the control group). The result of this experiment is that the mean reading speed of those in the green paper group is 255 words per minute, while the mean for the white paper group was only 240 words per minute. The company then begins to manufacture and market green paper. In their advertising the company confidently claims that green paper is superior to white paper.

However, the company soon comes under heavy criticism from the white paper lobby. While the white paper lobby accepts the statements that the experiment was conducted and that the mean reading speed with green paper was greater than the mean reading speed with white paper, the lobby rejects the conclusion that people in general will read faster on green paper. After all, the lobby points out, the experiment involved only 200 people out of the billions in the world. And the experiment was only done once. Certainly, if the experiment were repeated, the means of the two groups would not be the same as they were in the first experiment. Instead, the means are bound to fluctuate just by chance from one experiment to the next experiment. Who is to say that the white paper group would not have a higher mean reading speed in the next experiment? It could happen.

In fact, the company could repeat the experiment with 10,000 subjects in each group (instead of 100), and the experiment could be repeated 10 times (instead of just once). But the lobby's criticism would still be just as valid as ever. No matter how large the sample and no matter how many times the experiment is repeated, the workings of chance cannot be eliminated. The only recourse is to understand the nature of chance in such situations and take it into account.

Suppose it could be determined that in this situation one should get a chance difference in mean reading speeds as large as the one obtained in this experiment only once in ten thousand times. If so, then we should be quite confident that green paper is, indeed, better than white paper.

This issue is what inferential statistical techniques are all about. We must understand how chance works in experimental situations and take it into account when we draw our conclusions. Our study of probability in Chapter Six has given us a start toward this understanding of chance, but now we need to take it further. Our next step is to develop some definitions. Some of these terms are common English words that are used rather loosely in ordinary conversation, but they have precise meanings in inferential statistics.

## Definitions

A *population* is a complete set of people, objects, or events having some common observable characteristic. For example, all of the people in Boston who have red hair constitutes a population. All of the honey bees in Texas is another population.

A *sample* is a subset (or a subgroup) of a population. For example, the red-haired people who attend Yale University is a sample of the population of red-haired people in New Haven.

A *random sample* is a sample in which each member of the population has an equal chance of being included in the sample. Note that this is *not* the same as an *arbitrary sample*, in which members of the sample are chosen because they are convenient or of particular interest. Rather, for a sample to be truly random we must take steps to assure that every member of the population has an equal chance to be included in the sample. Tables of random numbers and computer programs that generate random samples are frequently used to ensure that a sample is truly random.

A *population parameter* is some characteristic of an entire population, such as its mean or its standard deviation.

A *sample statistic* is some characteristic of a sample, such as its mean or its standard deviation. Note that the value of a sample statistic (such as a sample mean) is almost certainly not exactly the same as the value of the corresponding population parameter (the population mean) for the population from which the sample was drawn.

A sample statistic is an *unbiased estimate* of the population parameter if the sample statistic does not systematically underestimate or overestimate the population parameter. For example, if the mean of all possible sample means is equal to the population mean, then the sample mean provides an unbiased estimate. In fact, the sample mean is an unbiased estimate.

However, if the sample statistic does, indeed, systematically underestimate or overestimate the population parameter, then it is a *biased estimate*. The sample standard deviation is a biased estimate, because the mean of all possible sample standard deviations will be smaller than the standard deviation of the population. That is, the sample standard deviation systematically underestimates the population standard deviation.

The *probability of an event* is the ratio of the number of favored outcomes to the total number of possible outcomes, when each possible outcome has an equal chance of occurring. We can write this as

$$\text{Probability} = \frac{\#\ \text{of favored outcomes}}{\text{Total}\ \#\ \text{of possible outcomes}}$$

We worked with this definition in Chapter Six. We repeat the definition here because probability is the basis for inferential statistics.

## Expanded Notation

So far in this book we have worked with means, standard deviations, and correlations; we introduced symbols for these characteristics as we developed the ideas concerning them. However, now we need a notation to denote whether we are referring to a population or a sample characteristic and a biased or unbiased estimate. Standard statistical notation uses a Latin (English) letter to denote a sample statistic and the corresponding Greek letter to denote a population parameter. A hat (^) is placed over the Greek letter to denote an unbiased estimate of the population parameter from a sample. Table 11-1 summarizes this new, expanded notation.

Table 11-1
Standard Statistical Notation

| Characteristic | Sample Statistic | Population Parameter | Unbiased Estimate of Population Parameter |
|---|---|---|---|
| Mean | $\overline{X}$ | $\mu$ (mu) | $\hat{\mu}$ * |
| Standard Deviation | s | $\sigma$ (sigma) | $\hat{\sigma}$ |
| Correlation | r | $\rho$ (rho) | $\hat{\rho}$ |

*Note that $\hat{\mu}$ is not needed because the sample mean is already an unbiased estimate.

## Unbiased Estimate of the Standard Deviation

As we noted earlier, the standard deviation of a sample is a biased estimate of the standard deviation of the population from which the sample was drawn, because it systematically underestimates the standard deviation of the population. Therefore, we need a method to produce an unbiased estimate of the population standard deviation.

Remember that the standard deviation formula that we have used until now is

$$s = \sqrt{\frac{\text{sum of squares}}{N}} = \sqrt{\frac{\Sigma(X - \overline{X})^2}{N}} = \sqrt{\frac{\Sigma X^2 - \frac{(\Sigma X)^2}{N}}{N}}$$

where X is a raw score and N is the number of scores. This formula does, indeed, give the standard deviation of a sample; or, if you have the scores for the entire population (that is, if the number of members in the population is equal to N), then this formula gives the population standard deviation.

However, to make an unbiased estimate of the population standard deviation from a sample we must modify the formula slightly. We must substitute N-1 in place of N in the denominator of the formula. Thus, the formula for the unbiased estimate of the population standard deviation from a sample is

$$\hat{\sigma} = \sqrt{\frac{\text{sum of squares}}{N-1}} = \sqrt{\frac{\Sigma(X - \overline{X})^2}{N-1}} = \sqrt{\frac{\Sigma X^2 - \frac{(\Sigma X)^2}{N}}{N-1}}$$

Note that an unbiased estimate when calculated from a small sample will be quite different from the biased estimate. However, when the sample is large, the difference between the biased and unbiased estimates will be small. As the sample size (N) approaches infinity, this difference will approach zero.

## Degrees of Freedom

We can define **degrees of freedom** as the effective sample size for making unbiased estimates. We talk about effective sample size because when we know (and use) the mean of a sample of scores (as we do when we calculate the sum of squares or standard deviation), then we have eliminated the freedom of one of the scores to vary. That is, when we know the mean of a set of scores, any one of the scores could be missing and we could recover it. For example, in the following set of three scores we know the value of two of the scores and we know the mean:

$$4 \quad 3 \quad ? \qquad \overline{X} = 4$$

We can easily determine that the missing score is 5. The fact that we have the mean of the set of scores has destroyed the freedom to vary for one of the scores. Hence, subtracting one from the sample size (N) provides the effective sample size (N-1).

In the case of making an unbiased estimate of the population standard deviation from a single sample the degrees of freedom equal N-1. In other cases the degrees of freedom will take on other values. The abbreviation for degrees of freedom is *df*. The concept of degrees of freedom is an important one that we will use throughout our work with inferential statistics.

## Common Problems Requiring Inferential Statistics

There are many problems that we can solve by making conclusions about populations based on samples drawn from those populations. In this book we will discuss four of these types of problems:

(1) *Establishing confidence limits*. When we establish confidence limits, we draw a single sample and estimate from it a set of limits within which we can be confident that the population mean will fall. This is what is involved when a political poll is conducted.

(2) *Testing the difference between a specific population mean and a sample mean*. When we test the difference between a population mean and a sample mean, we draw a single sample and ask whether or not it could reasonably be expected to have come from a population with a particular mean. For example, a manufacturer claims that its bags of potato chips contain 8 ounces of potato chips. Suppose the 10 bags of potato chips that we bought average only 7.96 ounces. Our task is to determine whether or not it is reasonable to believe that the mean weight of potato chips in the bags marketed by this manufacturer is 8 ounces.

(3) *Testing the significance of a correlation coefficient.* When we test the significance of a correlation coefficient, we are asking whether or not we can be reasonably confident that the single sample from which we calculated our correlation coefficient came from a population whose correlation is not zero. That is, our sample correlation is probably not zero; but can we be reasonably sure that this sample came from a population whose correlation is not zero?

(4) *Testing the significance of the difference between sample means.* When we test the significance of the difference between two sample means, we are asking whether these two samples came from two different populations (with different population means) or from a single population. For example, consider the experiment we discussed earlier that compared the reading speeds of two samples, one reading material printed on green paper and one reading material printed on white paper. Almost certainly we would obtain different mean reading speeds from the two samples. Our question is: could these two means be reasonably considered to be just two samples from a single population with a single mean, or are the two means different enough to tell us that the two samples represent two different populations with different population means? This is the most common type of problem in inferential statistics. This type of problem is encountered in nearly every experiment in most sciences.

In each of these four problems we draw a sample(s) that constitute a tiny proportion of the entire population(s) and we wish to make inferences about the whole population. We cannot prevent chance variation from operating in each of these problems. However, we can come to understand the way chance works, and we can take chance into account in each of these problems. This is what inferential statistical techniques are about.

The ability to understand chance and take it into account requires us to develop an understanding of *sampling distributions*. In Chapter Six we described the binomial distribution and indicated that it is one example of a relatively simple sampling distribution. We also stated that a sampling distribution links every possible value (outcome) of a variable with an associated probability. In this chapter and in subsequent chapters we will be depending primarily on the sampling distribution of the mean to tell us how sample means behave. So the sampling distribution of the mean serves as the key to answering questions (about chance) the we frequently encounter in inferential statistics.

## The Sampling Distribution of the Mean

Suppose that we are interested in the study skills of incoming students at American universities. In particular, we are interested in determining how fast they read. Of course, we can not afford to test the entire population of several million incoming college students; so we draw a random sample of 25 and give them a test of reading speed. The mean reading speed of our sample of 25 students is 290 words per minute.

What dos this tell us? We know that almost certainly this sample mean is not equal to the population mean, but how far from the population mean can we reasonably expect it to be? Can we feel confident that it is quite close to the population mean, or is there a good chance that it might be very far from the population mean? We need to understand the sampling distribution of the mean to be able to answer this question.

To shed some light on this subject, suppose that we were to play a sampling game. Suppose that we took several thousand samples (all of size 25) and found the mean of each sample. This set of several thousand sample means would form a distribution of sample means. In other words, we have created a sampling distribution of the mean. Figure 11-3 shows what this distribution would look like.

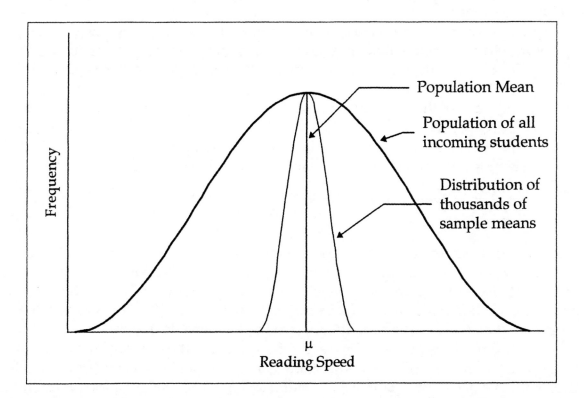

Figure 11-3. Distribution of sample means around the population mean.

The mean of our distribution of sample means would be equal to the population mean. But what would be the standard deviation of this distribution of sample means?

It turns out that the standard deviation of the set of sample means will be equal to the standard deviation of the population from which the samples were drawn (reading speeds of all incoming college students) divided by the square root of the number of subjects in each sample (25 in our case). This standard deviation of sample means is called the ***standard error of the mean***; it is the key for understanding the sampling distribution of the mean. The symbol for the standard error of the mean is $\sigma_{\overline{x}}$. We can write the standard error of the mean as

$$\sigma_{\overline{x}} = \text{standard error of the mean} = \text{standard deviation of sample means}$$

$$= \frac{\begin{array}{c}\text{standard deviation of the population}\\ \text{from which the sample means were drawn}\end{array}}{\sqrt{\text{\# of subjects in each sample}}} = \frac{\sigma}{\sqrt{N}}$$

This value for the standard error of the mean is derived from the ***central limit theorem***, which states:

> If random samples of a fixed size (N) are drawn from any population (regardless of the shape of the population distribution), then as N becomes larger
> (1) The shape of the distribution of sample means approaches the shape of the normal distribution,
> (2) The mean of the distribution of sample means approaches the population mean ($\mu$), and
> (3) The standard deviation of the distribution of sample means approaches the standard deviation of the population divided by the square root of the number of scores in each sample $\left(\dfrac{\sigma}{\sqrt{N}}\right)$.

The central limit theorem gives us a handle on how sample means behave and, hence, how chance works in a sampling situation. It is truly the key to understanding inferential statistics. Therefore we suggest that you make an extra effort to thoroughly learn the central limit theorem and its principles (much like in Chapter Four when we recommended that you pay special attention to the standard deviation).

Now we return to our sampling game. Suppose that the standard deviation of reading speed scores for the population of incoming students is 100 words per minute. Armed with this population standard deviation and our knowledge of the central limit theorem and the standard error of the mean, we can calculate how much sampling error we should expect if we draw samples of different sizes. We simply plug the sample size and the population standard deviation into the formula for the standard error of the mean:

$$\sigma_{\overline{x}} = \text{standard error of the mean} = \text{standard deviation of sample means}$$

$$= \frac{\text{standard deviation of the population}}{\sqrt{\text{sample size}}} = \frac{\sigma}{\sqrt{N}}$$

For example, if we draw samples with 9, 25, or 100 subjects in each sample, the standard deviation of the sample means will be:

(1) For samples with 9 subjects in each sample, the standard deviation of the sample means is

$$\sigma_{\bar{x}} = \frac{\sigma}{\sqrt{N}} = \frac{100}{\sqrt{9}} = \frac{100}{3} = 33.33$$

(2) For samples with 25 subjects in each sample, the standard deviation of the sample means is

$$\sigma_{\bar{x}} = \frac{\sigma}{\sqrt{N}} = \frac{100}{\sqrt{25}} = \frac{100}{5} = 20$$

(3) For samples with 100 subjects in each sample, the standard deviation of the sample means is

$$\sigma_{\bar{x}} = \frac{\sigma}{\sqrt{N}} = \frac{100}{\sqrt{100}} = \frac{100}{10} = 10$$

Figure 11-4 shows the shapes of these three sampling distributions relative to the population distribution. Figure 11-4 shows that when our sample size (the number of cases in each sample) gets larger, the standard deviation of our sample means (sampling error) gets smaller. This relationship should come as no surprise; (almost) anyone on the street, if asked, would tell you that a large sample is more reliable than a small sample. However, now we can also tell *how reliable* a sample of any size will be.

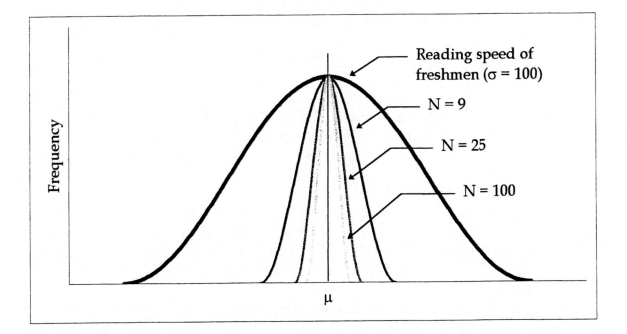

Figure 11-4. Sampling distributions of means with different sample sizes.

And since the distribution of the sample means in our student reading speed example should be approaching the normal distribution (by the central limit theorem), the distribution of sample means should be approximately normal with a standard deviation of about 20. Now recall from Chapter Five on the normal curve that about 95% of the cases in a normal distribution fall within two standard deviations of the mean. So, for our example problem, there is about a 95% chance that our sample mean of 290 words per minute falls within about 40 words per minute of the population mean (2 standard deviations of size 20 = 40). This relationship is illustrated in Figure 11-5.

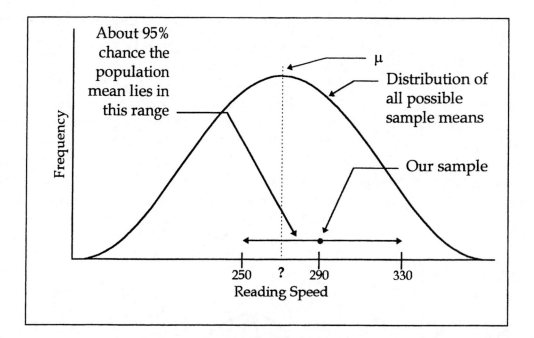

Figure 11-5. An interval established with a single sample within which we can be confident the population mean falls.

Following this reasoning, we can be quite confident that the population mean lies within the range of 250 to 330 words per minute. This range is based on our sample of only 25 incoming students. If we had used a larger, but still modest sized, sample, our range (within which we would be confident that the population mean lies) would be even narrower.

This system of establishing an interval within which we are confident that the population mean lies by going two standard errors above and below the sample mean has the advantage of being simple to understand, easy to calculate, and requiring no special tables or other aids. It works about as well as any other system when the sample is large (when N = 200 or more). However, it does lead to some serious inaccuracies when the sample is small. In the next chapter we will develop a system for making more precise inferences about a population from a small sample.

## Study Questions
*Answers to selected study questions may be found in Appendix A.*

1.  Compute the unbiased estimate of the population standard deviation based on each of the following samples:

    a.  Verbal SAT scores for a sample of incoming college freshmen at Old Sywash University.

| Student | Verbal SAT Score |
|---------|------------------|
| 1 | 650 |
| 2 | 435 |
| 3 | 550 |
| 4 | 505 |
| 5 | 490 |
| 6 | 585 |
| 7 | 605 |
| 8 | 565 |
| 9 | 530 |

    b.  Annual salaries (in thousands of dollars) for a sample of college professors at Old Sywash University.

| Professor | Salary |
|-----------|--------|
| 1 | 28.5 |
| 2 | 42.0 |
| 3 | 35.5 |
| 4 | 38.5 |
| 5 | 40.0 |
| 6 | 32.0 |

c. Hourly widget production rates for a sample of employees at Acme Widgets.

| Employee | Production Rate |
|----------|-----------------|
| 1 | 3 |
| 2 | 5 |
| 3 | 6 |
| 4 | 8 |
| 5 | 4 |
| 6 | 5 |
| 7 | 2 |
| 8 | 7 |
| 9 | 9 |
| 10 | 5 |
| 11 | 6 |
| 12 | 4 |

2. Compute the standard error of the mean (sampling error) for each of the following:

a. Verbal SAT scores for a sample of incoming college freshmen where N = 100 and $\sigma$ = 92.
b. Hourly widget production rates for a sample of employees where N = 36 and $\sigma$ = 5.02.
c. Average length in centimeters for a sample of salmon caught in the Klamath River where N = 64 and $\sigma$ = 12.38.

CHAPTER TWELVE
# Making Inferences about a
# Population from a Single Sample

At the end of Chapter Eleven we developed a system for establishing an interval within which we are confident that the population mean will lie. This interval is found by going two standard errors above and below the sample mean (since about 95% of the cases in a normal distribution lie within about two standard deviations of the mean of the distribution). Recall that we said that this system is reasonably accurate for large samples, but not for small samples. This raises two questions. First, why is this system less than optimal for small samples? Second, when our sample is small, how can we make more accurate estimates?

The answer to the first question lies within the central limit theorem, which we presented in Chapter Eleven. Recall that the central limit theorem states that as sample size (N) becomes larger, the shape of the distribution of sample means approaches that of the normal distribution. So if our sample size is less than infinite, our distribution of sample means is not yet normal in shape. However, the convergence on the normal shape is rather fast; so with samples of several hundred cases, the shape of the sampling distribution of the mean is, for practical purposes, normal. But with small samples there is considerable departure from normality.

Recall that the central limit theorem also says that the standard deviation of sample means (the standard error of the mean) approaches

$$\frac{\sigma}{\sqrt{N}} = \frac{\text{the standard deviation of the population}}{\sqrt{\text{the number of subjects in each sample}}}$$

However, when we are trying to estimate a population mean from a sample, we rarely know the exact value of the population standard deviation. Usually, we have only an unbiased estimate of the population standard deviation computed from our single sample. This estimated standard deviation can differ considerably from the population standard deviation when the sample is small. These two problems -- lack of a perfectly normal distribution of sample means and the fact that we are relying on an estimate of the population standard deviation -- will introduce an unacceptable degree of inaccuracy into our estimates if we use a system based on normal curve statistics when we try to estimate population means using small samples.

## The *t* Distribution

The answer to the second question posed earlier -- how can we make more accurate estimates of population means from small samples? -- was provided by William Sealy Gosset. Gosset was an employee of the Guinness Brewing Company of Dublin, Ireland. In the course of his work he discovered that when estimating population means from small samples while also using the sample to estimate the population standard deviation, the sampling distribution fit what is now called a *t distribution*, not a normal distribution.

A *t* distribution is "fatter" than the normal distribution when sample sizes are small; and the *t* distribution approaches the shape of the normal distribution as sample size increases. At an infinite sample size the *t* distribution is identical to the normal distribution. By the time the sample size reaches about 200, the difference between the *t* distribution and the normal distribution is inconsequential.

Since Gosset had discovered the *t* distribution as a Guinness employee, it was proprietary information belonging to the company. However, Gosset felt that his discovery was of sufficient importance to society in general that it should be available to the public. Therefore he published it anonymously under the pen name "Student," and even today it is sometimes referred to as "Student's *t*."

Just as we need a normal curve table to work with the normal distribution, we need a *t* table to work with the *t* distribution. A *t* table is provided in Appendix C and it is reproduced here as Table 12-1. Since the *t* distribution has a different shape for every possible sample size, we could have a whole table (like a normal curve table) for every possible sample size. Unfortunately, that would fill a whole book by itself. To make the table manageable it contains only values for a few proportions of particular interest to us for each sample size. Each row of the table represents a different sample size (remember that degrees of freedom, abbreviated df, is the effective sample size for making unbiased estimates). Each column head of the table gives the proportion of scores that lies in the tails of the *t* distribution, beyond the number of standard deviations equal to the tabled value.

For example, a single sample of size 10 has N-1 or 9 degrees of freedom. If we look at the value entered in the table at the intersection of the row labeled 9 df and the column headed by .05, we find the value of 2.262. This tabled value of 2.262 tells us that .05 (or 5%) of the cases in that *t* distribution lie 2.262 standard deviations or more from the mean. This example is illustrated in Figure 12-1.

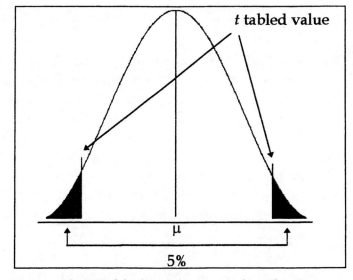

Figure 12-1. Tabled values in a *t* distribution.

Table 12-1
Critical Values of *t*

*Level of Significance for Two-Tailed Tests*

| df | .20 | .10 | .05 | .02 | .01 | .001 |
|----|-----|-----|-----|-----|-----|------|
| 1 | 3.078 | 6.314 | 12.706 | 31.821 | 63.657 | 636.619 |
| 2 | 1.886 | 2.920 | 4.303 | 6.965 | 9.925 | 31.598 |
| 3 | 1.638 | 2.353 | 3.182 | 4.541 | 5.841 | 12.941 |
| 4 | 1.533 | 2.132 | 2.776 | 3.747 | 4.604 | 8.610 |
| 5 | 1.476 | 2.015 | 2.571 | 3.365 | 4.032 | 6.859 |
| 6 | 1.440 | 1.943 | 2.447 | 3.143 | 3.707 | 5.959 |
| 7 | 1.415 | 1.895 | 2.365 | 2.998 | 3.499 | 5.405 |
| 8 | 1.397 | 1.860 | 2.306 | 2.896 | 3.355 | 5.041 |
| 9 | 1.383 | 1.833 | 2.262 | 2.821 | 3.250 | 4.781 |
| 10 | 1.372 | 1.812 | 2.228 | 2.764 | 3.169 | 4.587 |
| 11 | 1.363 | 1.796 | 2.201 | 2.718 | 3.106 | 4.437 |
| 12 | 1.356 | 1.782 | 2.179 | 2.681 | 3.055 | 4.318 |
| 13 | 1.350 | 1.771 | 2.160 | 2.650 | 3.012 | 4.221 |
| 14 | 1.345 | 1.761 | 2.145 | 2.624 | 2.977 | 4.140 |
| 15 | 1.341 | 1.753 | 2.131 | 2.602 | 2.947 | 4.073 |
| 16 | 1.337 | 1.746 | 2.120 | 2.583 | 2.921 | 4.015 |
| 17 | 1.333 | 1.740 | 2.110 | 2.567 | 2.898 | 3.965 |
| 18 | 1.330 | 1.734 | 2.101 | 2.552 | 2.878 | 3.922 |
| 19 | 1.328 | 1.729 | 2.093 | 2.539 | 2.861 | 3.883 |
| 20 | 1.325 | 1.725 | 2.086 | 2.528 | 2.845 | 3.850 |
| 21 | 1.323 | 1.721 | 2.080 | 2.518 | 2.831 | 3.819 |
| 22 | 1.321 | 1.717 | 2.074 | 2.508 | 2.819 | 3.792 |
| 23 | 1.319 | 1.714 | 2.069 | 2.500 | 2.807 | 3.767 |
| 24 | 1.318 | 1.711 | 2.064 | 2.492 | 2.797 | 3.745 |
| 25 | 1.316 | 1.708 | 2.060 | 2.485 | 2.787 | 3.725 |
| 26 | 1.315 | 1.706 | 2.056 | 2.479 | 2.779 | 3.707 |
| 27 | 1.314 | 1.703 | 2.052 | 2.473 | 2.771 | 3.690 |
| 28 | 1.313 | 1.701 | 2.048 | 2.467 | 2.763 | 3.674 |
| 29 | 1.311 | 1.699 | 2.045 | 2.462 | 2.756 | 3.659 |
| 30 | 1.310 | 1.697 | 2.042 | 2.457 | 2.750 | 3.646 |
| 40 | 1.303 | 1.684 | 2.021 | 2.423 | 2.704 | 3.551 |
| 60 | 1.296 | 1.671 | 2.000 | 2.390 | 2.660 | 3.460 |
| 120 | 1.289 | 1.658 | 1.980 | 2.358 | 2.617 | 3.373 |
| ∞ | 1.282 | 1.645 | 1.960 | 2.326 | 2.576 | 3.291 |

Note that at the bottom of the *t* table when the sample size is infinitely large (when df is infinite) the *t* distribution is equivalent to the normal distribution. We can see this by looking at the bottom row of the *t* table; 5% of the cases lie more than 1.96

standard deviations from the mean. However, as we move up the table we can see that the *t* distribution is, indeed, "fatter" than the normal distribution with smaller sample sizes, because 5% of the cases lie farther (more standard deviations) from the mean than would be the case with a normal distribution.

Armed with our *t* table, we are now able to make the most accurate possible estimate of the population mean from a single small sample. This procedure is called establishing confidence limits.

## Establishing Confidence Limits

Now consider a problem that we first posed in Chapter Eleven. We wanted to estimate the mean reading speed of the population of all incoming freshmen at American universities, using a small sample (n = 25) of them. Of course, we cannot know a population mean unless we measure the reading speed of every member of the population (virtually an impossible task in this case). What we can do is establish a set of limits, based on a single sample, within which there is an acceptably high probability that the population lies. By convention this probability is often 95% in the social sciences. This procedure is called establishing confidence limits, because we have a specific degree of confidence (usually 95%) that the population mean lies within the limits we have established. This procedure is the same as that outlined in Chapter Eleven except that we use the more accurate *t* distribution, instead of the normal distribution, as our model when working with small samples.

To illustrate the calculations involved in establishing a set of confidence limits, we will use a step-by-step procedure for the example of reading speeds of entering college freshmen. Recall that we had a sample of 25 randomly selected entering freshmen. The mean reading speed for this sample was 290 words per minute. The unbiased estimate of the population standard deviation, calculated from the sample, was 100 words per minute. Suppose that we wish to establish 95% confidence limits (that is, we want to be 95% confident that the population mean falls in the interval created by our confidence limits).

*Step 1.* Calculate the standard error of the mean.

$$\hat{\sigma}_{\bar{x}} = \text{standard error of the mean} = \text{standard deviation of sample means}$$

$$= \frac{\hat{\sigma}}{\sqrt{N}} = \frac{\text{estimated standard deviation of the population}}{\sqrt{\text{sample size}}} = \frac{100}{\sqrt{25}} = \frac{100}{5} = 20$$

*Step 2.* In the *t* table look up the critical value of *t* for N-1 degrees of freedom for the confidence level you are interested in (usually 95%). For 95% confidence limits use the column headed .05. The tabled value (the critical value of *t*) tells how many standard errors are required to have 95% of the possible sample means within the limits and only 5% of the sample means outside the limits.

In our example, degrees of freedom = N - 1 = 25 - 1 = 24. The value from the $t$ table in the row for 24 degrees of freedom and in the column headed by .05 is 2.064.

*Step 3.* Calculate the confidence limits by applying the formula

$$\text{Limits} = \overline{X} \pm \hat{\sigma}_{\overline{X}}(t_{crit})$$

where $\overline{X}$ is the sample mean, $\hat{\sigma}_{\overline{X}}$ is the standard error of the mean calculated in Step 1, and $t_{crit}$ is the critical value of $t$ (which is the value found in the $t$ table in Step 2).

In our example, we plug the values into our formula as shown below.

$$\text{Limits} = 290 \pm 20(2.064)$$
$$= 290 \pm 41.28$$

$$\text{Upper limit} = 290 + 41.28 = 331.28$$
$$\text{Lower limit} = 290 - 41.28 = 248.72$$

We now have good reason to believe that there is a .95 probability that the mean reading speed of the population of college freshmen lies between 248.72 words per minute and 331.28 words per minute. We were able to make this estimate by testing only 25 out of the millions of college freshmen.

We could establish a narrower interval if we had drawn a larger sample, but that would have been more costly. The decision of how large the sample should be in any study is a tradeoff between the cost of collecting the data for this sample size and the degree of accuracy (the size of the interval) we need for our estimate.

By the same token, we could have a higher degree of confidence that the population mean will lie within our interval by using the critical value of $t$ from the $t$ table in the column headed .01 (for example). This would produce 99% confidence limits, but it would also produce a wider interval.

We cannot have perfect certainty that the population mean is exactly a particular value, but we need not be entirely at the mercy of chance. We can choose the degree of uncertainty we are willing to risk and the cost of collecting data that we are willing to bear. Often we can achieve results that are nearly as useful as if we had measured the entire population while actually measuring only a modest sized sample that is only a tiny proportion of the total population.

## Testing the Significance of the Difference between a Single Sample Mean and a Known Population Mean or other Known Value

Sometimes the issue that concerns us with a single sample is somewhat different from that of establishing confidence limits. Sometimes we want to know whether or not our single sample came from a population whose mean is a particular known value. Suppose, for example, that we work in quality control for the Tasty Dip Potato Chip Company. Tasty Dip Potato Chip advertising states that its bags contain 8 ounces of potato chips. We know, of course, that every bag cannot contain *exactly* 8 ounces; some will contain a little more than 8 ounces and some a little less.

However, we fear that the company could be accused of false advertising if the mean weight of the chips in the bags were less than the advertised 8 ounces. In fact, because we are a responsible company, we want our bags to actually contain a little more than 8 ounces on average, just to be safe. Therefore we conduct a test by randomly selecting 25 bags of chips and weighing the chips in each bag. The mean of this sample is 8.09 ounces and the unbiased estimate of the population standard deviation is .12. We feel better to learn that our sample mean is a little more than 8 ounces, but we cannot be totally comfortable unless we are confident that the (population) average bag of chips contains more than 8 ounces.

If the mean bag of chips contains 8 ounces, the sampling distribution of the mean would look like that shown in Figure 12-2. The statistical question is whether our sample mean is likely to be a member of this distribution (as shown in Figure 12-2) or, alternatively, if it is very unlikely to be a member of this sampling distribution. In this alternate case, our sample mean would be a member of some sampling distribution with a higher mean, as illustrated in Figure 12-3.

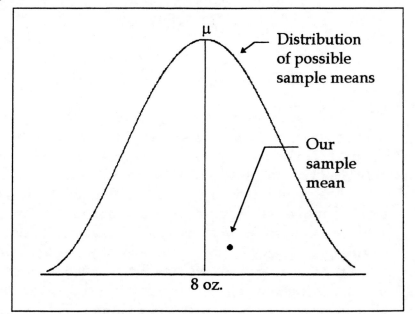

Figure 12-2. Distribution of sample means with our sample as a member of the population.

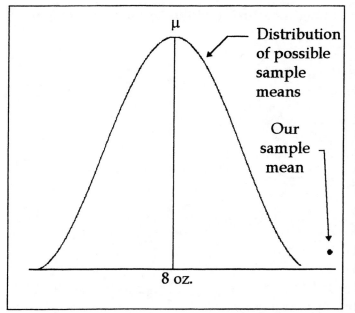

μ

Distribution of possible sample means

Our sample mean

8 oz.

Figure 12-3. Distribution of sample means with our sample not a member.

We can easily test whether we have reason to be confident that our hoped for alternate explanation of the situation is correct. We know that the standard error of the mean is the standard deviation of possible sample means around the population mean. We also know that these sample means should form a *t* distribution around the population mean. To make our test we take the difference between our sample mean and the population mean (8 oz) and see how many standard errors (standard deviations) the sample mean lies from the population mean. The formula for making this comparison is

$$t = \frac{\text{population mean - sample mean}}{\text{standard error of the mean}} = \frac{\mu - \overline{X}}{\hat{\sigma}_{\overline{x}}}$$

If the difference between our sample mean and the population mean is great enough, then our results will look like Figure 12-3. It would be very unlikely that our sample mean could have come from a population with a mean of 8 ounces. In this case we could feel comfortable; otherwise we could not.

The question now arises -- how unlikely is unlikely enough to feel comfortable? The convention most often used in the behavioral sciences is that the difference must be large enough that the probability it could have occurred by chance is less than .05. If this probability is less than .05, we consider the difference to be a real, non-chance difference.

The *t* table (see Appendix C) contains critical values of t. That is, if our calculated *t* value is equal to or greater than the critical value of *t* from the *t* table (at the intersection of the column headed .05 and the row for the appropriate degrees of freedom), then the probability that our difference could have occurred by chance is less than .05. Therefore, we can be reasonably confident that the average bag contains more than 8 ounces of chips. On the other hand, if our calculated *t* value is less than the critical value of *t* from the table, then we can not be confident that our difference was not due to chance.

Now we will illustrate the computations for our potato chip example using a step-by-step procedure. Remember that we sampled 25 bags of chips, found the sample mean to be 8.09 ounces, and found the unbiased estimate of the population standard deviation to be .12.

*Step 1.* Compute the standard error of the mean.

$$\hat{\sigma}_{\bar{X}} = \frac{\text{standard deviation}}{\sqrt{\text{sample size}}} = \frac{\hat{\sigma}}{\sqrt{N}} = \frac{.12}{\sqrt{25}} = \frac{.12}{5} = 0.024$$

*Step 2.* Calculate the value of *t* for this problem.

$$t = \frac{\text{population mean - sample mean}}{\text{standard error of the mean}} = \frac{\mu - \bar{X}}{\hat{\sigma}_{\bar{X}}} = \frac{8.00 - 8.09}{.024} = \frac{.09}{.024} = 3.75$$

*Step 3.* Look up the critical value of *t* in the *t* table (Appendix C) using the row for N-1 degrees of freedom and the column headed .05.

Critical *t* for our example with 24 degrees of freedom and .05 probability = 2.064

*Step 4.* Compare the calculated value of *t* with the critical value of *t* from the table. If the calculated *t* is equal to or greater than the critical value of *t*, then we can feel confident that the difference between the sample mean and value it was tested against was not due to chance. Otherwise, we cannot.

In our example, the calculated *t* of 3.75 is greater than the critical *t*, from the table, of 2.064. Therefore, we can conclude that the probability of this difference being due to chance is less than .05; we are justified in believing that the difference is not due to chance. The Tasty Dip Potato Chip Company's bags of potato chips really do contain more than 8 ounces of potato chips.

## Testing the Significance of a Correlation

The purpose of the Pearson Product-Moment Correlation (Pearson r) is to measure the strength of the relationship between two variables. It accomplishes this purpose with great precision when we compute the correlation on the entire population. However, it is easy to forget that this is seldom the case. In fact, correlations are almost always calculated on samples.

When the correlation is calculated on a sample, rather than an entire population, the correlation coefficient has all the sampling problems that the mean has and more. A sample correlation (r) will almost certainly not be exactly the same as the population correlation (ρ). One particularly distressing possibility is that the sample for which we have calculated a correlation may has been drawn from a population where the actual correlation is zero. In fact, correlations of rather impressive size can arise by chance in small samples taken from a population in which the true population correlation is zero. To interpret such a sample correlation would put us in the position of reading deep meaning into a chance event.

What is needed to prevent this sort of error is the ability to test the probability that the sample correlation we have computed could have arisen by chance alone. If it turns out that our correlation would be highly unlikely to have arisen by chance, then we can be confident that it represents a real relationship in the population.

This test can be done easily by using the Fisher's z conversion table (Appendix D), which we used in Chapter Ten to average correlations. Since the sampling distribution of Fisher's z is normal, in a population where the correlation ($\rho$) is zero this normal distribution would have a mean of zero and a standard error (standard deviation) of $\frac{1}{\sqrt{N - 3}}$. Using this information we can easily calculate a standard score (z score) for our sample correlation that will tell us how many standard deviations from the center of this chance (sampling) distribution our sample correlation would lie. If it lies so many standard deviations out in the tail of this distribution that such a sample correlation would be very unlikely to occur by chance (usually .05 or less by convention in the behavioral sciences), then we can feel confident that our sample correlation indicates that there is a real correlation in the population. Figure 12-4 describes this situation graphically.

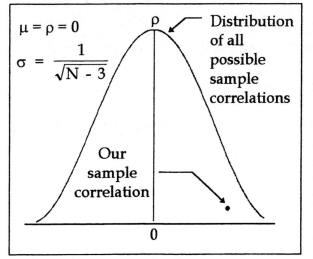

Figure 12-4. Sampling distribution of Fisher's z.

As always, the standard score for our sample correlation in this chance distribution would be

$$z = \text{standard score} = \frac{\text{raw score - mean}}{\text{standard deviation}}$$

Our raw score in this case is Fisher's z for our sample correlation. The mean of the distribution of chance correlations is zero. The standard deviation is the standard deviation of the distribution of Fisher's z scores, which is $\frac{1}{\sqrt{N-3}}$, where N is the number of paired observations used to compute the sample correlation.

So we can write the formula for the standard score used to test the significance of a correlation as

$$z = \text{standard score} = \frac{z_r - 0}{\dfrac{1}{\sqrt{N-3}}} = \frac{z_r}{\dfrac{1}{\sqrt{N-3}}}$$

The only tricky thing here is to be sure not to confuse z (a plain old standard score) with $z_r$ (Fisher's z), which is a conversion of the correlation coefficient using Appendix D.

Once we have calculate our z score for our correlation, we can compare it to our critical value. For a probability of .05 our critical value is 1.96, because in a normal distribution .95 of the scores fall within 1.96 standard deviations of the mean (and the remaining .05 of the scores fall outside this range). If our calculated standard score (z score) is equal to or greater than this critical value of 1.96, then we can feel confident that our sample correlation indicates that there is a real correlation in the population.

To illustrate these computations consider the following example. Suppose we had a theory that intelligence is an important component of bowling ability. In an effort to test this idea we give IQ tests to 20 randomly selected bowlers and calculate the correlation between their IQ scores and their bowling scores. Our sample correlation turns out to be r = .40. Can we feel confident that this represents a real correlation between intelligence test scores and bowling ability? We will answer this question using a step-by-step procedure.

*Step 1.* Convert the sample correlation to a Fisher's z using the table in Appendix D.

For our sample correlation of r = .40 the corresponding Fisher's z is $z_r$ = .424.

*Step 2.* Calculate the standard error for our correlation in the sampling distribution of Fisher's z.

$$z = \text{standard score} = \frac{\text{Fisher's } z}{\text{standard error of Fisher's } z} = \frac{z_r}{\dfrac{1}{\sqrt{N-3}}}$$

$$= \frac{.424}{\dfrac{1}{\sqrt{20-3}}} = \frac{.424}{\dfrac{1}{\sqrt{17}}} = \frac{.424}{\dfrac{1}{4.12}} = \frac{.424}{.243} = 1.74$$

*Step 3.* Determine the critical value of the standard score (from the normal curve table in Appendix B). By convention we usually choose the critical value of the standard score at the .05 probability level.

Critical value of z = 1.96

*Step 4.* Compare the calculated value of the standard score with the critical value of the standard score. If the calculated z is greater than or equal to the critical z, then we can feel confident that the sample correlation did not occur by chance. Otherwise we cannot.

In our example the z of 1.74 calculated from our sample is less than the critical z of 1.96. Therefore, we cannot be confident that our sample correlation did not occur by chance. We cannot conclude that intelligence is related to bowling ability.

This problem serves as a good example of what we said earlier that a correlation of rather impressive size can easily arise by chance when the sample is small. This is a stern reminder that we should always test the significance of any correlation we compute before we put our faith in it.

There is an even easier method for determining whether there is adequate reason to believe that a sample correlation came from a population with a real, non-zero correlation. In this method we simply look up the critical value of the Pearson r in the table in Appendix E. Degrees of freedom are listed as row headers down the left side of the table. The appropriate degrees of freedom for the Pearson r is N-2. (Since a straight line is defined by two points, we can put a regression line perfectly through *any* two data points in a scattergram. Thus, the correlation for *any* two data points is always r = 1.0) Some common probability levels are listed as column heads across the top of the table. Again, by convention, we usually use the .05 probability level. The tabled value is the minimum correlation (critical value of the Pearson r) that could occur by chance with a probability less than or equal to the probability listed as the column head.

To use this method to determine the significance of a sample correlation we follow three steps. First, calculate the sample correlation coefficient (a Pearson r). Second, find the critical value of the correlation in the table in Appendix E. Third, compare the calculated r to the critical r. If the calculated r is greater than or equal to the critical r, then we can feel confident that the sample correlation did not occur by chance alone. Otherwise, we cannot.

## Study Questions
*Answers to selected study questions may be found in Appendix A.*

1. The Parks and Wildlife Department has a newly developed lake that has been stocked with fish. The department wishes to know the mean length of fish that would be caught if the lake were opened to fishing. The department test-fishes the lake and catches 121 fish with a mean length of 17 cm and an unbiased estimate of the population standard deviation of 3.5 cm. Establish confidence limits for the mean length of the fish.

2. The time to harvest a particular variety of wine grapes comes when the mean sugar concentration of the grapes has reached 22 parts per hundred. The vintner randomly samples the grapes from 61 sprigs and finds a mean of 25 parts per hundred with an unbiased estimate of the population standard deviation of 5. Are the grapes ready to harvest?

3. A company has tested eight workers who have just completed its widget training program. The company wants to know the mean widget production for workers who have completed the widget training program. Using the data provided below, establish 95% confidence limits for the mean widget production. Can the company be confident that the mean widget production is above 50?

| Worker | # Widgets Produced |
|--------|--------------------|
| 1 | 70 |
| 2 | 45 |
| 3 | 62 |
| 4 | 58 |
| 5 | 71 |
| 6 | 43 |
| 7 | 64 |
| 8 | 54 |

4. The national mean on a third grade spelling test is 20. An elementary school teacher wonders how the mean of third-graders at her school compares with the national mean. She administers the test to a random sample of 12 students. Using the data provided below, determine whether the mean of the teacher's random sample of students is likely to be drawn from a population with a mean of 20.

| Student | Spelling Test Score |
|---------|---------------------|
| 1       | 13                  |
| 2       | 18                  |
| 3       | 24                  |
| 4       | 20                  |
| 5       | 19                  |
| 6       | 21                  |
| 7       | 25                  |
| 8       | 17                  |
| 9       | 20                  |
| 10      | 22                  |
| 11      | 16                  |
| 12      | 21                  |

5. A behavioral neuroscientist is interested in the effect of a drug used to treat attention deficit hyperactivity disorder (ADHD) on reaction time in a task designed to measure attentional processes. He randomly selects a group of 20 college students from whom he has obtained informed consent. Each subject is administered a small amount of the drug and tested on the task 30 minutes later. The mean reaction time of the experimental subjects is 248 ms with an unbiased estimate of the population standard deviation of 13.3 ms. The scientist knows that many previous studies have found the mean reaction time on this task to be 264 ms in normal subjects. Is it likely that this sample was drawn from a population with a mean of 264 ms? What does this suggest about the effect of the drug on reaction time?

6. A researcher has produced a new strain of transgenic mice that lack a particular type of neurotransmitter receptor. From previous studies it is known that normal mice will explore a novel object in preference to an object they have seen previously, spending an average of 8.2 minutes (out of a 10 minute interval) exploring the novel object and 1.8 minutes exploring the known object. The researcher tests a sample of 5 transgenic mice in the novel object task and finds that they spend an average of 5.7 minutes exploring the novel object with an unbiased estimate of the population standard deviation equal to 0.8 minutes. Is it likely that this sample was drawn

from a population with a mean of 8.2 minutes? What does this suggest about the role of the missing receptor?

7. According to a particular personality theory, the need for achievement (nAch) is negatively correlated with the need for affiliation (nAff). A psychologist measures nAch and nAff in a sample of 20 college students and finds that r = -.37. Do her results support the theory?

8. A college admissions officer finds a correlation of .32 between verbal SAT scores and college GPA based on a sample of 39 college students. Can he say that there a real correlation between verbal SAT score and college GPA in the population?

9. A football coach is interested in increasing the conditioning of his players. He samples a group of 12 players and finds that the correlation between percentage of body fat and endurance is -.43. Can he conclude that there is a real relationship between body fat and endurance?

# CHAPTER THIRTEEN

# Testing the Difference Between Means: Independent Samples

In Chapter Eleven, when we began this section on inferential statistics, we introduced the example of an experimenter trying to determine whether green paper or white paper produced faster reading speeds. The experimenter arranged for one group of subjects to read a passage printed on white paper and another group of subjects to read the same passage printed on green paper. The experimenter measured each subject's reading speed (number of words per minute) and then calculated a mean reading speed for each group. The result is that the mean reading speed for the green paper group is greater (faster) than for the white paper group.

However, before she can be confident that this result means that people, in general, read faster on green paper than on white paper, the experimenter must determine whether or not chance might be a reasonable explanation for the difference she found in this experiment. After all, even if both groups had read the passage on white paper, they would not have had exactly the same mean reading speeds.

This is a question that must be faced and answered in every scientific experiment that we do. We cannot eliminate the workings of chance from our experiments. All we can do is come to understand its principles and take them into account in our research. How do we do this? The approach that we use today derives primarily from the work of the great 20th century statistician Sir Ronald Fisher. Fisher set out to create a system of inductive logic that was as rigorous and mechanical as the older deductive logic. The system Fisher created is called **Classical Statistical Decision Theory.** Today, Classical Statistical Decision Theory is the way we deal with the issue of chance in our scientific experiments in the social sciences and many other disciplines.

To understand the nature of Fisher's Classical Statistical Decision Theory, its place in scientific research, and its place in our broader culture we need to look back into the historical development of science within philosophy. While inductive logic only began to be understood at all well in 20th century, deductive logic has been well understood and much used since the time of the ancient Greeks. Over 2000 years ago the philosopher Aristotle (384-322 BC) wrote an exhaustive treatise on the principles of deductive logic and it has not been much improved upon since. **Deductive logic** has a set of rules that wring specific implications out of general statements, called premises, in a very mechanical way. Deductive logic is sometimes called formal logic because the wringing of the implications (or conclusions) from the premises is purely a matter of form. That is, if the rules are properly observed (and the premises are true), then the conclusion **must** be true. These rules are too numerous to be dealt with here, but we can illustrate the way deductive logic works by considering the famous example syllogism shown in Table 13-1.

In a syllogism all statements are divided into a subject (S) and a predicate (P) portion. Each predicate portion tells us something about the subject portion. Note that in the form of syllogism shown in Table 13-1 the subject portion of the major premise is

Table 13-1
Parts of a Syllogism

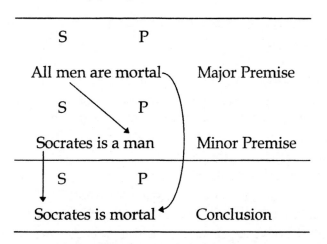

the same as the predicate portion of the minor premise. When they are linked in this way, the subject portion of the minor premise becomes the subject portion of the conclusion and the predicate portion of the major premise becomes the predicate portion of the conclusion. Thus, the implications of the premises are wrung out of them to form the conclusion as mechanically as a cookie cutter produces a cookie. Furthermore, any set of statements of the same form (with the same relationships) will produce a true conclusion.

The thing about this system of deductive logic that appealed to philosophers was its objective and mechanical rules. For over 1500 years it was regarded as *the* system for producing knowledge. The scholars of the Middle Ages became obsessed with it and gave names (such as Barbara) to each of the possible syllogistic forms. The study of (deductive) logic was an important part of the curriculum of every university student in the Middle Ages. One of the pilgrims in Chaucer's **Canterbury Tales** was an Oxford student (a student was called a clerk in those days). Chaucer wrote of him:

A clerk of Oxenford there was also,
Had taken to his logic long ago.

In the Renaissance some philosophers, notably Francis Bacon (1561-1626), began to become skeptical about the usefulness of deductive logic for discovering truth. They felt that, at best, deductive logic only brought out the knowledge already inherent in statements that were assumed to be true, and that it was rather barren in terms of its ability to discover original (new) truth.

What was really needed was a system that allowed new knowledge to be synthesized from direct observations of nature. That is, general principles were to be formulated by making multiple observations of phenomena in the natural world. These multiple observations were to be put together, or synthesized, into general principles. As a simple example, suppose that we want to study swans. We go to one pond and see seven swans, all of which are white. Next, we go to another pond and see five swans, all of which are also white. At a third pond we see ten white swans. We then form the general principle "swans are white." The separate observations have been synthesized into a general principle. This process, illustrated in Figure 13-1, has come to be called **inductive logic** because the general principle is "induced" by the observations.

This was a very appealing idea and much can be said for it. The chief problem, however, was that, in contrast to the neat, rigorous, and mechanical rules of deductive logic, inductive logic was a poorly understood and rather slipshod process. It was not

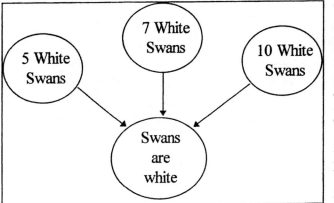

Figure 13-1. Synthesizing a general principle by induction.

clear how many observations were necessary in order to form a generalization. If we had gone to one more pond, perhaps we would have seen a black swan (or a green one). There was also no way to conclusively check the validity of the generalization. The whole process was like "flying by the seat of one's pants." What was needed was the ability to employ the creative richness and empirical contact with the natural world inherent in inductive logic with an objective, rigorous, and mechanical system comparable to that of the older

deductive logic. It was to this task that Fisher addressed himself and Classical Statistical Decision Theory was the result.

## Fisher's Classical Statistical Decision Theory

To illustrate how Fisher's Classical Statistical Decision Theory works consider, again, our example experiment on the effects of paper color on reading speed. We have drawn two samples of subjects and exposed them to different treatments -- reading the passage printed on green paper or on white paper. Then we calculated the mean reading speed of each group. We can count on the fact that there will be a difference between these two sample means. However, there are two possible explanations for why this difference occurred. These two explanations are related to one another in two important ways. They are (1) *mutually exclusive*, which means that they cannot both be true, and (2) *exhaustive*, which means that there are no other possible explanations. Together, these two characteristics of the two explanations mean that one of the explanations *must* be true.

The two possible explanations for the observed difference in our two sample means are (1) the null hypothesis, and (2) the alternate hypothesis. The *null hypothesis*, symbolized by $H_0$, states that both samples came from a single population (in our reading speed example, the population of people who read). The observed difference between the two sample means is due entirely to sampling error. For our example the null hypothesis is illustrated in Figure 13-2.

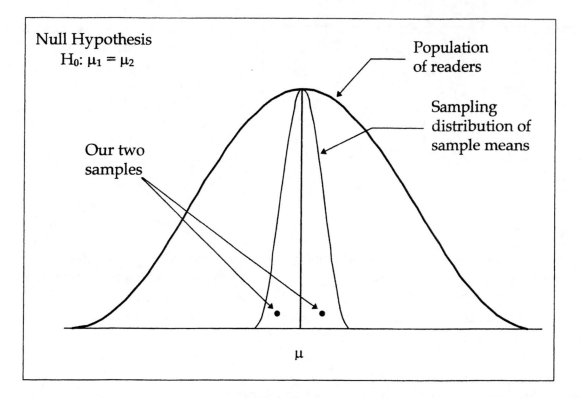

Figure 13-2. How the Null Hypothesis explains a difference between sample means.

The **alternate hypothesis** is represented by the symbol $H_1$. The alternate hypothesis states that our two samples came from different populations with different population means. Therefore, the observed difference between our two sample means is due to the combination of a real difference between the two populations and sampling error. In our reading speed example the alternate hypothesis is that paper color really does influence reading speed; the observed difference in sample means reflects a real population difference between readers of material on white paper and readers of material on green paper **and** sampling error. Figure 13-3 illustrates the alternate hypothesis for our example.

Now, how do we decide between these two hypotheses? Both are possible -- even plausible. According to Fisher's Classical Statistical Decision Theory, our reasoning should continue as follows: We cannot directly test the alternate hypothesis, because we do not have enough information to be able to make this test. We do not know how large the difference between the two populations is -- we are not even sure that there really are two populations. On the other hand, we can indirectly test the alternate hypothesis by determining how good an explanation the null hypothesis is for the observed difference between sample means. If the null hypothesis is false, then the alternate hypothesis **must** be true (remember that they are mutually exclusive and exhaustive).

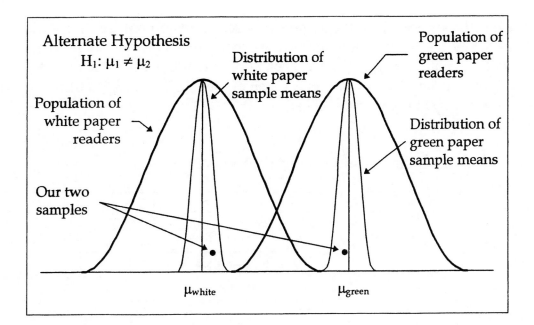

Figure 13-3. How the Alternate Hypothesis explains the difference between two means.

To assess the null hypothesis we use our knowledge of the sampling behavior of means drawn from a single population. That is, we use our knowledge of the standard error of the mean. Our task is to calculate the probability of getting a difference between sample means at least as large as the one we actually got when we randomly select two samples from a single population. In other words, if the null hypothesis were true how likely would it be for us to get a difference between sample means at least as large as the difference we did get? Or, what is the probability of obtaining a difference at least this large simply by chance?

If the probability of getting a chance difference at least as large as the one we actually got is very low (less than .05), then we can reasonably conclude that the null hypothesis is unlikely to be true. In this case we would reject the null hypothesis because it is a poor explanation of our results. Having rejected the null hypothesis, we must turn to the alternate hypothesis. There is no other explanation, because the two hypotheses are mutually exclusive and exhaustive. On the other hand, if the probability of getting a difference at least as large as the one we got is *not* very low (that is, greater than .05), then we cannot conclude that the null hypothesis is an unreasonable explanation for our result and we cannot reject it.

When we make this decision, there are four possible outcomes, as shown in Table 13-2. If we reject the null hypothesis, concluding that there is a real difference between population means, and the null hypothesis is, indeed, false, then we have made a correct decision. However, if we reject the null hypothesis and it is actually true, then we have made an error. This error is called a *Type I error*. The probability of committing a type I error is $\alpha$ (the lower case Greek letter alpha). The value of $\alpha$ should be set by the experimenter *before* the experiment is conducted. It is the risk the experimenter is willing to run of falsely concluding that there is a real difference between group means. By convention $\alpha$ is usually set at .05, but could be made either more or less stringent if the situation calls for it.

Table 13-2
Possible Outcomes in the Statistical Decision Process

|  |  | The Truth | |
|---|---|---|---|
|  |  | $H_0$ is True | $H_0$ is False |
| Our Decision | Reject the $H_0$ | Type I Error (probability = $\alpha$) | Correct Decision |
|  | Do not Reject the $H_0$ | Correct Decision | Type II Error (probability = $\beta$) |

If we do not reject the null hypothesis and it is actually true, then we have made the correct decision that there is no real difference between the population means. On the other hand, if we fail to reject the null hypothesis and it is actually false, then we have made another error -- a *Type II error*. The probability of committing a Type II error is $\beta$ (the lower case Greek letter beta). Unlike alpha ($\alpha$), beta ($\beta$) is not under the direct control of the experimenter and its value is unknown in most experiments.

Another related probability called the *power* of the test is $1 - \beta$. The power of the test is the probability of rejecting the null hypothesis when it is, indeed, false. In other words, the power of a test is the probability of detecting a true difference (if one actually exists). It is highly desirable to make our tests as powerful as possible. When beta ($\beta$) is minimized, power is maximized. The art of maximizing the power of our tests is a central part of what is called experimental design. It is covered extensively in advanced courses in research methodology.

When we reject the null hypothesis we say that we have a *significant difference*. A significant difference is a difference that is sufficiently unlikely to have occurred by chance that we can feel justified in regarding it as representing a real difference between population means. Alpha ($\alpha$) is the criterion that must be met to make this decision. When $\alpha$ is set at .05, a significant difference means that the probability that our difference could have occurred by chance is less than .05. Note that the common English word "significant" generally means "important," as when a speaker says "a significant event has occurred today." However, in statistical terminology "significant" is a specialized, technical term indicating only that the difference is unlikely to have occurred by chance. It does not carry the additional meaning of "importance." As such, a significant difference may be small and have little impact on anything of great value. The term tells us only that the difference is "statistically reliable." In fact, a less confusing way to express the idea of a significant difference would be to use the term "statistically reliable difference."

## Testing the Significance of the Difference Between the Means of Independent Samples

Suppose that the null hypothesis is true and we are, indeed, drawing our samples from a single population. Now we draw a pair of samples, calculate the mean of each sample (group), and calculate the chance difference between the two sample means. If we repeat this process for lots and lots of pairs of sample means and build a distribution of differences between pairs of means, then our distribution would have the following characteristics:

(1) The mean of our distribution of chance differences would be zero.

(2) Our distribution would form a $t$ distribution, which would approach the shape of a normal distribution as the sample size increases.

(3) If our samples were independent, the standard deviation of our distribution (called the ***standard error of the difference between means***, represented by the symbol $\sigma_{D_{\overline{x}}}$ )

would approach

$$\sigma_{D_{\overline{X}}} = \sqrt{\sigma_{\overline{X}_1}^2 + \sigma_{\overline{X}_2}^2}$$

where $\sigma_{\overline{X}_1}$ is the standard error of the mean for the first set of sample means and $\sigma_{\overline{X}_2}$ is the standard error of the mean for the second set of sample means.

When the samples are small (and, therefore, the approach to the normal distribution is not yet extremely close), the best estimate of the standard error of the difference between means can be made by the formula:

$$\sigma_{D_{\overline{X}}} = \text{standard error of the difference between means} = \sqrt{\left(\frac{SS_1 + SS_2}{N_1 + N_2 - 2}\right)\left(\frac{N_1 + N_2}{N_1 * N_2}\right)}$$

where $SS_1$ is the sum of squares for the first sample, $SS_2$ is the sum of squares for the second sample, $N_1$ is the number of scores in the first sample, and $N_2$ is the number of scores in the second sample. Remember that the sum of squares (first discussed in Chapter Four, it is the heart of the standard deviation formula) is the sum of the squared deviations of raw scores around the mean. The raw score formula for computing the sum of squares is

$$SS = \sum X^2 - \frac{(\sum X)^2}{N}$$

where $\sum X$ is the sum of the scores in the group, $\sum X^2$ is the sum of the squared scores in the group, and N is the number of scores in the group.

We realize that this second formula for the standard error of the difference between means does not look much like the first formula. In this case we ask you to trust us. It turns out that the two formulas for the standard error of the difference between means are closely related and, in some circumstances, give exactly the same results.

Using this standard deviation of chance differences between means (the standard error of the difference between means), we can take our *one* difference between sample means and see where it lies in the distribution of possible sample differences. We accomplish this by converting our difference to a standard score in the *t* distribution:

$$t = \frac{\text{our difference}}{\substack{\text{standard error of the} \\ \text{difference between means}}} = \frac{\overline{X}_1 - \overline{X}_2}{\sqrt{\left(\dfrac{SS_1 + SS_2}{N_1 + N_2 - 2}\right)\left(\dfrac{N_1 + N_2}{N_1 * N_2}\right)}}$$

where $\overline{X}_1$ is the mean of the first sample (group), $\overline{X}_2$ is the mean of the second sample (group), $SS_1$ is the sum of squares for the first group, $SS_2$ is the sum of squares for the second group, $N_1$ is the number of scores in the first group, and $N_2$ is the number of scores in the second group. This formula is used to perform a *t test for independent samples*. A *t* test for independent samples should be used when the subjects in our samples have not been paired or matched in any way.

To illustrate how a *t* test for independent samples is performed, consider the example data in Table 13-3. In this example we are testing the effects of caffeine on ability to perform clerical tasks. We give one group of subjects two cups of decaffeinated coffee and another group two cups of regular coffee. Then each subject looks up 50 telephone numbers in the telephone book. The scores are the time (in minutes) required to complete this task.

Table 13-3
Number of Minutes Required to Complete a Clerical
Task as a Function of Type of Coffee

| Regular Coffee | Decaffeinated Coffee |
|:---:|:---:|
| 5 | 9 |
| 7 | 8 |
| 5 | 8 |
| 8 | 10 |
| 6 | 10 |
| $\sum X_1 = 31$ | $\sum X_2 = 45$ |
| $\sum X_1^2 = 199$ | $\sum X_2^2 = 409$ |

To determine whether the caffeine had a real effect on the time required to complete the clerical task, we perform a $t$ test on the scores in Table 13-3 using a step-by-step procedure:

***Step 1.*** Calculate the value of $\sum X$ and $\sum X^2$ for each group, as shown in Table 13-3.

***Step 2.*** Calculate the mean of each group. In our example,

$$\overline{X}_1 = \frac{\sum X_1}{N_1} = \frac{31}{5} = 6.20$$

$$\overline{X}_2 = \frac{\sum X_2}{N_2} = \frac{45}{5} = 9.00$$

***Step 3.*** Find the sum of squares (sum of the squared deviations around the mean) for each group. In our example,

$$SS_1 = \sum X_1^2 - \frac{(\sum X_1)^2}{N_1} = 199 - \frac{(31)^2}{5} = 199 - \frac{961}{5} = 199 - 192.20 = 6.80$$

$$SS_2 = \sum X_2^2 - \frac{(\sum X_2)^2}{N_2} = 409 - \frac{(45)^2}{5} = 409 - \frac{2025}{5} = 409 - 405 = 4.00$$

*Step 4.* Calculate the value of $t$. In our example,

$$t = \frac{\overline{X}_1 - \overline{X}_2}{\sqrt{\left(\dfrac{SS_1 + SS_2}{N_1 + N_2 - 2}\right)\left(\dfrac{N_1 + N_2}{N_1 * N_2}\right)}} = \frac{6.20 - 9.00}{\sqrt{\left(\dfrac{6.80 + 4.00}{5 + 5 - 2}\right)\left(\dfrac{5 + 5}{5 * 5}\right)}} = \frac{-2.80}{\sqrt{\left(\dfrac{10.80}{8}\right)\left(\dfrac{10}{25}\right)}}$$

$$= \frac{-2.80}{\sqrt{(1.35)(.40)}} = \frac{-2.80}{\sqrt{.54}} = \frac{-2.80}{.73} = -3.84$$

*Step 5.* Find the critical value of $t$ in the $t$ table (Appendix C) for $N_1 + N_2 - 2$ degrees of freedom at the .05 level of significance for a two-tailed test. In our example the critical value of $t$ is 2.306 (for a two-tailed test with 8 degrees of freedom at the .05 level of significance):

$$t_{crit} = 2.306$$

*Step 6.* Compare the absolute value (the value without regard to whether it is positive or negative) of the calculated $t$ with the critical value of $t$ from the table. In our example the calculated $t$ is larger than the critical value of $t$:

Calculated $t$ (absolute value) = 3.84          Critical value of $t$ (from table) = 2.306

*Step 7.* Make the decision. This decision is a choice between two options:
(A) If the calculated $t$ is equal to or greater than the critical value of $t$ from the table, then we reject the null hypothesis ($H_0$) and conclude that the alternate hypothesis ($H_1$) is correct. The difference between means is significant. That is, we conclude that the probability that this difference occurred by chance is sufficiently low that chance as an explanation can be rejected as implausible. We are left with the conclusion that the difference between the sample means represents a real difference between population means. Or,
(B) If the calculated $t$ is less than the critical value of $t$ from the table, then we fail to reject the null hypothesis ($H_0$). We cannot conclude that the difference between means is significant. That is, we cannot confidently reject the explanation that this difference arose by chance alone due to sampling error. We cannot conclude that the difference between our sample means represents a real difference between population means.

In our example, since our calculated $t$ of 3.84 is greater than the critical $t$ from the table (2.306), we make decision A. We reject the null hypothesis ($H_0$) and conclude that we have a significant difference. That is, it is sufficiently unlikely to be due to chance that we can conclude that the difference represents a real difference between population means. We have sufficient reason to conclude that people who have had regular coffee with caffeine really can look up telephone numbers faster than people who have had decaffeinated coffee. In other words, caffeine does affect the speed of a clerical task. In a professional publication our result could be summarized as $t(8) = 3.84$, p<.05, which is read "$t$ with 8 degrees of freedom is equal to 3.84 which is significant at the .05 level."

The generalized logic of the decision making process for significance testing, for any test of significance, is shown in the form of a flowchart in Figure 13-4.

## Assumptions of the $t$-Test

In Chapter Ten we discussed the idea that all statistical procedures are based on some kind of theoretical model. Each model, in turn, is based on a set of assumptions. Three assumptions underlie the $t$-test. First, scores on the dependent variable are assumed to be of *interval or ratio level of measurement*. Second, scores on the dependent variable in each treatment group are assumed to be *normally distributed*. Third, variances of the scores in the two treatment groups are assumed to be *equal*.

## A Note on "Proving" the Null Hypothesis

In cases where our difference is sufficiently large to produce a significant difference, we are able make a rather strong statement in our conclusion. We have found our difference to be very unlikely to be due to chance (very unlikely defined as the probability being less than or equal to alpha, usually set at .05). Therefore we say that we "reject the null hypothesis" and "accept the alternate hypothesis." We can conclude with confidence that the difference represents a real difference between population means.

However, when we fail to reject the null hypothesis, our statement cannot be nearly so strong. We can only conclude that we did not find sufficient justification for rejecting the null hypothesis. We cannot assign a specific probability to the likelihood that the null hypothesis is true. Indeed, sloppy design of our experiment, very small sample sizes, and other problems may give us a very high probability of failing to reject the null hypothesis when it is actually not true (thereby committing a Type II error). For this reason it is inappropriate to simply say that we "accept the null hypothesis." Instead, we say that we "fail to reject the null hypothesis." This apparent clumsiness in our wording reflects the very real asymmetry in the strength of the conclusions we can draw in the two situations.

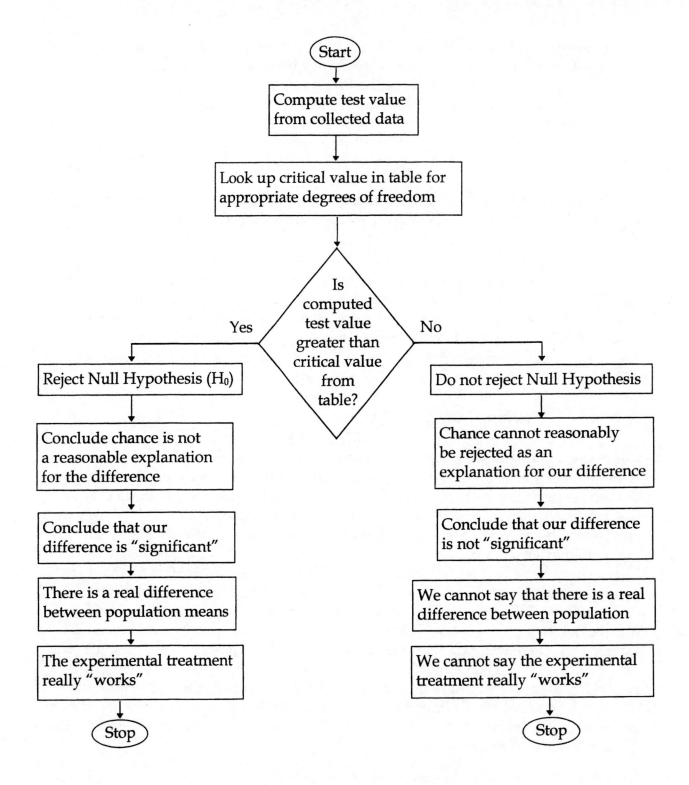

Figure 13-4. Flowchart of the reasoning process for a significance test.

## Study Questions
*Answers to selected study questions may be found in Appendix A.*

1. A psychologist wants to see if a new drug improves recall. One group of subjects is given the drug and one group is given a placebo. Both groups are then asked to memorize a list of 20 nonsense syllables. One week later all subjects are tested for memory and the number of syllables each correctly recalls is recorded. These data are reproduced below. Is there reason to believe that the drug improves memory?

Number of syllables correctly recalled

| Drug group | Placebo group |
| --- | --- |
| 18 | 11 |
| 12 | 13 |
| 15 | 9 |
| 13 | 12 |
| 15 | 8 |

2. A psychologist is interested in the effects of food reward on maze running behavior. Two groups of rats were run in a straight alley runway. The experimental group received a food pellet at the completion of each trial; the control group received no food. After a series of training trials the rats were timed on a test trial. These data are reproduced below. Was there a true difference in running times?

Running time in seconds

| Experimental (food pellet) | Control (no food) |
| --- | --- |
| 7 | 12 |
| 5 | 10 |
| 8 | 13 |
| 6 | 10 |
| 5 | 15 |

3.  A clinical psychologist at a university psychology clinic is interested in testing the effectiveness of a new type of treatment for depression. She randomly assigns a new group of 11 clients to receive either the standard type of therapy used in the clinic or the new therapy for a 12-week period. After completion of the therapy sessions, each client is given the Beck Depression Scale (a high score indicates greater depression). Her data are reproduced below. Can she conclude that one therapy works better than the other?

Beck Depression Scale Score

| Experimental (new therapy) | Control (standard therapy) |
| --- | --- |
| 6 | 8 |
| 3 | 6 |
| 8 | 11 |
| 2 | 4 |
| 9 | 9 |
| 4 | |

# CHAPTER FOURTEEN

# Testing the Difference Between Means: Related Samples

We can think of *any* test of significance as a ratio of a measure of the effect of the treatment being tested to a measure of error. The effect of the treatment is usually reflected in the difference between treatment group means, while error is measured by some indicator of unaccounted for variability, such as the standard error of the difference between means. This ratio can be written as

$$\text{Test value} = \frac{\text{Effect of the treatment}}{\text{Error}} = \frac{\text{Difference}}{\text{Standard error}}$$

The more we can minimize the error, the larger will be the test value and, hence, the greater will be the opportunity to find a significant difference, if a real difference exists. The art of minimizing error is the heart of the process called experimental design. Any experiment should be set up to minimize error, and to do so as efficiently as possible. Sometimes we can reduce the error (usually called the *error term* in our ratio) by matching or pairing similar subjects before the data are collected. There are three ways in which this matching is commonly accomplished:

(1) *Genetic matching* - Subjects with a high genetic similarity, such as twins or siblings (litter mates in animal studies) are used. One member of each pair is randomly assigned to each treatment group.

(2) *Matched samples* - Subjects are matched into pairs on the basis of some relevant variable before the experiment is conducted. One member of each pair is randomly assigned to each treatment group.

(3) *Test-retest procedure* - Each subject participates in both treatment groups and, therefore, is matched with himself.

The general formula for testing the significance of the difference between two means is

$$\frac{\overline{X}_1 - \overline{X}_2}{\sqrt{\sigma_{\overline{X}_1}^2 + \sigma_{\overline{X}_2}^2 - 2r\sigma_{\overline{X}_1}\sigma_{\overline{X}_2}}}$$

When samples are independent, r is assumed to be zero and the part of the denominator to the right of the minus sign disappears, leaving the formula presented in Chapter Thirteen. However, if subjects have been matched successfully, the correlation in the paired scores may be quite high. This reduces the size of the error term (the denominator in the formula).

When samples are small and we have only an estimate of the population standard deviation, the appropriate test is the $t$ test. A convenient version of the formula for the $t$ **test for related samples** is called the **direct differences version**:

$$t = \frac{\dfrac{\Sigma D}{N}}{\sqrt{\dfrac{\Sigma D^2 - \dfrac{(\Sigma D)^2}{N}}{N(N-1)}}}$$

where D is the difference between a paired set of scores, and N is the number of pairs of scores in the experiment. While this direct differences formula does not look like the general formula, it will give very similar (and under some conditions exactly the same) results.

## Computing the $t$ test for Related Samples

As an example, suppose we want to determine whether or not paper color affects reading speed. We know that people are very heterogeneous with regard to reading speed. So, before we begin our study, we would like to match our subjects on reading speed. We give each subject a test of reading speed, then pair each subject with the other subject whose reading speed score is the closest to her own reading speed score. Next, next we randomly assign one subject from each pair to a green paper group and the other subject in each pair to a white paper group. Having done this, we have each subject read a passage printed on the assigned color of paper. Finally, we count the number of 10 word lines read by each subject in the allotted time. The results of this example study are presented in Table 14-1.

Table 14-1
Number of Lines Read as a Function of Paper Color

| Pair | Green Paper Group | White Paper Group |
|------|-------------------|-------------------|
| 1 | 35 | 32 |
| 2 | 21 | 19 |
| 3 | 52 | 49 |
| 4 | 18 | 15 |
| 5 | 37 | 32 |

To determine whether paper color had a real effect on the number of lines read we perform a *t* test for related samples on the matched pairs of scores in Table 14-1. We use a step-by-step procedure to illustrate the computations.

*Step 1.* Calculate the difference (D) between each pair of scores and find the sum of these differences ($\Sigma$D). For our example this step is shown in Table 14-2.

$$\Sigma D = 16$$

*Step 2.* Square each difference to get D² for each pair of scores and find the sum of these squared differences ($\Sigma$D²). For our example this step is also shown in Table 14-2.

$$\Sigma D^2 = 56$$

Table 14-2
Number of Lines Read as a Function of Paper Color

| Pair | Green Paper Group | White Paper Group | D | D² |
|------|-------------------|-------------------|---|----|
| 1 | 35 | 32 | 3 | 9 |
| 2 | 21 | 19 | 2 | 4 |
| 3 | 52 | 49 | 3 | 9 |
| 4 | 18 | 15 | 3 | 9 |
| 5 | 37 | 32 | 5 | 25 |
| | | | $\Sigma D = 16$ | $\Sigma D^2 = 56$ |

*Step 3.* Calculate the value of *t*. Remember that N is the number of **pairs** of scores and D is the difference between a pair of scores. In our example,

$$t = \frac{\dfrac{\Sigma D}{N}}{\sqrt{\dfrac{\Sigma D^2 - \dfrac{(\Sigma D)^2}{N}}{N(N-1)}}} = \frac{\dfrac{16}{5}}{\sqrt{\dfrac{56 - \dfrac{(16)^2}{5}}{5(5-1)}}} = \frac{3.20}{\sqrt{\dfrac{56 - \dfrac{256}{5}}{5(4)}}} = \frac{3.20}{\sqrt{\dfrac{56 - 51.20}{20}}}$$

$$= \frac{3.20}{\sqrt{\dfrac{4.80}{20}}} = \frac{3.20}{\sqrt{.24}} = \frac{3.20}{.49} = 6.53$$

*Step 4.* Find the critical value of *t* in the *t* table (Appendix C) for a two-tailed test at the .05 level of significance for degrees of freedom equal to the number of pairs of scores - 1. In our example the critical value of *t* is 2.776 (for a two-tailed test with 4 degrees of freedom at the .05 level of significance):

$$t_{crit} = 2.776$$

*Step 5.* Compare the absolute value (the value without regard to whether it is positive or negative) of the calculated *t* with the critical value of *t* from the table. In our example the calculated *t* is larger than the critical value of *t*:

Calculated *t* (absolute value) = 6.53          Critical value of *t* (from table) = 2.776

*Step 6.* Make the decision. As in all significance tests, this decision is a choice between two options:
(A) If the calculated *t* is equal to or greater than the critical value of *t* from the table, then we reject the null hypothesis ($H_0$) and conclude that there is a significant difference; we conclude that the experimental treatment is effective. Or,
(B) If the calculated *t* is less than the critical value of *t* from the table, then we fail to reject the null hypothesis ($H_0$) and conclude that there is not a significant difference; we cannot say that the experimental treatment is effective.

In our example, since the calculated *t* of 6.53 is greater than the critical *t* from the table (2.776), we make decision A. We reject the null hypothesis ($H_0$) and conclude that the difference is significant. That is, paper color does affect reading speed. People reading on green paper do read faster than people reading on white paper. In a professional publication our result could be summarized by $t(4) = 6.53$, $p < .05$, which is read "*t* with 4 degrees of freedom is equal to 6.53 which is significant at the .05 level."

## One-Tailed and Two-Tailed Tests

The significance tests presented in Chapter Thirteen and in this chapter have been two-tailed tests. In a two-tailed test the *region of rejection* (the area in the sampling distribution that will cause the null hypothesis to be rejected if our sample value falls in it) is equally split between the two tails of the sampling distribution. This means that our alternate hypothesis is *non-directional*. If the alternate hypothesis is non-directional, it means that, when we test for the significance of a difference between two means, the alternate hypothesis does not specify which mean is larger. Rather, the alternate hypothesis merely states that the population means are different:

Null hypothesis ($H_0$): $\mu_1 = \mu_2$
Alternate hypothesis ($H_1$): $\mu_1 \neq \mu_2$

The sampling distribution and region of rejection under the null hypothesis for a two-tailed test are shown in Figure 14-1.

However, if the experimenter is willing to specify in the alternate hypothesis the direction of the difference, then the region of rejection can be placed entirely in one tail of the sampling distribution. This will allow a smaller difference to be significant. Thus, the advantage of a one-tailed test is that it is a more powerful test. The price we pay for this increased power is that any difference in the opposite (unexpected) direction, no matter how large, cannot be considered significant. When we have predicted (in advance) that $\overline{X}_1$ will be larger than $\overline{X}_2$, our null hypothesis is that $\mu_1$ is not greater than $\mu_2$ and the

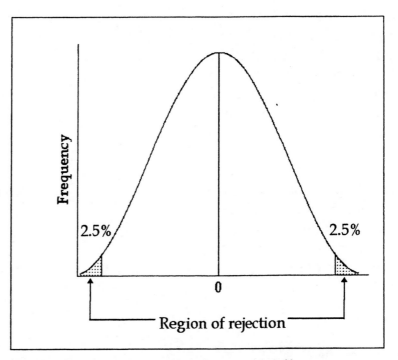

Figure 14-1. Sampling distribution of differences between means with the region of rejection for a two-tailed test.

alternate hypothesis is that $\mu_1$ is greater than $\mu_2$:

Null hypothesis ($H_0$): $\mu_1 \not> \mu_2$
Alternate hypothesis (H ): $\mu_1 > \mu_2$

Figure 14-2 shows the sampling distribution and region of rejection under the null hypothesis for a one-tailed test.

One-tailed tests are not frequently used and some researchers question whether they should ever be used. It seems silly to be unable to conclude that a difference in the unpredicted direction is significant, no matter how huge the difference may be.

The $t$ table in this book (Appendix C) is arranged for two-tailed tests, because two-tailed tests are, by far, the most commonly used. However, if a one-tailed test is used, the proper critical value of $t$ can be found in this table by using the column headed by two times the chosen value of alpha. For example, to find the critical value of $t$ for a one-tailed test with alpha = .05 we use the column headed by (2)(.05) = .10.

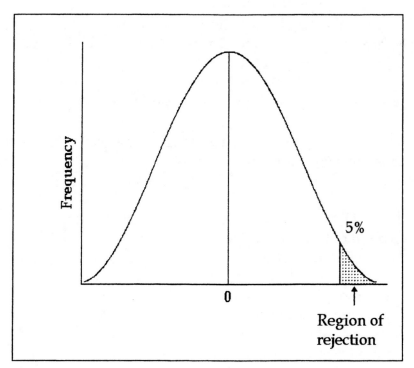

Figure 14-2. Sampling distribution of differences between means with the region of rejection for a one-tailed test.

## Study Questions
*Answers to selected study questions may be found in Appendix A.*

1. A psychologist wanted to know if students learned math better using a new interactive computer program instead of the standard textbook. She pretested a group of students for intelligence and then paired them by selecting the two highest scorers, the second highest two scorers, and so on down to the lowest two scorers. One subject from each pair was randomly assigned to the computer group and the other was assigned to the standard text group. Based on the semester average scores earned by the students shown on the next page, was there a difference in average scores based on teaching strategy (computer program versus standard text)?

| Pair # | Computer | Standard Text |
|--------|----------|---------------|
| 1 | 92 | 93 |
| 2 | 85 | 80 |
| 3 | 78 | 73 |
| 4 | 75 | 67 |
| 5 | 58 | 45 |

2. A company wants to know if a special training program reduces breakage by its china packers. A group of packers is monitored for breakage levels, given the training, and again monitored for breakage levels. Did the program have an effect on breakage?

| Packer # | Pieces Broken before Training | Pieces Broken after Training |
|----------|-------------------------------|------------------------------|
| 1 | 4 | 2 |
| 2 | 6 | 3 |
| 3 | 9 | 9 |
| 4 | 7 | 4 |
| 5 | 6 | 2 |
| 6 | 8 | 3 |

3. A physiologist wishes to know if a new experimental blood pressure medication reduces blood pressure. He selects a sample of 12 subjects and measures each subject's blood pressure. He then pairs the subjects who are closest in blood pressure. From each pair one subject is randomly assigned to the treatment group that gets the new experimental medication. The other subject from each pair is assigned to the control group that gets a sugar pill placebo. All subjects' blood pressures are measured again after the treatment. Does the medication have an effect?

| Pair # | Treatment (medication) | Control (placebo) |
|--------|------------------------|-------------------|
| 1 | 109 | 118 |
| 2 | 90 | 104 |
| 3 | 115 | 118 |
| 4 | 120 | 125 |
| 5 | 96 | 105 |
| 6 | 88 | 95 |

CHAPTER FIFTEEN
# Analysis of Variance

Analysis of variance is a test of the significance of the difference among means. It can be seen as an extension of the *t* test. The *t* test is limited because only two means can be tested at a time. But what about the situation where we have several treatment groups and we wish to test the differences among the means? We could compare these means two at a time using *t* tests. However, this would create two problems. First, we would have to do a lot of *t* tests. For example, with six groups it would require 15 *t* tests to test the differences between all possible pairs of means. Second, and much worse, this process tends to capitalize on chance. If we perform 15 tests each with a probability of .05 of producing a Type I error, it is very likely that at least one Type I error will be made. That is, it is very likely that at least one of these *t* tests should be significant simply by chance.

Analysis of variance allows us to avoid these problems and use a single overall test to determine whether or not there are real differences among several means. In other words, analysis of variance allows us to test the null hypothesis that k groups were drawn from a single population. The alternate hypothesis states that k groups did not come from a single population.

## The Linear Model

Analysis of variance is based on the linear model. The linear model can be illustrated by considering the set of hypothetical data shown in Table 15-1. The scores in Table 15-1 represent scores on a test of attitude toward toughness in foreign trade policy and are grouped according to the type of persuasive message to which people were exposed. High scores indicate attitudes favoring a "get tough" foreign trade policy. Table 15-1 shows these scores arranged in an unusual way for purposes of illustration -- larger scores are printed toward the top of the table and smaller scores are printed toward the bottom of the table. On the table each group mean is circled and the grand (or overall) mean is indicated by a dashed line. Note that the groups of scores appear to have been pushed up or pulled down from the grand mean by the treatments experienced by the groups.

Table 15-1
Attitudes toward toughness in foreign trade policy as a function of type of persuasion

| Movie on Free Trade | Editorial on Free Trade | No Persuasion |
|---|---|---|
| | 9 | 9 |
| $\overline{X}_{grand} = 6$ | ⑦ | ⑧ |
| | | 7 |
| 5 | 5 | |
| ③ | | |
| 1 | | |
| $\overline{X}_1 = 3$ | $\overline{X}_2 = 7$ | $\overline{X}_3 = 8$ |

The linear model grows out of this idea. It assumes that each individual score is a sum of several influences or components. In our example there are three components. That is, an individual's score is determined by the overall mean for everyone, plus the influence of the treatment she has received, plus differences among people in her treatment group. In other words,

an individual's score = the grand mean + treatment effect + error

More formally, this can be written

$X = \mu + T + e$

where X is an individual score, $\mu$ is the grand mean, T is the treatment group's influence, and e is random error.

If this is true, then all of the variation of a set of scores around the grand mean as measured by the sum of squares (the sum of the squared deviation of each score from the grand mean) can be broken into two components. The first component is the variation due to the treatment -- a person's score is pushed up or pulled down from the grand mean by the treatment she receives. The second component is the variation due to error -- each person's score contains some unexplained, possibly random influences. That is,

| total sum of squares | = | sum of squares due to treatment | + | sum of squares due to error |
|---|---|---|---|---|

188

More formally, this can be written

$$SS_{Total} = SS_{Treatment} + SS_{Error}$$

## Deviation Score Formulae

These components of variation can be computed using the following *deviation score formulae*, which express the variation in terms of deviations around the appropriate mean:

(1) $SS_{Total}$ = $\sum\limits_{\text{for all subjects}}$ (individual score - grand mean)$^2$

(2) $SS_{Treatment}$ = $\sum\limits_{\text{for all groups}}\left[(\text{\# of scores in a group})(\text{group mean - grand mean})^2\right]$

(3) $SS_{Error}$ = $\sum\limits_{\text{for all groups}}\left[\sum\limits_{\text{for all subjects in a group}}\left(\text{individual score - group mean}\right)^2\right]$

More formally, we can write these deviation score formulae as

(1) $SS_{Total} = \sum\limits_{1}^{N}\left(X - \overline{X}_{grand}\right)^2$

(2) $SS_{Treatment} = \sum\limits_{1}^{k}\left[n\left(\overline{X}_{group} - \overline{X}_{grand}\right)^2\right]$

(3) $SS_{Error} = \sum\limits_{1}^{k}\left[\sum\limits_{1}^{n}\left(X - \overline{X}_{group}\right)^2\right]$

where N is the total number of scores, n is the number of scores in a treatment group, and k is the number of treatment groups. So, we have broken the total sum of squares for a set of scores into its component parts.

Now, remember that every test of significance is a ratio in the form

$$\frac{\text{strength of treatment}}{\text{sampling error}}$$

In analysis of variance we use the variance due to the treatment in the numerator of the ratio and the variance due to error in the denominator. So our test of significance, which is called an F ratio, can be written

$$F = \frac{\text{variance due to treatment}}{\text{variance due to error}}$$

Remember that a variance is an average of the sum of the squared deviations around the mean (an average sum of squares) or a *mean square*. The variance components used in the F ratio are, in fact, mean squares derived by dividing sums of squares by the appropriate *degrees of freedom* (df). So, we can write our F ration as

$$F = \frac{\text{mean square}_{\text{treatment}}}{\text{mean square}_{\text{error}}} = \frac{\dfrac{SS_{\text{treatment}}}{df_{\text{treatment}}}}{\dfrac{SS_{\text{error}}}{df_{\text{error}}}}$$

$$= \frac{\dfrac{SS_{\text{treatment}}}{\text{number of treatment groups} - 1}}{\dfrac{SS_{\text{error}}}{\text{total number of scores} - \text{number of treatment groups}}}$$

## Raw Score or Computational Formulae

The deviation-based formulae for sums of squares were presented to show how the variance components grew out of the linear model. However, there is a set of equivalent formulae that are computationally much simpler. These formulae require only raw scores (rather than deviations from a mean) and therefore are recommended for hand computations. We will use these *raw score* or *computational formulae* for all further computations in this analysis of variance section:

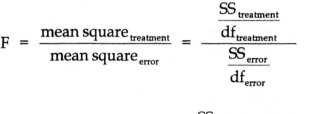

(1) $SS_{\text{total}} = \sum_{1}^{N} X_{\text{grand}}^2 - \dfrac{\left( \sum_{1}^{N} X_{\text{grand}} \right)^2}{N}$

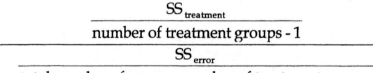

(2) $SS_{\text{treatment}} = \dfrac{\sum_{1}^{k} \left( \sum_{1}^{n} X_{\text{group}} \right)^2}{n} - \dfrac{\left( \sum_{1}^{N} X_{\text{grand}} \right)^2}{N}$

$$(3)\ SS_{error} = \sum_{1}^{k}\left[\sum_{1}^{n}X_{group}^2 - \frac{\left(\sum_{1}^{n}X_{group}\right)^2}{n}\right]$$

where N is the total number of scores, n is the number of scores in each treatment group, and k is the number of treatment groups.

## Analysis of Variance Calculations

Now we return to our example data showing attitudes toward foreign trade toughness as a function of persuasion type, shown here as Table 15-2.

Table 15-2
Attitudes toward toughness in foreign trade policy as a function of type of persuasion

| Movie | Editorial | No persuasion | |
|---|---|---|---|
| 5 | 9 | 9 | |
| 3 | 7 | 8 | |
| 1 | 5 | 7 | |
| $\sum X_1 = 9$ | $\sum X_2 = 21$ | $\sum X_3 = 24$ | $\sum X_{grand} = 54$ |
| $\sum X_1^2 = 35$ | $\sum X_2^2 = 155$ | $\sum X_3^2 = 194$ | $\sum X_{grand}^2 = 384$ |

The steps involved in calculating an analysis of variance are as follows:

*Step 1.* Calculate the sum of the scores and the sum of the squared scores for each group and for the total set of scores as shown in Table 15-2.

*Step 2.* Calculate the total sum of squares.

$$SS_{Total} = \sum X_{grand}^2 - \frac{(\sum X_{grand})^2}{N}$$

$$= 384 - \frac{(54)^2}{9} = 384 - \frac{2916}{9} = 384 - 324 = 60$$

*Step 3.* Calculate the treatment sum of squares.

$$SS_{treatment} = \frac{\sum(\sum X_{group})^2}{n} - \frac{(\sum X_{grand})^2}{N}$$

$$= \frac{(9)^2 + (21)^2 + (24)^2}{3} - \frac{(54)^2}{9} = \frac{81 + 441 + 576}{3} - \frac{2916}{9}$$

$$= \frac{1098}{3} - 324 = 366 - 324 = 42$$

*Step 4.* Calculate the error sum of squares.

$$SS_{error} = \sum \left[ \sum X_{group}^2 - \frac{(\sum X_{group})^2}{n} \right]$$

$$SS_{group1} = 35 - \frac{(9)^2}{3} = 35 - \frac{81}{3} = 35 - 27 = 8$$

$$SS_{group2} = 155 - \frac{(21)^2}{3} = 155 - \frac{441}{3} = 155 - 147 = 8$$

$$SS_{group3} = 194 - \frac{(24)^2}{3} = 194 - \frac{576}{3} = 194 - 192 = 2$$

$$SS_{error} = 8 + 8 + 2 = 18$$

*Step 5.* Check:

$$SS_{Total} = SS_{treatment} + SS_{error}$$
$$60 = 42 + 18$$
$$60 = 60$$

*Step 6.* Make our F ratio.

$$F = \frac{MS_{treatment}}{MS_{error}} = \frac{\dfrac{SS_{treatment}}{\text{number of groups} - 1}}{\dfrac{SS_{error}}{\text{number of scores} - \text{number of groups}}}$$

$$= \frac{\dfrac{42}{3-1}}{\dfrac{18}{9-3}} = \frac{\dfrac{42}{2}}{\dfrac{18}{6}} = \frac{21}{3} = 7.0$$

*Step 7.* Look up the critical value of F in the F table (Appendix F). To find the critical value of F in the table we must use the number of degrees of freedom (df) in the numerator term and the number of degrees of freedom in the denominator term. The critical F is found at the intersection of the column headed df numerator (which is equal to the number of groups - 1) and the row headed df denominator (which is equal to the number of scores - the number of groups). In our case the critical value for the .05 level of significance will be the upper (light-faced) value at the intersection of column 2 and row 6. Thus, the critical value of F for the .05 level of significance is 5.14.

*Step 8.* We now make our decision. If the calculated F is greater than or equal to the critical value of F from the table, we reject the null hypothesis and conclude that our treatment groups were not drawn from a single population. If, on the other hand, the calculated F is less than the critical F, then we fail to reject the null hypothesis and cannot conclude that our treatment groups are significantly different. In our example the calculated F of 7.0 is greater than the critical F of 5.14. Therefore, we conclude that a significant difference exists among the treatment groups. In a professional publication our result could be summarized by $F(2,6) = 7.0$, $p<.05$, which is read "F with 2 and 6 degrees of freedom is equal to 7.0 which is significant at the .05 level."

## Assumptions of Analysis of Variance

Analysis of variance, like all significance tests, rests on a set of assumptions that determine the conditions in which the test is appropriate. Four assumptions underlie analysis of variance. The first, and distinguishing, assumption is that of *linear additivity*. That is, the linear model, which holds that an individual score on the dependent variable is a sum of several influences or components, is an appropriate description of the data.

The second assumption is that the dependent variable is of *interval level of measurement or higher*. As discussed in Chapter One, an interval level of measurement involves equal sized units throughout the range of measurement. So the difference between scores of 10 and 12 (for example) should equal the difference between scores of 20 and 22.

The third assumption is that the dependent variable is *normally distributed within treatment groups*. That is, the scores within each cell of an analysis of variance design should form a normal distribution.

The fourth assumption is that the *variances within treatment groups are homogeneous*. That is, the variances of the scores within the cells of an analysis of variance design should be equal to one another.

## Determining Where the Differences Lie in a Significant Analysis of Variance: Posteriori Tests

Having found a significant treatment effect in our analysis of variance, we can be quite confident that the set of means of our treatment groups were not drawn by chance from a single population. However, this does not usually constitute a complete answer to the question we had at the outset of our experiment. We would also like to know where the difference(s) between groups lie(s). That is, specifically which group means are different from each other?

To answer this question we need to test all possible pairs of means against each other to determine whether each difference is significant. Such tests are called *posteriori tests* or *post hoc tests*, because they are appropriate only after the analysis of variance has revealed a significant overall treatment effect. The significant overall analysis of variance tells us that there is a real difference among the treatment groups, but not specifically which groups are different from each other.

The problems associated with multiple comparisons of means mentioned at the beginning of this chapter also apply to posteriori tests. If we make a large number of comparisons between pairs of means with the probability of making a Type I error ($\alpha$) set at .05 for each comparison, the probability that we will make one or more Type I errors in our set of comparisons will be higher than we intended. The probability that we will make one or more Type I errors in a set of comparisons grows as the number of means being compared increases. For example, if we made all the possible comparisons between pairs of means for the example experiment on the effect of types of persuasion (discussed earlier in this chapter), the probability that we would make one or more Type I errors (an error in which we incorrectly reject the null hypothesis) would be .14, rather than .05 as we intended.

When we set the probability of making a Type I error ($\alpha$) at .05 for each comparison, we are using a *per comparison error rate.* A per comparison error rate assumes that we are making only one comparison. Therefore, while the per comparison error rate is fine for experiments with only two treatment groups, it is inappropriate when there are more than two treatment groups. The appropriate Type I error rate when there are more than two treatment groups (and, therefore, we wish to make more than one comparison) is the *per experimentwise error rate.* The per experimentwise error rate is the probability that our entire set of comparisons is not free of Type I errors. Posteriori (or post hoc) tests are designed to hold the per experimentwise error rate constant at .05 (or whatever $\alpha$ level we choose), regardless of the number of comparisons in our set. Tukey's Honestly Significant Difference (HSD) Test is a popular and relatively simple test designed to accomplish this task.

## Tukey's Honestly Significant Difference (HSD) Test

Tukey's Honestly Significant Difference Test makes use of something called the *Studentized Range Statistic.* A table of critical values of the Studentized Range Statistic is provided in Appendix G. The values in this table could be considered replacements for the critical values of *t* from the *t* table (Appendix C), which would be used when we do a *t* test comparing a single pair of treatment groups. The Studentized Range table tells us for any number of groups, if all groups differences were actually due to chance, how many standard errors apart the two most different group means would be five percent of the time. This allows us to maintain a constant five percent (.05) per experimentwise error rate.

Once we have obtained the critical value of the Studentized Range Statistic from the table, we can compute the Honestly Significant Difference using the formula

$$\text{Honestly Significant Difference} = \text{HSD} = q\sqrt{\frac{\text{mean square error}}{\text{\# of subjects per group}}} = q\sqrt{\frac{MS_{error}}{n}}$$

where q is the critical value of the Studentized Range Statistic for the .05 level of $\alpha$ from the table (Appendix G) in the column for k = # of treatment groups in the whole experiment and the row = # of error degrees of freedom for the whole experiment, and n is the number of scores in each group. The mean square error and the error degrees of freedom are those used in the analysis of variance which must have been computed before the HSD test is considered. Any difference between treatment group means that is larger than the value of the Honestly Significant Difference (HSD) is significant at the .05 level.

## Step-by-Step Example

To illustrate the use of a posteriori test to follow-up our analysis of variance we will compare the three treatment group means from our example experiment, using Tukey's HSD test. The group means and the results of the overall analysis of variance are reproduced here as Table 15-3. Then, using this information, a step-by-step procedure for computing the Tukey's HSD test to determine which difference(s) between pairs of treatment group means is(are) significant is presented.

Table 15-3
Attitudes toward Toughness in Foreign Trade Policy as a Function of Type of Persuasion: Treatment Group Means and Summary of Analysis of Variance

|  | Movie | Editorial | No Persuasion |
| --- | --- | --- | --- |
| Mean | 3 | 7 | 8 |

Error Degrees of Freedom = 6
Mean Square Error $\quad = 3$

$$F = \frac{MS_{treatment}}{MS_{error}} = \frac{\dfrac{SS_{treatment}}{df_{treatment}}}{\dfrac{SS_{error}}{df_{error}}} = \frac{\dfrac{42}{(3-1)}}{\dfrac{18}{(9-3)}} = \frac{\dfrac{42}{2}}{\dfrac{18}{6}} = \frac{21}{3} = 7$$

Or, $F(2,6) = 7.0$, $p<.05$

*Step 1.* Find the critical value of the Studentized Range Statistic (q) for the .05 level of significance in the table in Appendix G. For our example, this value is found at the intersection of the column for k = 3 groups (since we have 3 treatment groups) and the row for 6 degrees of freedom (since the error degrees of freedom was 6 in our analysis of variance). In this case the critical value from the table is

Critical Value of the Studentized Range Statistic = q = 4.34

***Step* 2.** Compute the Honestly Significant Difference (HSD), using the critical value of q from Step 1 and the mean square error from the analysis of variance.

$$\text{Honestly Significant Difference} = \text{HSD} = q\sqrt{\frac{\text{mean square error}}{\text{\# of subjects per group}}}$$

$$= q\sqrt{\frac{MS_{error}}{n}} = 4.34\sqrt{\frac{3}{3}} = 4.34\sqrt{1} = 4.34\,(1) = 4.34$$

***Step* 3.** Make a matrix with each treatment group mean listed as a column head. Then list each treatment group mean again, this time as a row head. Finally, enter the difference between each pair of means at the intersection of the row and column representing that pair. Table 15-4 shows this matrix for our example.

***Step* 4.** Compare the absolute value (the value without regard to whether it is positive or negative) of each difference between pairs of means to the Honestly Significant Difference (HSD). Place an asterisk (*) beside any difference whose absolute value exceeds the value of HSD to indicate that it is significant. Table 15-4 shows an asterisk beside the significant difference between treatment group means for our example.

Table 15-4
Matrix Summarizing Tukey's HSD Test Results for Attitudes toward Toughness in Foreign Trade Policy as a Function of Type of Persuasion

|  |  | $\overline{X}$ Movie 3.00 | $\overline{X}$ Editorial 7.00 | $\overline{X}$ No Persuasion 8.00 |
|---|---|---|---|---|
| $\overline{X}$ Movie | = 3.00 |  |  |  |
| $\overline{X}$ Editorial | = 7.00 | 4.00 |  |  |
| $\overline{X}$ No Persuasion | = 8.00 | 5.00* | 1.00 |  |

The results of our HSD test shows a significant difference between the mean attitude scores of the group that saw a movie advocating a tolerant trade policy and the control group that received no persuasion concerning trade policy. We can be confident that the movie does, indeed, influence people's attitudes toward trade policy. However, we cannot be confident that the other two comparisons represent genuine differences between populations means.

Note that Tukey's HSD test assumes that there are equal numbers of subjects in all treatment groups. When this is not the case, the average group size is sometimes used for n in the formula (if the group sizes are not very different). There are also other multiple comparison tests that do not make this assumption of equal numbers of subjects in all treatment groups. Finally, remember that posteriori multiple comparison tests, such as Tukey's HSD test, are only appropriate after a significant analysis of variance has shown that a real, overall treatment effect exists. Only then does it make sense to look for real differences between specific treatment groups.

## Study Questions

*Answers to selected study questions may be found in Appendix A.*

1. A behavioral psychologist is interested in how the type of reinforcement a person receives on a preliminary task affects his or her performance on a subsequent task. She randomly assigns college students to one of three groups. The first group receives contingent reinforcement in which subjects are given accurate feedback ("correct" or "incorrect") about their performance on a preliminary task. The second group receives noncontingent reinforcement in which subjects are given random feedback ("correct" or "incorrect") without regard to their actual performance on the preliminary task. The third group receives no reinforcement on the preliminary task. After completion of the preliminary task, all subjects then complete the second task and are scored on their performance (number of correct responses). These data are reproduced below. Based on this data set, does the type of reinforcement affect subjects' performance? If appropriate, perform a post hoc test to determine which groups are significantly different from one another.

| Contingent Reinforcement | Noncontingent Reinforcement | No Reinforcement |
|:---:|:---:|:---:|
| 12 | 6 | 8 |
| 9 | 7 | 9 |
| 11 | 10 | 7 |
| 15 | 8 | 8 |

2. A quality control engineer at ACME Widgets is interested in the effect of shift work on widget production. A group of newly hired employees is randomly assigned to one of three work shifts – days, evenings, or nights – and their daily widget production is determined after allowing them 4 weeks to become accustomed to their work hours. These data are reproduced below. Does shift work affect widget production? If appropriate, perform a post hoc test to determine which groups are significantly different from one another.

| Days | Evenings | Nights |
|------|----------|--------|
| 8 | 6 | 5 |
| 5 | 7 | 3 |
| 7 | 4 | 6 |

3. To test the effects of stimulants on maze running time, a psychologist randomly assigns mice to one of 4 groups. Three of the groups receive a drug (caffeine, cocaine, or methamphetamine) in their drinking water. The control group receives sugar in their drinking water. All mice are tested in the same maze and their running times (in seconds) are recorded below. Does the treatment affect maze running behavior? If appropriate, perform a post hoc test to determine which groups are significantly different from one another.

| Caffeine | Cocaine | Methamphetamine | Sugar |
|----------|---------|-----------------|-------|
| 3 | 6 | 7 | 5 |
| 4 | 7 | 8 | 6 |
| 5 | 8 | 9 | 7 |

CHAPTER SIXTEEN
# Chi-Square: An Introduction to Non-Parametric Tests

## Parametric and Non-Parametric Tests

Nearly all of the statistical tests that we have discussed up to this point in this book make very restrictive assumptions about the population characteristics of the data being analyzed. That is, they make assumptions about the population parameters. For this reason these techniques are called *parametric statistics*. In earlier chapters we discussed the assumptions of the Pearson r, the *t*-test, and analysis of variance. While we may bend these requirements a little bit (and we often do), any radical departure from the assumptions of a statistical technique makes its use inappropriate. Although it would still be possible to plug in the numbers and crank out a test value, the conclusions we draw from this test value are likely to be seriously inaccurate and misleading.

The central assumption of all parametric statistics is that the data are of interval level of measurement or higher. This assumption is made when we calculate a mean, standard deviation, Pearson r, *t*-test, analysis of variance, or any extension of these statistics. This list includes most of the techniques we like to use.

There is another class of statistical techniques that make much less stringent assumptions about the nature of the data. These techniques are called *non-parametric statistics*, because they make either few assumptions or no assumptions about the population characteristics (parameters). The most central difference between parametric and non-parametric statistics is that non-parametric statistics do not require the scores to be of interval level of measurement or higher.

We generally prefer to use parametric statistics whenever possible, because these tests have more power than the comparable non-parametric tests. That is, parametric tests are more likely to detect a difference between groups if one truly exists (remember that power = $1 - \beta$). There are, however, many good non-parametric techniques which can and should be used when our data do not fit the assumptions of parametric statistics. For example, we have already discussed the Spearman's rho correlation coefficient, which assumes the data are of ordinal (rank order), rather than interval, level of measurement.

## The Chi-Square Test

One of the most useful and widely applicable non-parametric tests is the Chi-square test. The Chi-square test is a test of the significance of differences among groups, based on counts of the number of members in each group. It has only one assumption -- the assumption of independence. That is, the Chi-square test assumes that one subject's membership in a particular group has no influence on the probability that any other subject will be a member of any particular group.

There are two main advantages of the Chi-square test, relative to parametric tests. First, the Chi-square test can be used with scores which are of nominal level of measurement. This is an important advantage because it allows us to do inferential tests any time we can get a count of group membership. Thus, if we can count it, we can do a relatively sophisticated statistical test on it. Second, unlike parametric tests, the Chi-square test makes no assumptions about the nature of the populations (such as the shape of the population distribution or its variability).

To illustrate the computation of Chi-square, consider the following example. A social psychologist wants to test the hypothesis that passersby are more likely to help a distressed motorist in a rural setting than in an urban setting. He stages a mock auto breakdown by parking his car by the side of the road with the hood raised and standing helplessly beside it. Sometimes he does this on a city street, and sometimes on a rural county road. Table 17-1 shows the numbers of passersby who stop to help and who do not stop to help in each of these two locations.

Table 17-1
Number of Passersby Who Help in Rural and Urban Settings

|                   | Help | Do Not Help |
|-------------------|------|-------------|
| Rural Setting     | 24   | 16          |
| Urban Setting     | 26   | 54          |

The computation of Chi-square is based on the disparity between the **observed frequency**, which is the obtained frequency or the actual count of the number of cases in each cell, and the **expected frequency** under the null hypothesis. The null hypothesis states that the proportion of cases in each outcome category should be equal across all treatment groups. In our example, the null hypothesis is that equal proportions of passersby should stop to help in both the rural and urban settings.

The expected frequency under the null hypothesis for any cell can be calculated using the following formula:

$$E = \frac{(\text{Sum of row for which cell is a member}) \times (\text{Sum of column for which cell is a member})}{\text{Grand total for all cells}}$$

$$= \frac{(\text{Row sum}) \times (\text{Column sum})}{N}$$

The alternate hypothesis states that the proportion of cases in each outcome category should **not** be equal across all treatment groups. That is, the disparity between the expected frequency and the actual observed frequency in each cell is not merely due to chance. In our example, the alternate hypothesis is that unequal proportions of passersby should stop to help in the two settings.

The computation of the Chi-square statistic rests on this disparity between the actually observed frequency and the expected frequency under the null hypothesis. We can compute the value of Chi-square using the following formula:

$$\chi^2 = \Sigma \left[ \frac{(\text{Observed frequency - Expected frequency})^2}{\text{Expected frequency}} \right] = \Sigma \left[ \frac{(O-E)^2}{E} \right]$$

where $\chi^2$ is the symbol for Chi-square, O is the actually observed frequency in each cell, and E is the expected frequency under the null hypothesis for each cell. Note that E must be calculated using the formula given just before this one.

To illustrate the computation of Chi-square using our example of helping by passersby in rural and urban settings, we consider the data first presented in Table 17-1 and reproduced here as Table 17-2. We have numbered the cells in Table 17-2 to more easily keep track of them as we do the computations.

Table 17-2
Number of Passersby Who Help in Rural and Urban Settings (Data from Table 17-1)

|  | Help | Do Not Help | Row Total |
|---|---|---|---|
| Rural Setting | ① 24 | ② 16 | 40 |
| Urban Setting | ③ 26 | ④ 54 | 80 |
| Column Total | 50 | 70 | 120 |

To compute Chi-square we complete the following steps:

**Step 1.** Calculate the sum for each row, the sum for each column, and the grand sum (the sum of all the cells in the whole table) as shown in Table 17-2.

*Step 2.* Calculate the expected frequency for each cell using the formula

$$E = \frac{(\text{Row sum}) \times (\text{Column sum})}{N}$$

For the four cells in our example,

$$E_{\text{CELL 1}} = \frac{(40)(50)}{120} = \frac{2000}{120} = 16.67$$

$$E_{\text{CELL 2}} = \frac{(40)(70)}{120} = \frac{2800}{120} = 23.33$$

$$E_{\text{CELL 3}} = \frac{(80)(50)}{120} = \frac{4000}{120} = 33.33$$

$$E_{\text{CELL 4}} = \frac{(80)(70)}{120} = \frac{5600}{120} = 46.67$$

*Step 3.* At this step we have all the components necessary to plug into the Chi-square formula. That is, we have O (the actual observed frequency) for each cell, and we have E (the expected frequency under the null hypothesis) for each cell. Now we use a table (Table 17-3) to organize our computations.

Table 17-3
Computation of Chi-Square Using the Data in Table 17-2

|  | O | E | O - E | $(O - E)^2$ | $\dfrac{(O - E)^2}{E}$ |
|---|---|---|---|---|---|
| Cell 1 | 24 | 16.67 | 7.33 | 53.73 | 3.22 |
| Cell 2 | 16 | 23.33 | -7.33 | 53.73 | 2.30 |
| Cell 3 | 26 | 33.33 | -7.33 | 53.73 | 1.61 |
| Cell 4 | 50 | 46.67 | 7.33 | 53.73 | 1.15 |

$$\chi^2 = \Sigma \left[ \frac{(O - E)^2}{E} \right] = 8.28$$

*Step 4*. Calculate the degrees of freedom (df) for this Chi-square test using the formula

df = (# of rows - 1)(# of columns - 1)

In our example, df = (2 - 1)(2 - 1) = (1)(1) = 1

*Step 5*. Find the critical value of Chi-square at the .05 level for this number of degrees of freedom in the Chi-square table (see Appendix H). In our example, the critical value of Chi-square is 3.841.

*Step 6*. Compare the calculated value of Chi-square with the critical value of Chi-square from the table. If the calculated value of Chi-square is equal to or larger than the critical value, then we conclude that there is a significant departure from the frequencies expected under the null hypothesis. In our example, the calculated value of Chi-square (8.28) is larger than the critical value of Chi-square (3.841). So, we conclude that rural passersby are significantly more likely to stop and help than are urban passersby. Our Chi-square test result can be summarized (for example, in the text of a research report) as $\chi^2 (1) = 8.28$, p<.05. This summary is read "the calculated value of Chi-square with one degree of freedom is 8.28, which is significant at the .05 level."

Note that the logic of the Chi-square test is basically the same as the logic used for all other significance tests. When the calculated value of the test statistic is equal to or greater than the critical value from the table, we reject chance as a reasonable explanation for the observed difference. But if the calculated value of the test statistic is less than the critical value from the table, then we cannot reject chance as an explanation for the observed difference.

## Sample Sizes with the Chi-Square Test

In general, it is recommended that the sample size for a Chi-square test be large enough that no more than 20 percent of the cells have an expected frequency of less than five and no cell has an expected frequency of less than one. This means that for a 2 x 2 table with one degree of freedom, the expected frequencies for all four cells must be at least five. When the table is larger than a 2 x 2, if more than 20 percent of the cells have expected frequencies of less than five, then we should combine categories based on a defensible rationale. For example, if our study of whether passersby stop to help had originally involved a 2 x 3 table -- help or not help, and urban, suburban, or rural settings -- the rural setting might have had too few members. To remedy this problem we might combine the suburban and rural categories into a single non-urban category.

## Choosing the Appropriate Significance Test

In this book we have discussed several significance tests. Each of these tests is appropriate under a different set of conditions. Since choosing the appropriate test is one of the most important tasks in statistics, at this point we can summarize the conditions under which each test is appropriate. Table 16-4 shows the appropriate significance test for each combination of level of measurement, number of samples (groups), and type of sample.

Table 16-4
Appropriate Significance Tests as a Function of Level of Measurement, Number of Samples, and Type of Samples

|  | Two Samples | | More than Two Samples | |
|---|---|---|---|---|
|  | Independent Samples | Related Samples | Independent Samples | Related Samples |
| Nominal or Ordinal Level Data (Non-parametric tests) | Chi Square Test | *McNemar Test for the Significance of Changes | Chi Square Test | *Cochran Q test |
| Interval or Ratio Level Data (Parametric Tests) | *t*-test for Independent Samples | *t*-test for Related Samples | Simple Analysis of Variance | **Within Subjects Analysis of Variance |

*Not covered in this book. See Siegel, S. & Castellan, N.S. (1988). *Non-parametric statistics for the Behavioral Sciences*. 2nd Edition. New York: McGraw-Hill.

**Not covered in this book. See Esser, J.K., Walker, J.L., & Kirk, E.E. (2005). *Analysis of variance and multivariate statistics with matrix algebra*. Acton, MA: Copley, or Ferguson, G.A. & Takane, Y. (1989). *Statistical analysis in psychology and education*. 6th Edition. New York: McGraw-Hill.

## Study Questions
*Answers to selected study questions may be found in Appendix A.*

1.  A researcher collected data on the incidence of conforming versus nonconforming behavior among individuals identified as introverts or extroverts on the basis of a personality inventory.

|  | Conforming | Nonconforming |
|---|---|---|
| Introverts | 55 | 39 |
| Extroverts | 22 | 84 |

Does personality type influence the likelihood of conformity?

2.  A political pollster asked voters of different political affiliations whether they voted for or against a municipal proposition as they were leaving the polling place. The table below shows the number of people in each category.

|  | Vote | |
|---|---|---|
|  | For | Against |
| Republican | 61 | 27 |
| Democrat | 36 | 55 |
| Other | 4 | 11 |

Did political affiliation affect the way people voted?

3. A nurse practitioner is concerned about the incidence of post-operative infections among patients receiving different types of antibiotics prior to surgery. She collects data on the incidence of infection and records the type of antibiotic the patient received. Her data reflecting the number of patients in each category are shown in the table below.

|  |  | Penicillin | Gentamicin | Erythromycin | Cephalexin |
|---|---|---|---|---|---|
| Post-Op | Yes | 21 | 11 | 7 | 15 |
| Infection | No | 71 | 47 | 62 | 66 |

Type of Antibiotic

Did the type of antibiotic therapy influence the incidence of infection?

# Answers to Selected Study Questions

## Chapter One

1. Nominal
3. Ratio
5. Ratio
7. Ordinal
9. Interval
11. Nominal

## Chapter Two

1.

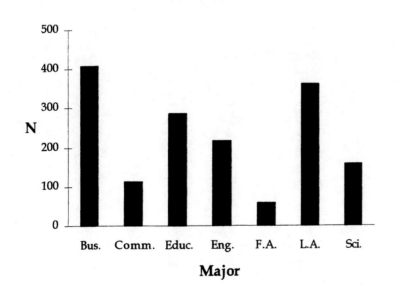

**Majors of Incoming Freshmen**
**Old Sywash University 1997**

3.

| Statistics Exam Grades | Frequency |
| --- | --- |
| 95 - 99 | 1 |
| 90 - 94 | 2 |
| 85 - 89 | 2 |
| 80 - 84 | 6 |
| 75 - 79 | 10 |
| 70 - 74 | 6 |
| 65 - 69 | 4 |
| 60 - 64 | 1 |
| 55 - 59 | 1 |
| 50 - 54 | 1 |
| 45 - 49 | 1 |
| 40 - 44 | 1 |

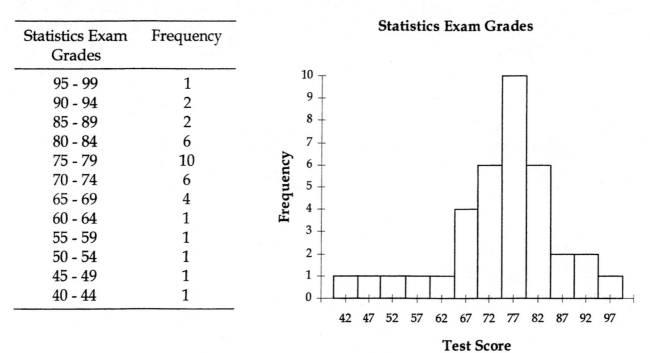

**Statistics Exam Grades**

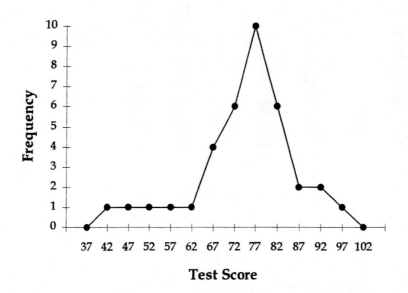

**Statistics Exam Grades**

5.

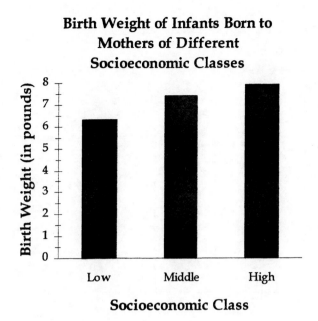

**Birth Weight of Infants Born to Mothers of Different Socioeconomic Classes**

6.

| Supervisor's Rating | Frequency |
|---|---|
| 120 - 129 | 1 |
| 110 - 119 | 2 |
| 100 - 109 | 3 |
| 90 - 99 | 4 |
| 80 - 89 | 4 |
| 70 - 79 | 6 |
| 60 - 69 | 6 |
| 50 - 59 | 5 |
| 40 - 49 | 6 |
| 30 - 39 | 2 |
| 20 - 29 | 1 |

6. cont.

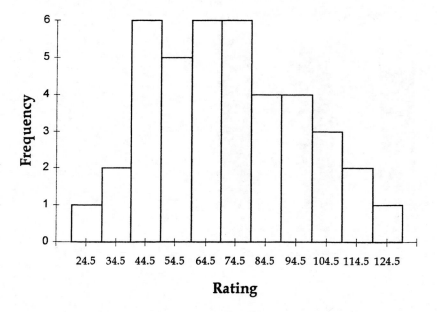

**Supervisor's Ratings of Employee Performance**

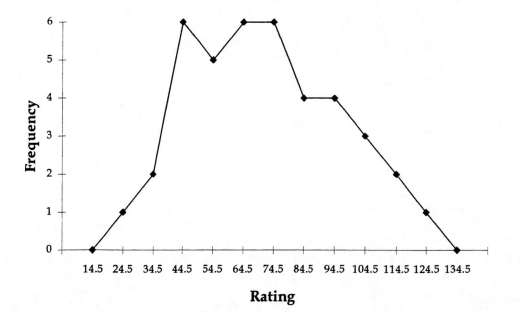

**Supervisor's Ratings of Employee Performance**

# Chapter Three

1. The following distribution of scores was obtained by introductory statistics students on the first exam.

| | | Statistics Test Scores | | | |
|---|---|---|---|---|---|
| 77 | 86 | 95 | 70 | 81 | 62 |
| 74 | 65 | 79 | 92 | 87 | 75 |
| 68 | 71 | 75 | 91 | 52 | 72 |

   a.  This distribution has one score that appears exactly twice (75) and no other score appears more than once.
   b.  To determine the median, the scores must first be counted and arranged in order. This distribution contains 18 scores (N = 18). Since the distribution contains an even number of scores, the median will lie halfway in between the two middle scores -- scores 9 and 10.

9th score ⌐

| 95 | 92 | 91 | 87 | 86 | 81 | 79 | 77 | 75 |
|---|---|---|---|---|---|---|---|---|
| 75 | 74 | 72 | 71 | 70 | 68 | 65 | 62 | 52 |

└ 10th score

   Therefore, the median is equal to: $\dfrac{75 + 75}{2}$ or 75.

   c.  To determine the mean, the scores must first be summed. The mean is calculated by dividing the sum by the number of scores:

   $$\overline{X} = \frac{\Sigma X}{N} = \frac{1372}{18} = 76.22$$

2.  a.  156
    b.  159
    c.  158.7

# Chapter Four

1.  a.  Range = Highest score - Lowest score + 1 = 95 - 55 + 1 = 41
    c.  91

2.  b.  $\overline{X} = \dfrac{\sum X}{N} = \dfrac{343}{5} = 68.6$

| Score | Score - Mean | (Score - Mean)² |
|:-----:|:------------:|:---------------:|
| X | $X - \overline{X}$ | $(X - \overline{X})^2$ |
| 64 | -4.6 | 21.16 |
| 73 | 4.4 | 19.36 |
| 71 | 2.4 | 5.76 |
| 69 | 0.4 | 0.16 |
| 66 | -2.6 | 6.76 |

$$SS = \sum(X - \overline{X})^2 = 53.20$$

$$SS = \sum(X - \overline{X})^2 = 53.20$$

$$s^2 = \frac{SS}{N} = \frac{\sum(X - \overline{X})^2}{N} = \frac{53.20}{5} = 10.64$$

$$s = \sqrt{s^2} = \sqrt{\frac{SS}{N}} = \sqrt{\frac{\sum(X - \overline{X})^2}{N}} = \sqrt{\frac{53.20}{5}} = \sqrt{10.64} = 3.26$$

   c.  SS = 4584.8
       s² = 916.9
       s = 30.28

3.  a.  SS = 71.43
        s² = 10.20
        s = 3.19

3. b.

| X | X² |
|-----|-------|
| 56 | 3136 |
| 76 | 5776 |
| 64 | 4096 |
| 32 | 1024 |
| 44 | 1936 |

$\sum X = 272 \qquad \sum X^2 = 15968$

$$SS = \sum X^2 - \frac{(\sum X)^2}{N} = 15968 - \frac{(272)^2}{5} = 15968 - \frac{73984}{5} = 15968 - 14796.8 = 1171.2$$

$$s^2 = \frac{SS}{N} = \frac{\sum X^2 - \dfrac{(\sum X)^2}{N}}{N} = \frac{1171.2}{5} = 234.24$$

$$s = \sqrt{\frac{SS}{N}} = \sqrt{\frac{\sum X^2 - \dfrac{(\sum X)^2}{N}}{N}} = \sqrt{\frac{1171.2}{5}} = \sqrt{234.24} = 15.30$$

4.

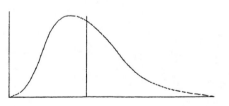

5.

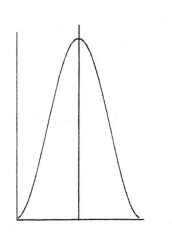

## Chapter Five

1.  a.  X = 48    $\overline{X}$ = 60    s = 8

$$z = \frac{X - \overline{X}}{s} = \frac{48 - 60}{8} = \frac{-12}{8} = -1.50$$

c.   $z = \frac{70 - 60}{8} = 1.25$

e.   0

2.  b.  X = 88    $\overline{X}$ = 100    s = 16

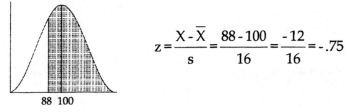

$$z = \frac{X - \overline{X}}{s} = \frac{88 - 100}{16} = \frac{-12}{16} = -.75$$

from the column headed *Prop. Above*, we get .7734 or 77.34%

d.  when X = 85, $z = \frac{85 - 100}{16} = \frac{-15}{16} = -.94$

when X = 120, $z = \frac{120 - 100}{16} = 1.25$

from the column headed *Prop. Above*, we get .8264 - .1056 = .7208 or 72.08%

3.  b.  X = 62    $\overline{X}$ = 50    s = 10

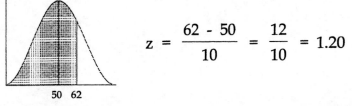

$$z = \frac{62 - 50}{10} = \frac{12}{10} = 1.20$$

from the column headed *Prop. Below*, we get .8849 or the 88th percentile rank

d.  $z = \frac{55 - 50}{10} = \frac{5}{10} = .50$

from the column headed *Prop. Below*, we get .6915 or the 69th percentile rank

3. f. 21st percentile rank

4. b. $\overline{X} = 500$   $s = 100$   67th centile point
   locate the value nearest .6700 in the column headed *Prop. Below* and read across
   to the column headed z to get the z score

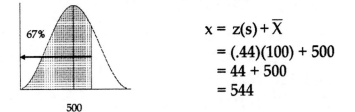

$$x = z(s) + \overline{X}$$
$$= (.44)(100) + 500$$
$$= 44 + 500$$
$$= 544$$

   d. 84th centile point: locate the value nearest .8400 in the column headed *Prop.
   Below* and read across to the column headed z to get the z score

$$X = .99(100) + 500 = 99 + 500 = 599$$

   f. 475

# Chapter Six

1. a. $p(\text{red}) = \dfrac{10 \text{ red marbles}}{100 \text{ total marbles}} = \dfrac{10}{100} = .10$
   b. .25

2. b. .23
   c. p(heart or face card) = p(heart) + p(face card) - p(heart)p(face card)
   $= 13/52 + 12/52 - (13/52)(12/52) = 25/52 - 156/2704 = 25/52 - 3/52$
   $= 22/52 = .42$

3. a. p(spade) = 13/52 = 1/4
   $p(\text{spade}|\text{spade}) = 12/51$
   $p(\text{spade and spade}) = p(\text{spade})p(\text{spade}|\text{spade}) = (1/4)(12/51) = 12/204 = .0588$

   c. .0045

4.

|  | 0 Heads | 1 Head | 2 Heads | 3 Heads | 4 Heads | 5 Heads |  |
|---|---|---|---|---|---|---|---|
|  | TTTTT | HTTTT | HHTTT | HHHTT | HHHHT | HHHHH |  |
|  |  | THTTT | HTHTT | HHTHT | HHHTH |  |  |
|  |  | TTHTT | HTTHT | HTHHT | HHTHH |  |  |
|  |  | TTTHT | HTTTH | THHHT | HTHHH |  |  |
|  |  | TTTTH | TTHHT | HHTTH | THHHH |  |  |
|  |  |  | THHTT | HTTHH |  |  |  |
|  |  |  | THTHT | HTHTH |  |  |  |
|  |  |  | THTTH | HTTHH |  |  |  |
|  |  |  | TTHTH | THTHH |  |  |  |
|  |  |  | TTTHH | TTHHH |  |  |  |
| Total # of ways | 1 | 5 | 10 | 10 | 5 | 1 | Grand Total 32 |
| Probability | 1/32 | 5/32 | 10/32 | 10/32 | 5/32 | 1/32 |  |

a. .16

c. p(at least two heads) = 10/32 + 10/32 + 5/32 + 1/32 = 26/32 = .81

5. b. P! = 10! = (10)(9)(8)(7)(6)(5)(4)(3)(2)(1) = 3,628,800

   c. 479,001,600

6. a. $_NC_r = {_6C_5} = \dfrac{6!}{(6-5)!5!} = \dfrac{(6)(5)(4)(3)(2)(1)}{1!(5)(4)(3)(2)(1)} = 6$

   c. 126

7. a. p(exactly 2 heads in 8 tosses) $= {_NC_r}p^r q^{N-r} = \dfrac{N!}{(N-r)!r!}p^r q^{N-r}$

$= \dfrac{8!}{(8-2)!2!}(1/2)^2(1/2)^6 = \dfrac{(8)(7)6!}{6!2!}(1/4)(1/64) = \dfrac{56}{2}(1/256) = 56/512 = .11$

   b. .11

8.  N = 100   r = 60    p = .5    q = .5

    Npq = 100 (.5)(.5) = 25

    $\overline{X}$ = Np = 100(.5) = 50

    $s = \sqrt{Npq} = \sqrt{25} = 5$

    $z = \dfrac{X - \overline{X}}{s} = \dfrac{60 - 50}{5} = \dfrac{10}{5} = 2$

    from the column headed *Prop. Above*, p(60 correct in 100 items) = .0228

9.  .1251

11. $p(B|A) = \dfrac{p(A \text{ and } B)}{p(A)} = \dfrac{.28}{.50} = .56$

12. .24

# Chapter Seven

1.

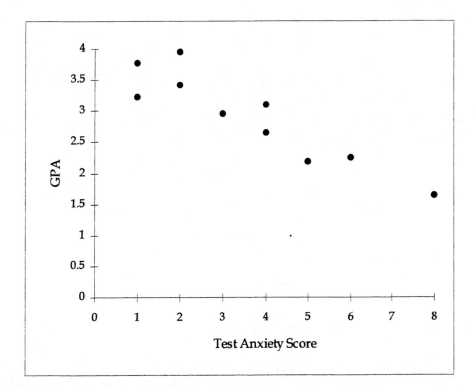

This relationship is very strong and negative. High scores on the anxiety measure are associated with lower GPAs.

2.

| Exec. | Ht (X) | X² | Salary (Y) | Y² | XY |
|---|---|---|---|---|---|
| 1 | 77 | 5929 | 46.5 | 2162.25 | 3580.5 |
| 2 | 64 | 4096 | 33.1 | 1095.61 | 2118.4 |
| 3 | 68 | 4624 | 36.5 | 1332.25 | 2482.0 |
| 4 | 70 | 4900 | 38.3 | 1466.89 | 2681.0 |
| 5 | 63 | 3969 | 33.1 | 1095.61 | 2085.3 |
| 6 | 60 | 3600 | 33.0 | 1089.00 | 1980.0 |
| 7 | 67 | 4489 | 42.1 | 1772.41 | 2820.7 |
| 8 | 69 | 4761 | 45.2 | 2043.04 | 3118.8 |
| 9 | 72 | 5184 | 46.1 | 2125.21 | 3319.2 |
| 10 | 67 | 4489 | 37.2 | 1383.84 | 2492.4 |
| Σ | 677 | 46041 | 391.1 | 15566.11 | 26678.3 |

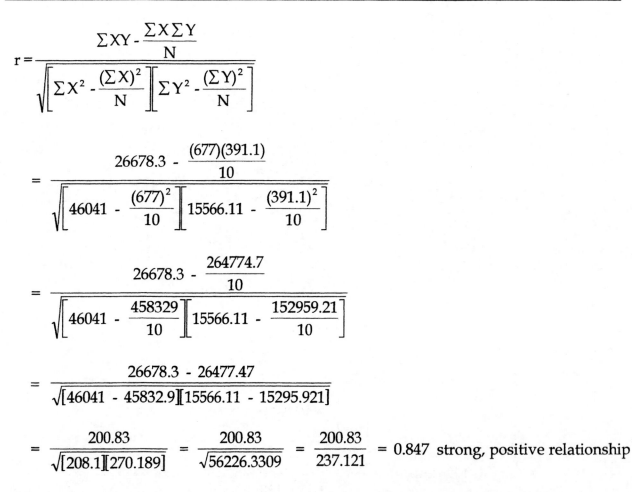

$$r = \frac{\sum XY - \frac{\sum X \sum Y}{N}}{\sqrt{\left[\sum X^2 - \frac{(\sum X)^2}{N}\right]\left[\sum Y^2 - \frac{(\sum Y)^2}{N}\right]}}$$

$$= \frac{26678.3 - \frac{(677)(391.1)}{10}}{\sqrt{\left[46041 - \frac{(677)^2}{10}\right]\left[15566.11 - \frac{(391.1)^2}{10}\right]}}$$

$$= \frac{26678.3 - \frac{264774.7}{10}}{\sqrt{\left[46041 - \frac{458329}{10}\right]\left[15566.11 - \frac{152959.21}{10}\right]}}$$

$$= \frac{26678.3 - 26477.47}{\sqrt{[46041 - 45832.9][15566.11 - 15295.921]}}$$

$$= \frac{200.83}{\sqrt{[208.1][270.189]}} = \frac{200.83}{\sqrt{56226.3309}} = \frac{200.83}{237.121} = 0.847 \text{ strong, positive relationship}$$

3. r = .97, very strong, positive relationship

# Chapter Eight

1.

| Student | Test Anxiety Score (X) | X² | GPA (Y) | XY |
|---------|------------------------|-----|---------|-------|
| 1 | 8 | 64 | 1.64 | 13.12 |
| 2 | 4 | 16 | 2.65 | 10.60 |
| 3 | 1 | 1 | 3.78 | 3.78 |
| 4 | 2 | 4 | 3.95 | 7.90 |
| 5 | 4 | 16 | 3.10 | 12.40 |
| 6 | 6 | 36 | 2.25 | 13.50 |
| 7 | 2 | 4 | 3.42 | 6.84 |
| 8 | 3 | 9 | 2.95 | 8.85 |
| 9 | 5 | 25 | 2.18 | 10.90 |
| 10 | 1 | 1 | 3.23 | 3.23 |
| $\Sigma$ | 36 | 176 | 29.15 | 91.12 |

$$\overline{X} = \frac{\Sigma X}{N} = \frac{36}{10} = 3.6 \qquad \overline{Y} = \frac{\Sigma Y}{N} = \frac{29.15}{10} = 2.915$$

$$b = \frac{\Sigma XY - \frac{\Sigma X \Sigma Y}{N}}{\Sigma X^2 - \frac{(\Sigma X)^2}{N}} = \frac{91.12 - \frac{(36)(29.15)}{10}}{176 - \frac{(36)^2}{10}} = \frac{91.12 - \frac{1049.4}{10}}{176 - \frac{1296}{10}} = \frac{91.12 - 104.94}{176 - 129.6}$$

$$= \frac{-13.82}{46.4} = -0.30$$

$a = \overline{Y} - b\overline{X} = 2.915 - (-0.30)(3.6) = 2.915 - (-1.08) = 4.0$

$Y' = -0.30X + 4$

$Y' = -0.30(7) + 4 = -2.1 + 4 = 1.9$

2.  $Y' = 2.15X + 2.71$; when X is 20, $Y' = 45.71$

# Chapter Nine

1.  r = .42

    coefficient of alienation = the proportion of guessing error remaining in our predictions = $k = \sqrt{1 - r^2} = \sqrt{1 - .42^2} = \sqrt{1 - .1764} = \sqrt{.8236} = .91$ or 91%

    index of forecasting efficiency = the proportion of guessing error eliminated from our predictions = $E = 1 - k = 1 - \sqrt{1 - r^2} = 1 - \sqrt{1 - .42^2} = 1 - .91 = 0.09$ or 9%

    coefficient of determination = the proportion of variance in Y that is shared with X $= r^2 = .42^2 = .1764$ or 18%

    coefficient of non-determination = the proportion of variance in Y that is not shared with X $= 1 - r^2 = 1 - .42^2 = 1 - .1764 = .8236$ or 82%

3.  r = .27
    coefficient of alienation = proportion of guessing error remaining = .96 or 96%
    index of forecasting efficiency = proportion of guessing error eliminated = .04 or 4%
    coefficient of determination = proportion of shared variance = .07 or 7%
    coefficient of non-determination = proportion of unshared variance = .93 or 93%

# Chapter Ten

1.  a. This distribution violates the assumption of linearity.
    c. This distribution does not violate any of the assumptions.
    d. This distribution violates the assumptions of continuous variables and interval level of measurement.

2.

| Book | Critic #1 Rank | Critic #2 Rank | D | D² |
|---|---|---|---|---|
| Gone with the Wind | 8 | 10 | -2 | 4 |
| Catcher in the Rye | 2 | 3 | -1 | 1 |
| For Whom the Bell Tolls | 6 | 6 | 0 | 0 |
| The Turn of the Screw | 7 | 5 | 2 | 4 |
| Portrait of the Artist as Young Man | 9 | 7 | 2 | 4 |
| Slaughterhouse Five | 1 | 1 | 0 | 0 |
| The Naked Lunch | 10 | 2 | 8 | 64 |
| The Unbearable Lightness of Being | 4 | 4 | 0 | 0 |
| The Great Gatsby | 5 | 9 | -4 | 16 |
| The Color Purple | 3 | 8 | -5 | 25 |
| | | | | $\sum D^2 = 118$ |

$$\text{rho} = 1 - \frac{6 \sum D^2}{N(N^2 - 1)} = 1 - \frac{6(118)}{10(10^2 - 1)} = 1 - \frac{708}{10(99)} = 1 - \frac{708}{990} = 1 - .715 = .285$$

These two book critics do not agree very much since the correlation is weak.

3.  rho = .583; there is moderate agreement between these two supervisors.

4.  a.

| r | $z_r$ |
|---|---|
| .45 | .485 |
| .33 | .343 |
| .76 | .996 |
| .51 | .563 |
| $\sum z_r = 2.387$ | |

$$\bar{z}_r = \frac{\sum z_r}{N} = \frac{2.387}{4} = .597$$

from Appendix D we find that this value of $\bar{z}_r$ corresponds to $\bar{r} = .53$

c.  $\bar{r} = .63$

# Chapter Eleven

1. a.

| Student | Verbal SAT Score (X) | X² |
|:---:|:---:|:---:|
| 1 | 650 | 422500 |
| 2 | 435 | 189225 |
| 3 | 550 | 302500 |
| 4 | 505 | 255025 |
| 5 | 490 | 240100 |
| 6 | 585 | 342225 |
| 7 | 605 | 366025 |
| 8 | 565 | 319225 |
| 9 | 530 | 280900 |
| Σ | 4915 | 2717725 |

$$\hat{\sigma} = \sqrt{\frac{\sum X^2 - \frac{(\sum X)^2}{N}}{N-1}} = \sqrt{\frac{2717725 - \frac{(4915)^2}{9}}{9-1}} = \sqrt{\frac{2717725 - \frac{24157225}{9}}{8}}$$

$$= \sqrt{\frac{2717725 - 2684136.11}{8}} = \sqrt{\frac{33588.89}{8}} = \sqrt{4198.61} = 64.80$$

b. 5.11

2. b. $\sigma_{\bar{x}} = \dfrac{\sigma}{\sqrt{N}} = \dfrac{5.02}{6} = 0.84$

c. 1.55

# Chapter Twelve

2. Upper limit = 26.28; Lower limit = 23.72. Yes, the grapes are ready to harvest.

3.

| Worker | # Widgets Produced (X) | $X^2$ |
|--------|------------------------|-------|
| 1 | 70 | 4900 |
| 2 | 45 | 2025 |
| 3 | 62 | 3844 |
| 4 | 58 | 3364 |
| 5 | 71 | 5041 |
| 6 | 43 | 1849 |
| 7 | 64 | 4096 |
| 8 | 54 | 2916 |
| $\Sigma$ | 467 | 28035 |

$$\overline{X} = \frac{\Sigma X}{N} = \frac{467}{8} = 58.38$$

$$\hat{\sigma} = \sqrt{\frac{\Sigma X^2 - \frac{(\Sigma X)^2}{N}}{N-1}} = \sqrt{\frac{28035 - \frac{(467)^2}{8}}{8-1}} = \sqrt{\frac{28035 - \frac{218089}{8}}{7}}$$

$$= \sqrt{\frac{28035 - 27261.13}{7}} = \sqrt{\frac{773.87}{7}} = \sqrt{110.55} = 10.51$$

$$\hat{\sigma}_{\overline{X}} = \frac{\hat{\sigma}}{\sqrt{N}} = \frac{10.51}{\sqrt{8}} = \frac{10.51}{2.83} = 3.71$$

$$df = N - 1 = 8 - 1 = 7 \qquad t_{crit}(7) = 2.37$$

$$\text{Upper limit} = \overline{X} + \hat{\sigma}_{\overline{X}}(t_{crit}) = 58.38 + (3.71)(2.37) = 58.38 + 8.79 = 67.17$$

$$\text{Lower limit} = \overline{X} - \hat{\sigma}_{\overline{X}}(t_{crit}) = 58.38 - (3.71)(2.37) = 58.38 - 8.79 = 49.59$$

Since the lower limit for the 95% confidence interval is below 50, the company can not be confident that the mean widget production is above 50.

4. $t = .34$; the probability is greater than 95% that this sample was drawn from a population with a mean of 20.

5. $\hat{\sigma}_{\bar{x}} = \dfrac{\hat{\sigma}}{\sqrt{N}} = \dfrac{13.3}{\sqrt{20}} = \dfrac{13.3}{4.47} = 2.98$

$t = \dfrac{\mu - \bar{X}}{\hat{\sigma}_{\bar{x}}} = \dfrac{264 - 248}{2.98} = \dfrac{16}{2.98} = 5.37$

$df = N - 1 = 20 - 1 = 19 \qquad t_{crit}(19) = 2.093$

Since the calculated value of $t$ (5.37) is greater than the critical value (2.093), the probability is less than 5% that this sample was drawn from a population with a mean of 264. This suggests that the drug decreases reaction time, at least when administered to normal subjects.

7. $z = \dfrac{\text{Fisher's z}}{\text{standard error of Fisher's z}} = \dfrac{z_r}{\dfrac{1}{\sqrt{N - 3}}} = \dfrac{.389}{\dfrac{1}{\sqrt{N - 3}}} = \dfrac{.389}{\dfrac{1}{\sqrt{20 - 3}}}$

$= \dfrac{.389}{\dfrac{1}{\sqrt{17}}} = \dfrac{.389}{\dfrac{1}{4.12}} = \dfrac{.389}{.24} = 1.62$

Since the calculated value of z (1.62) is less than the critical value (1.96), we can not conclude that there is a real negative correlation between these two needs.

9. $z = 1.39$; the probability is greater than 95% that the population correlation is zero. No, he can not conclude that there is a real relationship between body fat and endurance.

# Chapter Thirteen

1.

| Drug group | Placebo group |
|:---:|:---:|
| 18 | 11 |
| 12 | 13 |
| 15 | 9 |
| 13 | 12 |
| 15 | 8 |
| $\sum X_1 = 73$ | $\sum X_2 = 53$ |
| $\sum X_1^2 = 1087$ | $\sum X_2^2 = 579$ |
| $\overline{X}_1 = 14.6$ | $\overline{X}_2 = 10.6$ |

$df = N_1 + N_2 - 2 = 5 + 5 - 2 = 8$

$$SS_1 = \sum X_1^2 - \frac{(\sum X_1)^2}{N_1} = 1087 - \frac{(73)^2}{5} = 1087 - \frac{5329}{5} = 1087 - 1065.8 = 21.2$$

$$SS_2 = \sum X_2^2 - \frac{(\sum X_2)^2}{N_2} = 579 - \frac{(53)^2}{5} = 579 - \frac{2809}{5} = 579 - 561.8 = 17.2$$

$$t = \frac{\overline{X}_1 - \overline{X}_2}{\sqrt{\left(\frac{SS_1 + SS_2}{N_1 + N_2 - 2}\right)\left(\frac{N_1 + N_2}{N_1 * N_2}\right)}} = \frac{14.6 - 10.6}{\sqrt{\left(\frac{21.2 + 17.2}{5 + 5 - 2}\right)\left(\frac{5 + 5}{5 * 5}\right)}} = \frac{4}{\sqrt{\left(\frac{38.4}{8}\right)\left(\frac{10}{25}\right)}}$$

$$= \frac{4}{\sqrt{(4.8)(.4)}} = \frac{4}{\sqrt{1.92}} = \frac{4}{1.39} = 2.88$$

$t_{crit} = 2.306$; $t_{calc} > t_{crit}$. So, $t(8) = 2.88$, $p < .05$; we reject the null hypothesis and conclude that the drug does improve memory.

2. $t_{crit} = 2.306$; $t(8) = 52$, $p < .05$. We reject the null hypothesis and conclude that there is a true difference in running times between the rats who received a food pellet and those who did not. The rats who received a food pellet ran faster.

## Chapter Fourteen

1.

| Pair # | Computer | Standard Text | D | D² |
|--------|----------|---------------|-----|-----|
| 1 | 92 | 93 | -1 | 1 |
| 2 | 85 | 80 | 5 | 25 |
| 3 | 78 | 73 | 5 | 25 |
| 4 | 75 | 67 | 8 | 64 |
| 5 | 58 | 45 | 13 | 169 |
| | | | $\Sigma D = 30$ | $\Sigma D^2 = 284$ |

$df = N - 1 = 5 - 1 = 4$

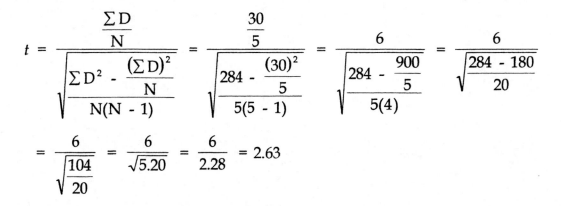

$$t = \frac{\dfrac{\Sigma D}{N}}{\sqrt{\dfrac{\Sigma D^2 - \dfrac{(\Sigma D)^2}{N}}{N(N-1)}}} = \frac{\dfrac{30}{5}}{\sqrt{\dfrac{284 - \dfrac{(30)^2}{5}}{5(5-1)}}} = \frac{6}{\sqrt{\dfrac{284 - \dfrac{900}{5}}{5(4)}}} = \frac{6}{\sqrt{\dfrac{284 - 180}{20}}}$$

$$= \frac{6}{\sqrt{\dfrac{104}{20}}} = \frac{6}{\sqrt{5.20}} = \frac{6}{2.28} = 2.63$$

$t_{calc} = 2.63 < t_{crit} = 2.776$; So, $t(4) = 2.63$, n.s. We cannot reject the null hypothesis -- we cannot say that the groups are different.

2. $t_{crit}(5) = 2.571$; $t_{calc}(5) = 4.04$, $p<.05$. We reject the null hypothesis and conclude that the training helped reduce breakage.

# Chapter Fifteen

1.

| | Contingent Reinforcement | Noncontingent Reinforcement | No Reinforcement | |
|---|---|---|---|---|
| | 12 | 6 | 8 | |
| | 9 | 7 | 9 | |
| | 11 | 10 | 7 | |
| | 15 | 8 | 8 | |
| | $\sum X_1 = 47$ | $\sum X_2 = 31$ | $\sum X_3 = 32$ | $\sum X_{grand} = 110$ |
| | $\sum X_1^2 = 571$ | $\sum X_2^2 = 249$ | $\sum X_3^2 = 258$ | $\sum X_{grand}^2 = 1078$ |

$$SS_{Total} = \sum X_{grand}^2 - \frac{\left(\sum X_{grand}\right)^2}{N}$$

$$= 1078 - \frac{(110)^2}{12} = 1078 - \frac{12100}{12} = 1078 - 1008.33 = 69.67$$

$$SS_{treatment} = \frac{\sum\left(\sum X_{group}\right)^2}{n} - \frac{\left(\sum X_{grand}\right)^2}{N}$$

$$= \frac{(47)^2 + (31)^2 + (32)^2}{4} - \frac{(110)^2}{12} = \frac{2209 + 961 + 1024}{4} - \frac{12100}{12}$$

$$= \frac{4194}{4} - 1008.33 = 1048.5 - 1008.33 = 40.17$$

$$SS_{error} = \sum\left[\sum X_{group}^2 - \frac{\left(\sum X_{group}\right)^2}{n}\right]$$

$$SS_{group1} = 571 - \frac{(47)^2}{4} = 571 - \frac{2209}{4} = 571 - 552.25 = 18.75$$

$$SS_{group2} = 249 - \frac{(31)^2}{4} = 249 - \frac{961}{4} = 249 - 240.25 = 8.75$$

$$SS_{group3} = 258 - \frac{(32)^2}{4} = 258 - \frac{1024}{4} = 258 - 256 = 2$$

$$SS_{error} = 18.75 + 8.75 + 2 = 29.5$$

Check:

$$SS_{Total} = SS_{treatment} + SS_{error}$$
$$69.67 = 40.17 + 29.5$$
$$69.67 = 69.67$$

$$F = \frac{MS_{treatment}}{MS_{error}} = \frac{\dfrac{SS_{treatment}}{\text{number of groups} - 1}}{\dfrac{SS_{error}}{\text{number of scores} - \text{number of groups}}}$$

$$= \frac{\dfrac{40.17}{3-1}}{\dfrac{29.5}{12-3}} = \frac{\dfrac{40.17}{2}}{\dfrac{29.5}{9}} = \frac{20.09}{3.28} = 6.13$$

$F_{calc} = 6.13 \quad > \quad F_{crit}(2,9) = 4.26$; therefore, reject the null hypothesis – the type of reinforcement significantly affected subjects' performance. Since there is a significant effect of reinforcement type on performance, a Tukey's HSD test is appropriate.

$$\text{Honestly Significant Difference} = HSD = q\sqrt{\frac{\text{mean square error}}{\text{\# of subjects per group}}}$$

$$= q\sqrt{\frac{MS_{error}}{n}} = 3.95\sqrt{\frac{3.28}{4}} = 3.95\sqrt{.82} = 3.95\,(.91) = 3.59$$

|  |  | $\overline{X}$ Contingent 11.75 | $\overline{X}$ Noncontingent 7.75 | $\overline{X}$ None 8.00 |
|---|---|---|---|---|
| $\overline{X}$ Contingent | = 11.75 | | | |
| $\overline{X}$ Noncontingent | = 7.75 | 4.00* | | |
| $\overline{X}$ None | = 8.00 | 3.75* | 0.25 | |

The number of correct responses given by the group who received contingent reinforcement is significantly different from that of the group who received noncontingent reinforcement and from that of the group who received no reinforcement. The number of correct responses given by the group who received noncontingent reinforcement is not significantly different from that of the group who received no reinforcement. Subjects who received contingent reinforcement performed better on the subsequent task than subjects who received noncontingent or no reinforcement.

3. $F_{calc} = 8.75 > F_{crit}(3,8) = 4.07$; HSD = 2.58. The mean running time for the group that received caffeine is significantly different from that of the groups that received cocaine and methamphetamine. The caffeine group does not differ significantly from the group that received sugar, and the groups that received cocaine, methamphetamine, or sugar do not differ significantly from one another. Mice that received caffeine ran the maze in less time than mice that received cocaine or methamphetamine, but not less time than mice that received sugar.

# Chapter Sixteen

2.

| | O | E | O - E | $(O - E)^2$ | $\dfrac{(O - E)^2}{E}$ |
|---|---|---|---|---|---|
| Cell 1 | 61 | 45.81 | 15.19 | 230.74 | 5.04 |
| Cell 2 | 27 | 42.19 | -15.19 | 230.74 | 5.47 |
| Cell 3 | 36 | 47.38 | -11.38 | 129.50 | 2.73 |
| Cell 4 | 55 | 43.62 | 11.38 | 129.50 | 2.97 |
| Cell 5 | 4 | 7.81 | -3.81 | 14.52 | 1.86 |
| Cell 6 | 11 | 7.19 | 3.81 | 14.52 | 2.02 |

$$\chi^2 = \Sigma \left[ \frac{(O - E)^2}{E} \right] = 20.09$$

$\chi^2_{crit}(2) = 5.991$; reject the null hypothesis -- political affiliation influenced how people voted.

3. $\chi^2 = \Sigma \left[ \dfrac{(O - E)^2}{E} \right] = 4.388$.

$\chi^2_{crit}(3) = 7.815$; fail to reject the null hypothesis -- type of antibiotic therapy did not seem to influence the incidence of post-op infection.

# Normal Curve Table

| z | Prop. Below | Prop. Above | Ht. Of Curve | z | Prop. Below | Prop. Above | Ht. Of Curve |
|---|---|---|---|---|---|---|---|
| -2.99 | .0014 | .9986 | .0046 | -2.59 | .0048 | .9952 | .0139 |
| -2.98 | .0014 | .9986 | .0047 | -2.58 | .0049 | .9951 | .0143 |
| -2.97 | .0015 | .9985 | .0048 | -2.57 | .0051 | .9949 | .0147 |
| -2.96 | .0015 | .9985 | .0050 | -2.56 | .0052 | .9948 | .0151 |
| -2.95 | .0016 | .9984 | .0051 | -2.55 | .0054 | .9946 | .0154 |
| -2.94 | .0016 | .9984 | .0053 | -2.54 | .0055 | .9945 | .0158 |
| -2.93 | .0017 | .9983 | .0055 | -2.53 | .0057 | .9943 | .0163 |
| -2.92 | .0018 | .9982 | .0056 | -2.52 | .0059 | .9941 | .0167 |
| -2.91 | .0018 | .9982 | .0058 | -2.51 | .0060 | .9940 | .0171 |
| -2.90 | .0019 | .9981 | .0060 | -2.50 | .0062 | .9938 | .0175 |
| -2.89 | .0019 | .9981 | .0061 | -2.49 | .0064 | .9936 | .0180 |
| -2.88 | .0020 | .9980 | .0063 | -2.48 | .0066 | .9934 | .0184 |
| -2.87 | .0021 | .9979 | .0065 | -2.47 | .0068 | .9932 | .0189 |
| -2.86 | .0021 | .9979 | .0067 | -2.46 | .0069 | .9931 | .0194 |
| -2.85 | .0022 | .9978 | .0069 | -2.45 | .0071 | .9929 | .0198 |
| -2.84 | .0023 | .9977 | .0071 | -2.44 | .0073 | .9927 | .0203 |
| -2.83 | .0023 | .9977 | .0073 | -2.43 | .0075 | .9925 | .0208 |
| -2.82 | .0024 | .9976 | .0075 | -2.42 | .0078 | .9922 | .0213 |
| -2.81 | .0025 | .9975 | .0077 | -2.41 | .0080 | .9920 | .0219 |
| -2.80 | .0026 | .9974 | .0079 | -2.40 | .0082 | .9918 | .0224 |
| -2.79 | .0026 | .9974 | .0081 | -2.39 | .0084 | .9916 | .0229 |
| -2.78 | .0027 | .9973 | .0084 | -2.38 | .0087 | .9913 | .0235 |
| -2.77 | .0028 | .9972 | .0086 | -2.37 | .0089 | .9911 | .0241 |
| -2.76 | .0029 | .9971 | .0088 | -2.36 | .0091 | .9909 | .0246 |
| -2.75 | .0030 | .9970 | .0091 | -2.35 | .0094 | .9906 | .0252 |
| -2.74 | .0031 | .9969 | .0093 | -2.34 | .0096 | .9904 | .0258 |
| -2.73 | .0032 | .9968 | .0096 | -2.33 | .0099 | .9901 | .0264 |
| -2.72 | .0033 | .9967 | .0099 | -2.32 | .0102 | .9898 | .0270 |
| -2.71 | .0034 | .9966 | .0101 | -2.31 | .0104 | .9896 | .0277 |
| -2.70 | .0035 | .9965 | .0104 | -2.30 | .0107 | .9893 | .0283 |
| -2.69 | .0036 | .9964 | .0107 | -2.29 | .0110 | .9890 | .0290 |
| -2.68 | .0037 | .9963 | .0110 | -2.28 | .0113 | .9887 | .0297 |
| -2.67 | .0038 | .9962 | .0113 | -2.27 | .0116 | .9884 | .0303 |
| -2.66 | .0039 | .9961 | .0116 | -2.26 | .0119 | .9881 | .0310 |
| -2.65 | .0040 | .9960 | .0119 | -2.25 | .0122 | .9878 | .0317 |
| -2.64 | .0041 | .9959 | .0122 | -2.24 | .0125 | .9875 | .0325 |
| -2.63 | .0043 | .9957 | .0126 | -2.23 | .0129 | .9871 | .0332 |
| -2.62 | .0044 | .9956 | .0129 | -2.22 | .0132 | .9868 | .0339 |
| -2.61 | .0045 | .9955 | .0132 | -2.21 | .0136 | .9864 | .0347 |
| -2.60 | .0047 | .9953 | .0136 | -2.20 | .0139 | .9861 | .0355 |

From Edwards, A.L., *Statistical Methods for the Behavioral Sciences*. Holt, 1954. Used with permission.

| z | Prop. Below | Prop. Above | Ht. Of Curve | z | Prop. Below | Prop. Above | Ht. Of Curve |
|---|---|---|---|---|---|---|---|
| -2.19 | .0143 | .9857 | .0363 | -1.74 | .0409 | .9591 | .0878 |
| -2.18 | .0146 | .9854 | .0371 | -1.73 | .0418 | .9582 | .0893 |
| -2.17 | .0150 | .9850 | .0379 | -1.72 | .0427 | .9573 | .0909 |
| -2.16 | .0154 | .9846 | .0387 | -1.71 | .0436 | .9564 | .0925 |
| -2.15 | .0158 | .9842 | .0396 | -1.70 | .0446 | .9554 | .0940 |
| -2.14 | .0162 | .9838 | .0404 | -1.69 | .0455 | .9545 | .0957 |
| -2.13 | .0166 | .9834 | .0413 | -1.68 | .0465 | .9535 | .0973 |
| -2.12 | .0170 | .9830 | .0422 | -1.67 | .0475 | .9525 | .0989 |
| -2.11 | .0174 | .9826 | .0431 | -1.66 | .0485 | .9515 | .1006 |
| -2.10 | .0179 | .9821 | .0440 | -1.65 | .0495 | .9505 | .1023 |
| -2.09 | .0183 | .9817 | .0449 | -1.64 | .0505 | .9495 | .1040 |
| -2.08 | .0188 | .9812 | .0459 | -1.63 | .0516 | .9484 | .1057 |
| -2.07 | .0192 | .9808 | .0468 | -1.62 | .0526 | .9474 | .1074 |
| -2.06 | .0197 | .9803 | .0478 | -1.61 | .0537 | .9463 | .1092 |
| -2.05 | .0202 | .9798 | .0488 | -1.60 | .0548 | .9452 | .1109 |
| -2.04 | .0207 | .9793 | .0498 | -1.59 | .0559 | .9441 | .1127 |
| -2.03 | .0212 | .9788 | .0508 | -1.58 | .0571 | .9429 | .1145 |
| -2.02 | .0217 | .9783 | .0519 | -1.57 | .0582 | .9418 | .1163 |
| -2.01 | .0222 | .9778 | .0529 | -1.56 | .0594 | .9406 | .1182 |
| -2.00 | .0228 | .9772 | .0540 | -1.55 | .0606 | .9394 | .1200 |
| -1.99 | .0233 | .9767 | .0551 | -1.54 | .0618 | .9382 | .1219 |
| -1.98 | .0239 | .9761 | .0562 | -1.53 | .0630 | .9370 | .1238 |
| -1.97 | .0244 | .9756 | .0573 | -1.52 | .0643 | .9357 | .1257 |
| -1.96 | .0250 | .9750 | .0584 | -1.51 | .0655 | .9345 | .1276 |
| -1.95 | .0256 | .9744 | .0596 | -1.50 | .0668 | .9332 | .1295 |
| -1.94 | .0262 | .9738 | .0608 | -1.49 | .0681 | .9319 | .1315 |
| -1.93 | .0268 | .9732 | .0620 | -1.48 | .0694 | .9306 | .1334 |
| -1.92 | .0274 | .9726 | .0632 | -1.47 | .0708 | .9292 | .1354 |
| -1.91 | .0281 | .9719 | .0644 | -1.46 | .0721 | .9279 | .1374 |
| -1.90 | .0287 | .9713 | .0656 | -1.45 | .0735 | .9265 | .1394 |
| -1.89 | .0294 | .9706 | .0669 | -1.44 | .0749 | .9251 | .1415 |
| -1.88 | .0301 | .9699 | .0681 | -1.43 | .0764 | .9236 | .1435 |
| -1.87 | .0307 | .9693 | .0694 | -1.42 | .0778 | .9222 | .1456 |
| -1.86 | .0314 | .9686 | .0707 | -1.41 | .0793 | .9207 | .1476 |
| -1.85 | .0322 | .9678 | .0721 | -1.40 | .0808 | .9192 | .1497 |
| -1.84 | .0329 | .9671 | .0734 | -1.39 | .0823 | .9177 | .1518 |
| -1.83 | .0336 | .9664 | .0748 | -1.38 | .0838 | .9162 | .1539 |
| -1.82 | .0344 | .9656 | .0761 | -1.37 | .0853 | .9147 | .1561 |
| -1.81 | .0351 | .9649 | .0775 | -1.36 | .0869 | .9131 | .1582 |
| -1.80 | .0359 | .9641 | .0790 | -1.35 | .0885 | .9115 | .1604 |
| -1.79 | .0367 | .9633 | .0804 | -1.34 | .0901 | .9099 | .1626 |
| -1.78 | .0375 | .9625 | .0818 | -1.33 | .0918 | .9082 | .1647 |
| -1.77 | .0384 | .9616 | .0833 | -1.32 | .0934 | .9066 | .1669 |
| -1.76 | .0392 | .9608 | .0848 | -1.31 | .0951 | .9049 | .1691 |
| -1.75 | .0401 | .9599 | .0863 | -1.30 | .0968 | .9032 | .1714 |

| z | Prop. Below | Prop. Above | Ht. Of Curve | z | Prop. Below | Prop. Above | Ht. Of Curve |
|---|---|---|---|---|---|---|---|
| -1.29 | .0985 | .9015 | .1736 | -0.84 | .2005 | .7995 | .2803 |
| -1.28 | .1003 | .8997 | .1758 | -0.83 | .2033 | .7967 | .2827 |
| -1.27 | .1020 | .8980 | .1781 | -0.82 | .2061 | .7939 | .2850 |
| -1.26 | .1038 | .8962 | .1804 | -0.81 | .2090 | .7910 | .2874 |
| -1.25 | .1056 | .8944 | .1826 | -0.80 | .2119 | .7881 | .2897 |
| -1.24 | .1075 | .8925 | .1849 | -0.79 | .2148 | .7852 | .2920 |
| -1.23 | .1093 | .8907 | .1872 | -0.78 | 2177 | .7823 | .2943 |
| -1.22 | .1112 | .8888 | .1895 | -0.77 | .2206 | .7794 | .2966 |
| -1.21 | .1131 | .8869 | .1919 | -0.76 | .2236 | .7764 | .2989 |
| -1.20 | .1151 | .8849 | .1942 | -0.75 | .2266 | .7734 | .3011 |
| -1.19 | .1170 | .8830 | .1965 | -0.74 | .2296 | .7704 | .3034 |
| -1.18 | .1190 | .8810 | .1989 | -0.73 | .2327 | .7673 | .3058 |
| -1.17 | .1210 | .8970 | .2012 | -0.72 | .2358 | .7642 | .3079 |
| -1.16 | .1230 | .8770 | .2036 | -0.71 | .2389 | .7611 | .3101 |
| -1.15 | .1251 | .8749 | .2059 | -0.70 | .2420 | .7580 | .3123 |
| -1.14 | .1271 | .8729 | .2083 | -0.69 | .2451 | .7549 | .3144 |
| -1.13 | .1292 | .8708 | .2107 | -0.68 | .2483 | .7517 | .3166 |
| -1.12 | .1314 | .8686 | .2131 | -0.67 | .2514 | .7486 | .3187 |
| -1.11 | .1335 | .8665 | .2155 | -0.66 | .2546 | .7454 | .3209 |
| -1.10 | .1357 | .8643 | .2179 | -0.65 | .2578 | .7422 | .3230 |
| -1.09 | .1379 | .8621 | .2203 | -0.64 | .2611 | .7389 | .3251 |
| -1.08 | .1401 | .8599 | .2227 | -0.63 | .2643 | .7357 | .3271 |
| -1.07 | .1423 | .8577 | .2251 | -0.62 | .2676 | .7324 | .3292 |
| -1.06 | .1446 | .8554 | .2275 | -0.61 | .2709 | .7291 | .3312 |
| -1.05 | .1469 | .8531 | .2299 | -0.60 | .2743 | .7257 | .3332 |
| -1.04 | .1492 | .8508 | .2323 | -0.59 | .2776 | .7224 | .3352 |
| -1.03 | .1515 | .8485 | .2347 | -0.58 | .2810 | .7190 | .3372 |
| -1.02 | .1539 | .8461 | .2371 | -0.57 | .2843 | .7157 | .3391 |
| -1.01 | .1562 | .8438 | .2396 | -0.56 | .2877 | .7123 | .3410 |
| -1.00 | .1587 | .8413 | .2420 | -0.55 | .2912 | .7088 | .3429 |
| -0.99 | .1611 | .8389 | .2444 | -0.54 | .2946 | .7054 | .3448 |
| -0.98 | .1635 | .8365 | .2468 | -0.53 | .2981 | .7019 | .3467 |
| -0.97 | .1660 | .8340 | .2492 | -0.52 | .3015 | .6985 | .3485 |
| -0.96 | .1685 | .8315 | .2516 | -0.51 | .3050 | .6950 | .3503 |
| -0.95 | .1711 | .8289 | .2541 | -0.50 | .3085 | .6915 | .3521 |
| -0.94 | .1736 | .8264 | .2565 | -0.49 | .3121 | .6879 | .3538 |
| -0.93 | .1762 | .8238 | .2589 | -0.48 | .3156 | .6844 | .3555 |
| -0.92 | .1788 | .8212 | .2613 | -0.47 | .3192 | .6808 | .3572 |
| -0.91 | .1814 | .8186 | .2637 | -0.46 | .3228 | .6772 | .3589 |
| -0.90 | .1841 | .8159 | .2661 | -0.45 | .3264 | .6736 | .3605 |
| -0.89 | .1867 | .8133 | .2685 | -0.44 | .3300 | .6700 | .3624 |
| -0.88 | .1894 | .8106 | .2709 | -0.43 | .3336 | .6664 | .3637 |
| -0.87 | .1922 | .8078 | .2732 | -0.42 | .3372 | .6628 | .3653 |
| -0.86 | .1949 | .8051 | .2756 | -0.41 | .3409 | .6591 | .3668 |
| -0.85 | .1977 | .8023 | .2780 | -0.40 | .3446 | .6554 | .3683 |

| z | Prop. Below | Prop. Above | Ht. Of Curve | z | Prop. Below | Prop. Above | Ht. Of Curve |
|---|---|---|---|---|---|---|---|
| -0.39 | .3483 | .6517 | .3697 | 0.00 | .5000 | .5000 | .3989 |
| -0.38 | .3520 | .6480 | .3712 | 0.01 | .5040 | .4960 | .3989 |
| -0.37 | .3557 | .6443 | .3725 | 0.02 | .5080 | .4920 | .3989 |
| -0.36 | .3594 | .6406 | .3739 | 0.03 | .5120 | .4880 | .3988 |
| -0.35 | .3632 | .6368 | .3752 | 0.04 | .5160 | .4840 | .3986 |
| -0.34 | .3669 | .6331 | .3765 | 0.05 | .5199 | .4801 | .3984 |
| -0.33 | .3707 | .6293 | .3778 | 0.06 | .5239 | .4761 | .3982 |
| -0.32 | .3745 | .6255 | .3790 | 0.07 | .5279 | .4721 | .3980 |
| -0.31 | .3783 | .6217 | .3802 | 0.08 | .5319 | .4681 | .3977 |
| -0.30 | .3821 | .6179 | .3814 | 0.09 | .5359 | .4641 | .3973 |
| -0.29 | .3859 | .6141 | .3825 | 0.10 | .5398 | .4602 | .3970 |
| -0.28 | .3897 | .6103 | .3836 | 0.11 | .5438 | .4562 | .3965 |
| -0.27 | .3936 | .6064 | .3847 | 0.12 | .5478 | .4522 | .3961 |
| -0.26 | .3974 | .6026 | .3857 | 0.13 | .5517 | .4483 | .3956 |
| -0.25 | .4013 | .5987 | .3867 | 0.14 | .5557 | .4443 | .3951 |
| -0.24 | .4052 | .5948 | .3876 | 0.15 | .5596 | .4404 | .3945 |
| -0.23 | .4090 | .5910 | .3885 | 0.16 | .5636 | .4364 | .3939 |
| -0.22 | .4129 | .5871 | .3894 | 0.17 | .5675 | .4325 | .3932 |
| -0.21 | .4168 | .5832 | .3902 | 0.18 | .5714 | .4286 | .3925 |
| -0.20 | .4207 | .5793 | .3910 | 0.19 | .5753 | .4247 | .3918 |
| -0.19 | .4247 | .5753 | .3918 | 0.20 | .5793 | .4207 | .3910 |
| -0.18 | .4286 | .5714 | .3925 | 0.21 | .5832 | .4168 | .3902 |
| -0.17 | .4325 | .5675 | .3932 | 0.22 | .5871 | .4129 | .3894 |
| -0.16 | .4364 | .5636 | .3939 | 0.23 | .5910 | .4090 | .3885 |
| -0.15 | .4404 | .5596 | .3945 | 0.24 | .5948 | .4052 | .3876 |
| -0.14 | .4443 | .5557 | .3951 | 0.25 | .5987 | .4013 | .3867 |
| -0.13 | .4483 | .5517 | .3956 | 0.26 | .6026 | .3974 | .3857 |
| -0.12 | .4522 | .5478 | .3961 | 0.27 | .6064 | .3936 | .3847 |
| -0.11 | .4562 | .5348 | .3966 | 0.28 | .6103 | .3897 | .3836 |
| -0.10 | .4602 | .5398 | .3970 | 0.29 | .6141 | .3859 | .3825 |
| -0.09 | .4641 | .5359 | .3973 | 0.30 | .6179 | .3821 | .3814 |
| -0.08 | .4681 | .5319 | .3977 | 0.31 | .6217 | .3783 | .3802 |
| -0.07 | .4721 | .5279 | .3980 | 0.32 | .6255 | .3745 | .3790 |
| -0.06 | .4761 | .5239 | .3982 | 0.33 | .6293 | .3707 | .3778 |
| -0.05 | .4801 | .5199 | .3984 | 0.34 | .6331 | .3669 | .3765 |
| -0.04 | .4840 | .5160 | .3986 | 0.35 | .6368 | .3632 | .3752 |
| -0.03 | .4880 | .5120 | .3988 | 0.36 | .6406 | .3594 | .3739 |
| -0.02 | .4920 | .5080 | .3989 | 0.37 | .6443 | .3557 | .3725 |
| -0.01 | .4960 | .5040 | .3989 | 0.38 | .6480 | .3520 | .3712 |
| 0.00 | .5000 | .5000 | .3989 | 0.39 | .6517 | .3483 | .3697 |
| | | | | 0.40 | .6554 | .3446 | .3683 |
| | | | | 0.41 | .6591 | .3409 | .3668 |
| | | | | 0.42 | .6628 | .3372 | .3653 |
| | | | | 0.43 | .6664 | .3336 | .3637 |
| | | | | 0.44 | .6700 | .3300 | .3621 |

| z | Prop. Below | Prop. Above | Ht. Of Curve | z | Prop. Below | Prop. Above | Ht. Of Curve |
|---|---|---|---|---|---|---|---|
| 0.45 | .6736 | .3264 | .3605 | 0.90 | .8159 | .1841 | .2661 |
| 0.46 | .6772 | .3228 | .3589 | 0.91 | .8186 | .1814 | .2637 |
| 0.47 | .6808 | .3192 | .3572 | 0.92 | .8212 | .1788 | .2613 |
| 0.48 | .6844 | .3156 | .3555 | 0.93 | .8238 | .1762 | .2589 |
| 0.49 | .6879 | .3121 | .3538 | 0.94 | .8264 | .1736 | .2565 |
| 0.50 | .6915 | .3085 | .3521 | 0.95 | .8289 | .1711 | .2541 |
| 0.51 | .6950 | .3050 | .3503 | 0.96 | .8315 | .1685 | .2516 |
| 0.52 | .6985 | .3015 | .3485 | 0.97 | .8340 | .1660 | .2492 |
| 0.53 | .7019 | .2981 | .3467 | 0.98 | .8365 | .1635 | .2468 |
| 0.54 | .7054 | .2946 | .3448 | 0.99 | .8389 | .1611 | .2444 |
| 0.55 | .7088 | .2912 | .3429 | 1.00 | .8413 | .1587 | .2420 |
| 0.56 | .7123 | .2877 | .3410 | 1.01 | .8438 | .1562 | .2396 |
| 0.57 | .7157 | .2843 | .3391 | 1.02 | .8461 | .1539 | .2371 |
| 0.58 | .7190 | .2810 | .3372 | 1.03 | .8485 | .1515 | .2347 |
| 0.59 | .7224 | .2776 | .3352 | 1.04 | .8508 | .1492 | .2323 |
| 0.60 | .7257 | .2743 | .3332 | 1.05 | .8531 | .1469 | .2299 |
| 0.61 | .7291 | .2709 | .3312 | 1.06 | .8554 | .1446 | .2275 |
| 0.62 | .7324 | .2676 | .3292 | 1.07 | .8577 | .1423 | .2251 |
| 0.63 | .7357 | .2643 | .3271 | 1.08 | .8599 | .1401 | .2227 |
| 0.64 | .7389 | .2611 | .3251 | 1.09 | .8621 | .1379 | .2203 |
| 0.65 | .7422 | .2578 | .3230 | 1.10 | .8643 | .1357 | .2179 |
| 0.66 | .7454 | .2546 | .3209 | 1.11 | .8665 | .1335 | .2155 |
| 0.67 | .7486 | .2514 | .3187 | 1.12 | .8686 | .1314 | .2131 |
| 0.68 | .7517 | .2483 | .3166 | 1.13 | .8708 | .1292 | .2107 |
| 0.69 | .7549 | .2451 | .3144 | 1.14 | .8729 | .1271 | .2083 |
| 0.70 | .7580 | .2420 | .3123 | 1.15 | .8749 | .1251 | .2059 |
| 0.71 | .7611 | .2389 | .3101 | 1.16 | .8770 | .1230 | .2036 |
| 0.72 | .7642 | .2358 | .3079 | 1.17 | .8790 | .1210 | .2012 |
| 0.73 | .7673 | .2327 | .3056 | 1.18 | .8810 | .1190 | .1989 |
| 0.74 | .7704 | .2296 | .3034 | 1.19 | .8830 | .1170 | .1965 |
| 0.75 | .7734 | .2266 | .3011 | 1.20 | .8849 | .1151 | .1942 |
| 0.76 | .7764 | .2236 | .2989 | 1.21 | .8869 | .1131 | .1919 |
| 0.77 | .7794 | .2206 | .2966 | 1.22 | .8888 | .1112 | .1895 |
| 0.78 | .7823 | .2177 | .2943 | 1.23 | .8907 | .1093 | .1872 |
| 0.79 | .7852 | .2148 | .2920 | 1.24 | .8925 | .1075 | .1849 |
| 0.80 | .7881 | .2119 | .2987 | 1.25 | .8944 | .1056 | .1826 |
| 0.81 | .7910 | .2090 | .2874 | 1.26 | .8962 | .1038 | .1804 |
| 0.82 | .7939 | .2061 | .2850 | 1.27 | .8980 | .1020 | .1781 |
| 0.83 | .7967 | .2033 | .2827 | 1.28 | .8997 | .1003 | .1758 |
| 0.84 | .7995 | .2005 | .2803 | 1.29 | .9015 | .0985 | .1736 |
| 0.85 | .8023 | .1977 | .2780 | 1.30 | .9032 | .0968 | .1714 |
| 0.86 | .8051 | .1949 | .2756 | 1.31 | .9049 | .0951 | .1691 |
| 0.87 | .8078 | .1922 | .2732 | 1.32 | .9066 | .0934 | .1669 |
| 0.88 | .8106 | .1894 | .2709 | 1.33 | .9082 | .0918 | .1647 |
| 0.89 | .8133 | .1867 | .2685 | 1.34 | .9099 | .0901 | .1626 |

| z | Prop. Below | Prop. Above | Ht. Of Curve | z | Prop. Below | Prop. Above | Ht. Of Curve |
|------|--------|-------|-------|------|-------|-------|-------|
| 1.35 | .9115 | .0885 | .1604 | 1.80 | .9641 | .0359 | .0790 |
| 1.36 | .9131 | .0869 | .1582 | 1.81 | .9649 | .0351 | .0775 |
| 1.37 | .9147 | .0853 | .1561 | 1.82 | .9656 | .0344 | .0761 |
| 1.38 | .9162 | .0838 | .1539 | 1.83 | .9664 | .0336 | .0748 |
| 1.39 | .9177 | .0823 | .1518 | 1.84 | .9671 | .0329 | .0734 |
| 1.40 | .9192 | .0808 | .1497 | 1.85 | .9678 | .0322 | .0721 |
| 1.41 | .9207 | .0793 | .1476 | 1.86 | .9686 | .0314 | .0707 |
| 1.42 | .9222 | .0778 | .1456 | 1.87 | .9693 | .0307 | .0694 |
| 1.43 | .9236 | .0764 | .1435 | 1.88 | .9699 | .0301 | .0681 |
| 1.44 | .9251 | .0749 | .1415 | 1.89 | .9706 | .0294 | .0669 |
| 1.45 | .99265 | .0735 | .1394 | 1.90 | .9713 | .0287 | .0565 |
| 1.46 | .9279 | .0721 | .1374 | 1.91 | .9719 | .0281 | .0644 |
| 1.47 | .9292 | .0708 | .1354 | 1.92 | .9726 | .0274 | .0632 |
| 1.48 | .9306 | .0694 | .1334 | 1.93 | .9732 | .0268 | .0620 |
| 1.49 | .9319 | .0681 | .1315 | 1.94 | .9738 | .0262 | .0608 |
| 1.50 | .9332 | .0668 | .1295 | 1.95 | .9744 | .0256 | .0596 |
| 1.51 | .9345 | .0665 | .1276 | 1.96 | .9750 | .0250 | .0584 |
| 1.52 | .9357 | .0643 | .1257 | 1.97 | .9756 | .0244 | .0573 |
| 1.53 | .9370 | .0630 | .1238 | 1.98 | .9761 | .0239 | .0562 |
| 1.54 | .9382 | .0618 | .1219 | 1.99 | .9767 | .0233 | .0551 |
| 1.55 | .9394 | .0606 | .1200 | 2.00 | .9772 | .0228 | .0540 |
| 1.56 | .9406 | .0594 | .1182 | 2.01 | .9778 | .0222 | .0529 |
| 1.57 | .9148 | .0582 | .1163 | 2.02 | .9783 | .0217 | .0519 |
| 1.58 | .9429 | .0571 | .1145 | 2.03 | .9788 | .0212 | .0508 |
| 1.59 | .9441 | .0559 | .1127 | 2.04 | .9793 | .0207 | .0498 |
| 1.60 | .9452 | .0548 | .1109 | 2.05 | .9798 | .0202 | .0488 |
| 1.61 | .9463 | .0537 | .1092 | 2.06 | .9803 | .0197 | .0478 |
| 1.62 | .9474 | .0526 | .1074 | 2.07 | .9808 | .0192 | .0468 |
| 1.63 | .9484 | .0516 | .1057 | 2.08 | .9812 | .0188 | .0459 |
| 1.64 | .9495 | .0505 | .1040 | 2.09 | .9817 | .0183 | .0449 |
| 1.65 | .9505 | .0495 | .1023 | 2.10 | .9821 | .0179 | .0440 |
| 1.66 | .9515 | .0485 | .1006 | 2.11 | .9826 | .0174 | .0431 |
| 1.67 | .9525 | .0475 | .0989 | 2.12 | .9830 | .0170 | .0422 |
| 1.68 | .9535 | .0465 | .0973 | 2.13 | .9834 | .0166 | .0413 |
| 1.69 | .9545 | .0455 | .0957 | 2.14 | .9838 | .0162 | .0404 |
| 1.70 | .9554 | .0446 | .0940 | 2.15 | .9842 | .0158 | .0396 |
| 1.71 | .9564 | .0436 | .0925 | 2.16 | .9846 | .0154 | .0387 |
| 1.72 | .9573 | .0427 | .0909 | 2.17 | .9850 | .0150 | .0379 |
| 1.73 | .9582 | .0418 | .0893 | 2.18 | .9854 | .0146 | .0371 |
| 1.74 | .9591 | .0409 | .0878 | 2.19 | .9857 | .0143 | .0363 |
| 1.75 | .9599 | .0401 | .0863 | 2.20 | .9861 | .0139 | .0356 |
| 1.76 | .9608 | .0392 | .0848 | 2.21 | .9864 | .0136 | .0347 |
| 1.77 | .9616 | .0384 | .0833 | 2.22 | .9868 | .0132 | .0339 |
| 1.78 | .9625 | .0375 | .0818 | 2.23 | .9871 | .0129 | .0332 |
| 1.79 | .9633 | .0367 | .0804 | 2.24 | .9875 | .0125 | .0325 |

| z | Prop. Below | Prop. Above | Ht. Of Curve | z | Prop. Below | Prop. Above | Ht. Of Curve |
|---|---|---|---|---|---|---|---|
| 2.25 | .9878 | .0122 | .0317 | 2.65 | .9960 | .0040 | .0119 |
| 2.26 | .9881 | .0119 | .0310 | 2.66 | .9961 | .0039 | .0116 |
| 2.27 | .9884 | .0116 | .0303 | 2.67 | .9962 | .0038 | .0113 |
| 2.28 | .9887 | .0113 | .0297 | 2.68 | .9963 | .0037 | .0110 |
| 2.29 | .9890 | .0110 | .0290 | 2.69 | .9964 | .0036 | .0107 |
| 2.30 | .9893 | .0107 | .0283 | 2.70 | .9965 | .0035 | .0104 |
| 2.31 | .9896 | .0104 | .0277 | 2.71 | .9966 | .0034 | .0101 |
| 2.32 | .9898 | .0102 | .0270 | 2.72 | .9967 | .0033 | .0099 |
| 2.33 | .9901 | .0099 | .0264 | 2.73 | .9968 | .0032 | .0096 |
| 2.34 | .9904 | .0096 | .0258 | 2.74 | .9969 | .0031 | .0093 |
| 2.35 | .9906 | .0094 | .0252 | 2.75 | .9970 | .0030 | .0091 |
| 2.36 | .9909 | .0091 | .0246 | 2.76 | .9971 | .0029 | .0088 |
| 2.37 | .9911 | .0089 | .0241 | 2.77 | .9972 | .0028 | .0086 |
| 2.38 | .9913 | .0087 | .0235 | 2.78 | .9973 | .0027 | .0084 |
| 2.39 | .9916 | .0084 | .0229 | 2.79 | .9974 | .0026 | .0081 |
| 2.40 | .9918 | .0082 | .0224 | 2.80 | .9974 | .0026 | .0079 |
| 2.41 | .9920 | .0080 | .0219 | 2.81 | .9975 | .0025 | .0077 |
| 2.42 | .9922 | .0078 | .0213 | 2.82 | .9976 | .0024 | .0075 |
| 2.43 | .9925 | .0075 | .0208 | 2.83 | .9977 | .0023 | .0073 |
| 2.44 | .9927 | .0073 | .0203 | 2.84 | .9977 | .0023 | .0071 |
| 2.45 | .9929 | .0071 | .0198 | 2.85 | .9978 | .0022 | .0069 |
| 2.46 | .9931 | .0069 | .0194 | 2.86 | .9979 | .0021 | .0067 |
| 2.47 | .9932 | .0068 | .0189 | 2.87 | .9979 | .0021 | .0065 |
| 2.48 | .9934 | .0066 | .0184 | 2.88 | .9980 | .0020 | .0063 |
| 2.49 | .9936 | .0064 | .0180 | 2.89 | .9981 | .0019 | .0061 |
| 2.50 | .9938 | .0062 | .0175 | 2.90 | .9981 | .0019 | .0060 |
| 2.51 | .9940 | .0060 | .0171 | 2.91 | .9982 | .0018 | .0058 |
| 2.52 | .9941 | .0059 | .0167 | 2.92 | .9982 | .0018 | .0056 |
| 2.53 | .9943 | .0057 | .0163 | 2.93 | .9983 | .0017 | .0055 |
| 2.54 | .9945 | .0055 | .0158 | 2.94 | .9984 | .0016 | 0053 |
| 2.55 | .9946 | .0054 | .0154 | 2.95 | .9984 | .0016 | .0051 |
| 2.56 | .9948 | .0052 | .0151 | 2.96 | .9985 | .0015 | .0050 |
| 2.57 | .9949 | .0051 | .0147 | 2.97 | .9985 | .0015 | .0048 |
| 2.58 | .9951 | .0049 | .0143 | 2.98 | .9986 | .0014 | .0047 |
| 2.59 | .9952 | .0048 | .0139 | 2.99 | .9986 | .0014 | .0046 |
| 2.60 | .9953 | .0047 | .0136 | | | | |
| 2.61 | .9955 | .0045 | .0132 | | | | |
| 2.62 | .9956 | .0044 | .0129 | | | | |
| 2.63 | .9957 | .0043 | .0126 | | | | |
| 2.64 | .9959 | .0041 | .0122 | | | | |

# APPENDIX C
# Critical Values of $t$

*Level of Significance for Two-Tailed Tests*

| df | .20 | .10 | .05 | .02 | .01 | .001 |
|---|---|---|---|---|---|---|
| 1 | 3.078 | 6.314 | 12.706 | 31.821 | 63.657 | 636.619 |
| 2 | 1.886 | 2.920 | 4.303 | 6.965 | 9.925 | 31.598 |
| 3 | 1.638 | 2.353 | 3.182 | 4.541 | 5.841 | 12.941 |
| 4 | 1.533 | 2.132 | 2.776 | 3.747 | 4.604 | 8.610 |
| 5 | 1.476 | 2.015 | 2.571 | 3.365 | 4.032 | 6.859 |
| 6 | 1.440 | 1.943 | 2.447 | 3.143 | 3.707 | 5.959 |
| 7 | 1.415 | 1.895 | 2.365 | 2.998 | 3.499 | 5.405 |
| 8 | 1.397 | 1.860 | 2.306 | 2.896 | 3.355 | 5.041 |
| 9 | 1.383 | 1.833 | 2.262 | 2.821 | 3.250 | 4.781 |
| 10 | 1.372 | 1.812 | 2.228 | 2.764 | 3.169 | 4.587 |
| 11 | 1.363 | 1.796 | 2.201 | 2.718 | 3.106 | 4.437 |
| 12 | 1.356 | 1.782 | 2.179 | 2.681 | 3.055 | 4.318 |
| 13 | 1.350 | 1.771 | 2.160 | 2.650 | 3.012 | 4.221 |
| 14 | 1.345 | 1.761 | 2.145 | 2.624 | 2.977 | 4.140 |
| 15 | 1.341 | 1.753 | 2.131 | 2.602 | 2.947 | 4.073 |
| 16 | 1.337 | 1.746 | 2.120 | 2.583 | 2.921 | 4.015 |
| 17 | 1.333 | 1.740 | 2.110 | 2.567 | 2.898 | 3.965 |
| 18 | 1.330 | 1.734 | 2.101 | 2.552 | 2.878 | 3.922 |
| 19 | 1.328 | 1.729 | 2.093 | 2.539 | 2.861 | 3.883 |
| 20 | 1.325 | 1.725 | 2.086 | 2.528 | 2.845 | 3.850 |
| 21 | 1.323 | 1.721 | 2.080 | 2.518 | 2.831 | 3.819 |
| 22 | 1.321 | 1.717 | 2.074 | 2.508 | 2.819 | 3.792 |
| 23 | 1.319 | 1.714 | 2.069 | 2.500 | 2.807 | 3.767 |
| 24 | 1.318 | 1.711 | 2.064 | 2.492 | 2.797 | 3.745 |
| 25 | 1.316 | 1.708 | 2.060 | 2.485 | 2.787 | 3.725 |
| 26 | 1.315 | 1.706 | 2.056 | 2.479 | 2.779 | 3.707 |
| 27 | 1.314 | 1.703 | 2.052 | 2.473 | 2.771 | 3.690 |
| 28 | 1.313 | 1.701 | 2.048 | 2.467 | 2.763 | 3.674 |
| 29 | 1.311 | 1.699 | 2.045 | 2.462 | 2.756 | 3.659 |
| 30 | 1.310 | 1.697 | 2.042 | 2.457 | 2.750 | 3.646 |
| 40 | 1.303 | 1.684 | 2.021 | 2.423 | 2.704 | 3.551 |
| 60 | 1.296 | 1.671 | 2.000 | 2.390 | 2.660 | 3.460 |
| 120 | 1.289 | 1.658 | 1.980 | 2.358 | 2.617 | 3.373 |
| ∞ | 1.282 | 1.645 | 1.960 | 2.326 | 2.576 | 3.291 |

From Table III of Fisher & Yates; *Statistical Tables for Biological, Agricultural and Medical Research.*
Published by Longman Group UK Ltd., 1974. Used with permission.

# Fisher's z

## Transformation of r to $z_r$

| r | $z_r$ | r | $z_r$ | r | $z_r$ |
|---|---|---|---|---|---|
| .01 | .010 | .34 | .354 | .67 | .811 |
| .02 | .020 | .35 | .366 | .68 | .829 |
| .03 | .030 | .36 | .377 | .69 | .848 |
| .04 | .040 | .37 | .389 | .70 | .867 |
| .05 | .050 | .38 | .400 | .71 | .887 |
| .06 | .060 | .39 | .412 | .72 | .908 |
| .07 | .070 | .40 | .424 | .73 | .929 |
| .08 | .080 | .41 | .436 | .74 | .950 |
| .09 | .090 | .42 | .448 | .75 | .973 |
| .10 | .100 | .43 | .460 | .76 | .996 |
| .11 | .110 | .44 | .472 | .77 | 1.020 |
| .12 | .121 | .45 | .485 | .78 | 1.045 |
| .13 | .131 | .46 | .497 | .79 | 1.071 |
| .14 | .141 | .47 | .510 | .80 | 1.099 |
| .15 | .151 | .48 | .523 | .81 | 1.127 |
| .16 | .161 | .49 | .536 | .82 | 1.157 |
| .17 | .172 | .50 | .549 | .83 | 1.188 |
| .18 | .181 | .51 | .563 | .84 | 1.221 |
| .19 | .192 | .52 | .577 | .85 | 1.256 |
| .20 | .203 | .53 | .590 | .86 | 1.293 |
| .21 | .214 | .54 | .604 | .87 | 1.333 |
| .22 | .224 | .55 | .618 | .88 | 1.376 |
| .23 | .234 | .56 | .633 | .89 | 1.422 |
| .24 | .245 | .57 | .648 | .90 | 1.472 |
| .25 | .256 | .58 | .663 | .91 | 1.528 |
| .26 | .266 | .59 | .678 | .92 | 1.589 |
| .27 | .277 | .60 | .693 | .93 | 1.658 |
| .28 | .288 | .61 | .709 | .94 | 1.738 |
| .29 | .299 | .62 | .725 | .95 | 1.832 |
| .30 | .309 | .63 | .741 | .96 | 1.946 |
| .31 | .321 | .64 | .758 | .97 | 2.092 |
| .32 | .332 | .65 | .775 | .98 | 2.298 |
| .33 | .343 | .66 | .793 | .99 | 2.647 |

From Runyon, R. and Haber, A., *Fundamentals of Behavioral Statistics*, 5th Edition (1984). Reproduced by permission of McGraw-Hill, Inc.

# Critical Values of the Pearson r

## Level of Significance

| df = N - 2 | .10 | .05 | .02 | .01 |
|---|---|---|---|---|
| 1 | .988 | .997 | .9995 | .9999 |
| 2 | .900 | .950 | .980 | .990 |
| 3 | .805 | .878 | .934 | .959 |
| 4 | .729 | .811 | .882 | .917 |
| 5 | .669 | .754 | .833 | .874 |
| 6 | .622 | .707 | .789 | .834 |
| 7 | .582 | .666 | .750 | .798 |
| 8 | .549 | .632 | .716 | .765 |
| 9 | .521 | .602 | .685 | .735 |
| 10 | .497 | .576 | .658 | .708 |
| 11 | .476 | .553 | .634 | .684 |
| 12 | .458 | .532 | .612 | .661 |
| 13 | .441 | .514 | .592 | .641 |
| 14 | .426 | .497 | .574 | .623 |
| 15 | .412 | .482 | .558 | .606 |
| 16 | .400 | .468 | .542 | .590 |
| 17 | .389 | .456 | .528 | .575 |
| 18 | .378 | .444 | .516 | .561 |
| 19 | .369 | .433 | .503 | .549 |
| 20 | .360 | .423 | .492 | .537 |
| 21 | .352 | .413 | .482 | .526 |
| 22 | .344 | .404 | .472 | .515 |
| 23 | .337 | .396 | .462 | .505 |
| 24 | .330 | .388 | .453 | .496 |
| 25 | .323 | .381 | .445 | .487 |
| 26 | .317 | .374 | .437 | .479 |
| 27 | .311 | .367 | .430 | .471 |
| 28 | .306 | .361 | .423 | .463 |
| 29 | .301 | .355 | .416 | .456 |
| 30 | .296 | .349 | .409 | .449 |
| 35 | .275 | .325 | .381 | .418 |
| 40 | .257 | .304 | .358 | .393 |
| 45 | .243 | .288 | .338 | .372 |
| 50 | .231 | .273 | .322 | .354 |
| 60 | .211 | .250 | .295 | .325 |
| 70 | .195 | .232 | .274 | .303 |
| 80 | .183 | .217 | .256 | .283 |
| 90 | .173 | .205 | .242 | .267 |
| 100 | .164 | .195 | .230 | .254 |

From Table III of Fisher & Yates; *Statistical Tables for Biological, Agricultural and Medical Research.* Published by Longman Group UK Ltd., 1974. Used with permission.

# Critical Values of F

*Degrees of Freedom for Numerator*

| | 1 | 2 | 3 | 4 | 5 | 6 | 7 | 8 | 9 | 10 | 11 | 12 |
|---|---|---|---|---|---|---|---|---|---|---|---|---|
| **1** | 161<br>4052 | 200<br>4999 | 216<br>5403 | 225<br>5625 | 230<br>5764 | 234<br>5859 | 237<br>5928 | 239<br>5981 | 241<br>6022 | 242<br>6056 | 243<br>6082 | 244<br>6106 |
| **2** | 18.51<br>98.49 | 19.00<br>99.01 | 19.16<br>99.17 | 19.25<br>99.25 | 19.30<br>99.30 | 19.33<br>99.33 | 19.36<br>99.34 | 19.37<br>99.36 | 19.38<br>99.38 | 19.39<br>99.40 | 19.40<br>99.41 | 19.41<br>99.42 |
| **3** | 10.13<br>34.12 | 9.55<br>30.81 | 9.28<br>29.46 | 9.12<br>28.71 | 9.01<br>28.24 | 8.94<br>27.91 | 8.88<br>27.67 | 8.84<br>27.49 | 8.81<br>27.34 | 8.78<br>27.23 | 8.76<br>27.13 | 8.74<br>27.05 |
| **4** | 7.71<br>21.20 | 6.94<br>18.00 | 6.59<br>16.69 | 6.39<br>15.98 | 6.26<br>15.52 | 6.16<br>15.21 | 6.09<br>14.98 | 6.04<br>14.80 | 6.00<br>14.66 | 5.96<br>14.54 | 5.93<br>14.45 | 5.91<br>14.37 |
| **5** | 6.61<br>16.26 | 5.79<br>13.27 | 5.41<br>12.06 | 5.19<br>11.39 | 5.05<br>10.97 | 4.95<br>10.67 | 4.88<br>10.45 | 4.82<br>10.27 | 4.78<br>10.15 | 4.74<br>10.05 | 4.70<br>9.96 | 4.68<br>9.89 |
| **6** | 5.99<br>13.74 | 5.14<br>10.92 | 4.76<br>9.78 | 4.53<br>9.15 | 4.39<br>8.75 | 4.28<br>8.47 | 4.21<br>8.26 | 4.15<br>8.10 | 4.10<br>7.98 | 4.06<br>7.87 | 4.03<br>7.79 | 4.00<br>7.72 |
| **7** | 5.59<br>12.25 | 4.74<br>9.55 | 4.35<br>8.45 | 4.12<br>7.85 | 3.97<br>7.46 | 3.87<br>7.19 | 3.79<br>7.00 | 3.73<br>6.84 | 3.68<br>6.71 | 3.63<br>6.62 | 3.60<br>6.54 | 3.57<br>6.47 |
| **8** | 5.32<br>11.26 | 4.46<br>8.65 | 4.07<br>7.59 | 3.84<br>7.01 | 3.69<br>6.63 | 3.58<br>6.37 | 3.50<br>6.19 | 3.44<br>6.03 | 3.39<br>5.91 | 3.34<br>5.82 | 3.31<br>5.74 | 3.28<br>5.67 |
| **9** | 5.12<br>10.56 | 4.26<br>8.02 | 3.86<br>6.99 | 3.63<br>6.42 | 3.48<br>6.06 | 3.37<br>5.80 | 3.29<br>5.62 | 3.23<br>5.47 | 3.18<br>5.35 | 3.13<br>5.26 | 3.10<br>5.18 | 3.07<br>5.11 |
| **10** | 4.96<br>10.04 | 4.10<br>7.56 | 3.71<br>6.55 | 3.48<br>5.99 | 3.33<br>5.64 | 3.22<br>5.39 | 3.14<br>5.21 | 3.07<br>5.06 | 3.02<br>4.95 | 2.97<br>4.85 | 2.94<br>4.78 | 2.91<br>4.71 |
| **11** | 4.84<br>9.65 | 3.98<br>7.20 | 3.59<br>6.22 | 3.36<br>5.67 | 3.20<br>5.32 | 3.09<br>5.07 | 3.01<br>4.88 | 2.95<br>4.74 | 2.90<br>4.63 | 2.86<br>4.54 | 2.82<br>4.46 | 2.79<br>4.40 |
| **12** | 4.75<br>9.33 | 3.88<br>6.93 | 3.49<br>5.95 | 3.26<br>5.41 | 3.11<br>5.06 | 3.00<br>4.82 | 2.92<br>4.65 | 2.85<br>4.50 | 2.80<br>4.39 | 2.76<br>4.30 | 2.72<br>4.22 | 2.69<br>4.16 |
| **13** | 4.67<br>9.07 | 3.80<br>6.70 | 3.41<br>5.74 | 3.18<br>5.20 | 3.02<br>4.86 | 2.92<br>4.62 | 2.84<br>4.44 | 2.77<br>4.30 | 2.72<br>4.19 | 2.67<br>4.10 | 2.63<br>4.02 | 2.60<br>3.96 |
| **14** | 4.60<br>8.86 | 3.74<br>6.51 | 3.34<br>5.56 | 3.11<br>5.03 | 2.96<br>4.69 | 2.85<br>4.46 | 2.77<br>4.28 | 2.70<br>4.14 | 2.65<br>4.03 | 2.60<br>3.94 | 2.56<br>3.86 | 2.53<br>3.80 |
| **15** | 4.54<br>8.68 | 3.68<br>6.36 | 3.29<br>5.42 | 3.06<br>4.89 | 2.90<br>4.56 | 2.79<br>4.32 | 2.70<br>4.14 | 2.64<br>4.00 | 2.59<br>3.89 | 2.55<br>3.80 | 2.51<br>3.73 | 2.48<br>3.67 |
| **16** | 4.49<br>8.53 | 3.63<br>6.23 | 3.24<br>5.29 | 3.01<br>4.77 | 2.85<br>4.44 | 2.74<br>4.20 | 2.66<br>4.03 | 2.59<br>3.89 | 2.54<br>3.78 | 2.49<br>3.69 | 2.45<br>3.61 | 2.42<br>3.55 |
| **17** | 4.45<br>8.40 | 3.59<br>6.11 | 3.20<br>5.18 | 2.96<br>4.67 | 2.81<br>4.34 | 2.70<br>4.10 | 2.62<br>3.93 | 2.55<br>3.79 | 2.50<br>3.68 | 2.45<br>3.59 | 2.41<br>3.52 | 2.38<br>3.45 |

*Degrees of Freedom for Denominator*

**Note:** upper value in each box is the critical value at the .05 level of significance, lower value is at .01. From Runyon, R., and Haber, A., *Fundamentals of Behavioral Statistics*, 5th Edition (1984). Reproduced by permission of McGraw-Hill, Inc.

*Degrees of Freedom for Numerator*

| | 14 | 16 | 20 | 24 | 30 | 40 | 50 | 75 | 100 | 200 | 500 | ∞ |
|---|---|---|---|---|---|---|---|---|---|---|---|---|
| **1** | 245 | 246 | 248 | 249 | 250 | 251 | 252 | 253 | 253 | 254 | 254 | 254 |
| | **6142** | **6169** | **6208** | **6234** | **6258** | **6286** | **6302** | **6323** | **6334** | **6352** | **6361** | **6366** |
| **2** | 19.42 | 19.43 | 19.44 | 19.45 | 19.46 | 19.47 | 19.47 | 19.48 | 19.49 | 19.49 | 19.50 | 19.50 |
| | **99.43** | **99.44** | **99.45** | **99.46** | **99.47** | **99.48** | **99.48** | **99.49** | **99.49** | **99.49** | **99.50** | **99.50** |
| **3** | 8.71 | 8.69 | 8.66 | 8.64 | 8.62 | 8.60 | 8.58 | 8.57 | 8.56 | 8.54 | 8.54 | 8.53 |
| | **26.92** | **26.83** | **26.69** | **26.60** | **26.50** | **26.41** | **26.30** | **26.27** | **26.23** | **26.18** | **26.14** | **26.12** |
| **4** | 5.87 | 5.84 | 5.80 | 5.77 | 5.74 | 5.71 | 5.70 | 5.68 | 5.66 | 5.65 | 5.43 | 5.63 |
| | **14.24** | **14.15** | **14.02** | **13.93** | **13.83** | **13.74** | **13.69** | **13.61** | **13.57** | **13.52** | **13.48** | **13.46** |
| **5** | 4.64 | 4.60 | 4.56 | 4.53 | 4.50 | 4.46 | 4.44 | 4.42 | 4.40 | 4.38 | 4.37 | 4.36 |
| | **9.77** | **9.68** | **9.55** | **9.47** | **9.39** | **9.29** | **9.24** | **9.17** | **9.13** | **9.07** | **9.04** | **9.02** |
| **6** | 3.96 | 3.92 | 3.87 | 3.84 | 3.81 | 3.77 | 3.75 | 3.72 | 3.71 | 3.69 | 3.68 | 3.67 |
| | **7.60** | **7.52** | **7.39** | **7.31** | **7.23** | **7.14** | **7.09** | **7.02** | **6.99** | **6.94** | **6.90** | **6.88** |
| **7** | 3.52 | 3.49 | 3.44 | 3.41 | 3.38 | 3.34 | 3.32 | 3.29 | 3.28 | 3.25 | 3.24 | 3.23 |
| | **6.35** | **6.27** | **6.15** | **6.07** | **5.98** | **5.90** | **5.85** | **5.78** | **5.75** | **5.70** | **5.67** | **5.65** |
| **8** | 3.23 | 3.20 | 3.15 | 3.12 | 3.08 | 3.05 | 3.03 | 3.00 | 2.98 | 2.96 | 2.94 | 2.93 |
| | **5.56** | **5.48** | **5.36** | **5.28** | **5.20** | **5.11** | **5.06** | **5.00** | **4.96** | **4.91** | **4.88** | **4.86** |
| **9** | 3.02 | 2.98 | 2.93 | 2.90 | 2.86 | 2.82 | 2.80 | 2.77 | 2.76 | 2.73 | 2.72 | 2.71 |
| | **5.00** | **4.92** | **4.80** | **4.73** | **4.64** | **4.56** | **4.51** | **4.45** | **4.41** | **4.36** | **4.33** | **4.31** |
| **10** | 2.86 | 2.82 | 2.77 | 2.74 | 2.70 | 2.67 | 2.64 | 2.61 | 2.59 | 2.56 | 2.55 | 2.54 |
| | **4.60** | **4.52** | **4.41** | **4.33** | **4.25** | **4.17** | **4.12** | **4.05** | **4.01** | **3.96** | **3.93** | **3.91** |
| **11** | 2.74 | 2.70 | 2.65 | 2.61 | 2.57 | 2.53 | 2.50 | 2.47 | 2.45 | 2.42 | 2.41 | 2.40 |
| | **4.29** | **4.21** | **4.10** | **4.02** | **3.94** | **3.86** | **3.80** | **3.74** | **3.70** | **3.66** | **3.62** | **3.60** |
| **12** | 2.64 | 2.60 | 2.54 | 2.50 | 2.46 | 2.42 | 2.40 | 2.36 | 2.35 | 2.32 | 2.31 | 2.30 |
| | **4.05** | **3.98** | **3.86** | **3.78** | **3.70** | **3.61** | **3.56** | **3.49** | **3.46** | **3.41** | **3.38** | **3.36** |
| **13** | 2.55 | 2.51 | 2.46 | 2.42 | 2.38 | 2.34 | 2.32 | 2.28 | 2.26 | 2.24 | 2.22 | 2.21 |
| | **3.85** | **3.78** | **3.67** | **3.59** | **3.51** | **3.42** | **3.37** | **3.30** | **3.27** | **3.21** | **3.18** | **3.16** |
| **14** | 2.48 | 2.44 | 2.39 | 2.35 | 2.31 | 2.27 | 2.24 | 2.21 | 2.19 | 2.16 | 2.14 | 2.13 |
| | **3.70** | **3.62** | **3.51** | **3.43** | **3.34** | **3.26** | **3.21** | **3.14** | **3.11** | **3.06** | **3.02** | **3.00** |
| **15** | 2.43 | 2.39 | 2.33 | 2.29 | 2.25 | 2.21 | 2.18 | 2.15 | 2.12 | 2.10 | 2.08 | 2.07 |
| | **3.56** | **3.48** | **3.36** | **3.29** | **3.20** | **3.12** | **3.07** | **3.00** | **2.97** | **2.92** | **2.89** | **2.87** |
| **16** | 2.37 | 2.33 | 2.28 | 2.24 | 2.20 | 2.16 | 2.13 | 2.09 | 2.07 | 2.04 | 2.02 | 2.01 |
| | **3.45** | **3.37** | **3.25** | **3.18** | **3.10** | **3.01** | **2.96** | **2.89** | **2.86** | **2.80** | **2.77** | **2.75** |
| **17** | 2.33 | 2.29 | 2.23 | 2.19 | 2.15 | 2.11 | 2.08 | 2.04 | 2.02 | 1.99 | 1.97 | 1.96 |
| | **3.35** | **3.27** | **3.16** | **3.08** | **3.00** | **2.92** | **2.86** | **2.79** | **2.76** | **2.70** | **2.67** | **2.65** |

*Degrees of Freedom for Denominator*

*Degrees of Freedom for Numerator*

| | 1 | 2 | 3 | 4 | 5 | 6 | 7 | 8 | 9 | 10 | 11 | 12 |
|---|---|---|---|---|---|---|---|---|---|---|---|---|
| **18** | 4.41<br>8.28 | 3.55<br>6.01 | 3.16<br>5.09 | 2.93<br>4.58 | 2.77<br>4.25 | 2.66<br>4.01 | 2.58<br>3.85 | 2.51<br>3.71 | 2.46<br>3.60 | 2.41<br>3.51 | 2.37<br>3.44 | 2.34<br>3.37 |
| **19** | 4.38<br>8.18 | 3.52<br>5.93 | 3.13<br>5.01 | 2.90<br>4.50 | 2.74<br>4.17 | 2.63<br>3.94 | 2.55<br>3.77 | 2.48<br>3.63 | 2.43<br>3.52 | 2.38<br>3.43 | 2.34<br>3.36 | 2.31<br>3.30 |
| **20** | 4.35<br>8.10 | 3.49<br>5.85 | 3.10<br>4.94 | 2.87<br>4.43 | 2.71<br>4.10 | 2.60<br>3.87 | 2.52<br>3.71 | 2.45<br>3.56 | 2.40<br>3.45 | 2.35<br>3.37 | 2.31<br>3.30 | 2.28<br>3.23 |
| **21** | 4.32<br>8.02 | 3.47<br>5.78 | 3.07<br>4.87 | 2.84<br>4.37 | 2.68<br>4.04 | 2.57<br>3.81 | 2.49<br>3.65 | 2.42<br>3.51 | 2.37<br>3.40 | 2.32<br>3.31 | 2.28<br>3.24 | 2.25<br>3.17 |
| **22** | 4.30<br>7.94 | 3.44<br>5.72 | 3.05<br>4.82 | 2.82<br>4.31 | 2.66<br>3.99 | 2.55<br>3.76 | 2.47<br>3.59 | 2.40<br>3.45 | 2.35<br>3.35 | 2.30<br>3.26 | 2.26<br>3.18 | 2.23<br>3.12 |
| **23** | 4.28<br>7.88 | 3.42<br>5.66 | 3.03<br>4.76 | 2.80<br>4.26 | 2.64<br>3.94 | 2.53<br>3.71 | 2.45<br>3.45 | 2.38<br>3.41 | 2.32<br>3.30 | 2.28<br>3.21 | 2.24<br>3.14 | 2.20<br>3.07 |
| **24** | 4.26<br>7.82 | 3.40<br>5.61 | 3.01<br>4.72 | 2.78<br>4.22 | 2.62<br>3.90 | 2.51<br>3.67 | 2.43<br>3.50 | 2.36<br>3.36 | 2.30<br>3.25 | 2.26<br>3.17 | 2.22<br>3.09 | 2.18<br>3.03 |
| **25** | 4.24<br>7.77 | 3.38<br>5.57 | 2.99<br>4.68 | 2.76<br>4.18 | 2.60<br>3.86 | 2.49<br>3.63 | 2.41<br>3.46 | 2.34<br>3.32 | 2.28<br>3.21 | 2.24<br>3.13 | 2.20<br>3.05 | 2.16<br>2.99 |
| **26** | 4.22<br>7.72 | 3.37<br>5.53 | 2.89<br>4.64 | 2.74<br>4.14 | 2.59<br>3.82 | 2.47<br>3.59 | 2.39<br>3.42 | 2.32<br>3.29 | 2.27<br>3.17 | 2.22<br>3.09 | 2.18<br>3.02 | 2.15<br>2.96 |
| **27** | 4.21<br>7.68 | 3.35<br>5.49 | 2.96<br>4.60 | 2.73<br>4.11 | 2.57<br>3.79 | 2.46<br>3.56 | 2.37<br>3.39 | 2.30<br>3.26 | 2.25<br>3.14 | 2.20<br>3.06 | 2.16<br>2.98 | 2.13<br>2.93 |
| **28** | 4.20<br>7.64 | 3.34<br>5.45 | 2.95<br>4.57 | 2.71<br>4.07 | 2.56<br>3.76 | 2.44<br>3.53 | 2.36<br>3.36 | 2.29<br>3.23 | 2.24<br>3.11 | 2.19<br>3.03 | 2.15<br>2.95 | 2.12<br>2.90 |
| **29** | 4.18<br>7.60 | 3.33<br>5.52 | 2.93<br>4.54 | 2.70<br>4.04 | 2.54<br>3.73 | 2.43<br>3.50 | 2.35<br>3.32 | 2.28<br>3.20 | 2.22<br>3.08 | 2.18<br>3.00 | 2.14<br>2.92 | 2.10<br>2.87 |
| **30** | 4.17<br>7.56 | 3.32<br>5.39 | 2.92<br>4.51 | 2.69<br>4.02 | 2.53<br>3.70 | 2.42<br>3.47 | 2.34<br>3.30 | 2.27<br>3.17 | 2.21<br>3.06 | 2.16<br>2.98 | 2.12<br>2.90 | 2.09<br>2.84 |
| **32** | 4.15<br>7.50 | 3.30<br>5.34 | 2.90<br>4.46 | 2.67<br>3.97 | 2.51<br>3.66 | 2.40<br>3.42 | 2.32<br>3.25 | 2.25<br>3.12 | 2.19<br>3.01 | 2.14<br>2.94 | 2.10<br>2.86 | 2.07<br>2.80 |
| **34** | 4.13<br>7.44 | 3.28<br>5.29 | 2.88<br>4.42 | 2.65<br>3.93 | 2.49<br>3.61 | 2.38<br>3.38 | 2.30<br>3.21 | 2.23<br>3.08 | 2.17<br>2.97 | 2.12<br>2.89 | 2.08<br>2.82 | 2.05<br>2.76 |
| **36** | 4.11<br>7.39 | 3.26<br>5.25 | 2.86<br>7.38 | 2.63<br>3.89 | 2.48<br>3.58 | 2.36<br>3.35 | 2.28<br>3.18 | 2.21<br>3.04 | 2.15<br>2.94 | 2.10<br>2.86 | 2.06<br>2.78 | 2.03<br>2.72 |
| **38** | 4.10<br>7.35 | 3.25<br>5.21 | 2.85<br>4.34 | 2.62<br>3.86 | 2.46<br>3.54 | 2.35<br>3.32 | 2.26<br>3.15 | 2.19<br>3.02 | 2.14<br>2.91 | 2.09<br>2.82 | 2.05<br>2.75 | 2.02<br>2.69 |
| **40** | 4.08<br>7.31 | 3.23<br>5.18 | 2.84<br>4.31 | 2.61<br>3.83 | 2.45<br>3.51 | 2.34<br>3.29 | 2.25<br>3.12 | 2.18<br>2.99 | 2.12<br>2.88 | 2.07<br>2.80 | 2.04<br>2.73 | 2.00<br>2.66 |

*Degrees of Freedom for Denominator*

Degrees of Freedom for Numerator

| | 14 | 16 | 20 | 24 | 30 | 40 | 50 | 75 | 100 | 200 | 500 | ∞ |
|---|---|---|---|---|---|---|---|---|---|---|---|---|
| 18 | 2.29 3.27 | 2.25 3.19 | 2.19 3.07 | 2.15 3.00 | 2.11 2.91 | 2.07 2.83 | 2.04 2.78 | 2.00 2.71 | 1.98 2.68 | 1.95 2.62 | 1.93 2.59 | 1.92 2.57 |
| 19 | 2.26 3.19 | 2.21 3.12 | 2.15 3.00 | 2.11 2.92 | 2.07 2.84 | 2.02 2.76 | 2.00 2.70 | 1.96 2.63 | 1.94 2.60 | 1.91 2.54 | 1.90 2.51 | 1.88 2.49 |
| 20 | 2.23 3.13 | 2.18 3.05 | 2.12 2.94 | 2.08 2.86 | 2.04 2.77 | 1.99 2.69 | 1.96 2.63 | 1.92 2.56 | 1.90 2.53 | 1.87 2.47 | 1.85 2.44 | 1.84 2.42 |
| 21 | 2.20 3.07 | 2.15 2.99 | 2.09 2.88 | 2.05 2.80 | 2.00 2.72 | 1.96 2.63 | 1.96 2.58 | 1.80 2.51 | 1.87 2.47 | 1.84 2.42 | 1.82 2.38 | 1.81 2.36 |
| 22 | 2.18 3.02 | 2.13 2.94 | 2.07 2.83 | 2.03 2.75 | 1.98 2.67 | 1.93 2.58 | 1.91 2.53 | 1.87 2.46 | 1.84 2.42 | 1.81 2.37 | 1.80 2.33 | 1.78 2.31 |
| 23 | 2.14 2.97 | 2.10 2.89 | 2.04 2.78 | 2.00 2.70 | 1.96 2.62 | 1.91 2.53 | 1.88 2.48 | 1.84 2.41 | 1.82 2.37 | 1.79 2.32 | 1.77 2.28 | 1.76 2.26 |
| 24 | 2.13 2.93 | 2.09 2.85 | 2.02 2.74 | 1.98 2.66 | 1.94 2.58 | 1.89 2.49 | 1.86 2.44 | 1.82 2.36 | 1.80 2.33 | 1.76 2.27 | 1.74 2.23 | 1.73 2.21 |
| 25 | 2.11 2.89 | 2.06 2.81 | 2.00 2.70 | 1.96 2.62 | 1.92 2.54 | 1.87 2.45 | 1.84 2.40 | 1.80 2.32 | 1.77 2.29 | 1.74 2.23 | 1.72 2.19 | 1.71 2.17 |
| 26 | 2.10 2.86 | 2.05 2.77 | 1.99 2.66 | 1.95 2.58 | 1.90 2.50 | 1.85 2.41 | 1.82 2.36 | 1.78 2.28 | 1.76 2.25 | 1.72 2.19 | 1.70 2.15 | 1.69 2.13 |
| 27 | 2.08 2.83 | 2.03 2.74 | 1.97 2.63 | 1.93 2.55 | 1.88 2.47 | 1.84 2.38 | 1.80 2.33 | 1.76 2.25 | 1.74 2.21 | 1.71 2.16 | 1.68 2.12 | 1.67 2.10 |
| 28 | 2.06 2.80 | 2.02 2.71 | 1.96 2.60 | 1.91 2.52 | 1.87 2.44 | 1.81 2.35 | 1.78 2.30 | 1.75 2.22 | 1.72 2.18 | 1.69 2.13 | 1.67 2.09 | 1.65 2.06 |
| 29 | 2.05 2.77 | 2.00 2.68 | 1.94 2.57 | 1.90 2.49 | 1.85 2.41 | 1.80 2.32 | 1.77 2.27 | 1.73 2.19 | 1.71 2.15 | 1.68 2.10 | 1.65 2.06 | 1.64 2.03 |
| 30 | 2.04 2.74 | 1.99 2.66 | 1.93 2.55 | 1.89 2.47 | 1.84 2.38 | 1.79 2.29 | 1.76 2.24 | 1.72 2.16 | 1.69 2.13 | 1.66 2.07 | 1.64 2.03 | 1.62 2.01 |
| 32 | 2.02 2.70 | 1.97 2.62 | 1.91 2.51 | 1.86 2.42 | 1.82 2.34 | 1.76 2.25 | 1.74 2.20 | 1.69 2.12 | 1.67 2.08 | 1.64 2.02 | 1.61 1.98 | 1.59 1.96 |
| 34 | 2.00 2.66 | 1.95 2.58 | 1.89 2.47 | 1.84 2.38 | 1.80 2.30 | 1.74 2.21 | 1.71 2.15 | 1.67 2.08 | 1.64 2.04 | 1.61 1.98 | 1.59 1.94 | 1.57 1.91 |
| 36 | 1.98 2.62 | 1.93 2.54 | 1.87 2.43 | 1.82 2.35 | 1.78 2.26 | 1.72 2.17 | 1.69 2.12 | 1.65 2.04 | 1.62 2.00 | 1.59 1.94 | 1.56 1.90 | 1.55 1.87 |
| 38 | 1.96 2.59 | 1.92 2.51 | 1.85 2.40 | 1.80 2.32 | 1.76 2.22 | 1.71 2.14 | 1.67 2.08 | 1.63 2.00 | 1.60 1.97 | 1.57 1.90 | 1.54 1.86 | 1.53 1.84 |
| 40 | 1.95 2.56 | 1.90 2.49 | 1.84 2.37 | 1.79 2.29 | 1.74 2.20 | 1.69 2.11 | 1.66 2.05 | 1.61 1.97 | 1.59 1.94 | 1.55 1.88 | 1.53 1.84 | 1.51 1.81 |

Degrees of Freedom for Denominator

*Degrees of Freedom for Numerator*

| | 1 | 2 | 3 | 4 | 5 | 6 | 7 | 8 | 9 | 10 | 11 | 12 |
|---|---|---|---|---|---|---|---|---|---|---|---|---|
| **42** | 4.07 **7.27** | 3.22 **5.15** | 2.83 **4.29** | 2.59 **3.80** | 2.44 **3.49** | 2.32 **3.26** | 2.24 **3.10** | 2.71 **2.96** | 2.11 **2.86** | 2.06 **2.77** | 2.02 **2.70** | 1.90 **2.64** |
| **44** | 4.06 **7.24** | 3.21 **5.12** | 2.82 **4.26** | 2.58 **3.78** | 2.43 **3.460** | 2.31 **3.24** | 2.23 **3.07** | 2.16 **2.94** | 2.10 **2.84** | 2.05 **2.75** | 2.01 **2.68** | 1.98 **2.62** |
| **46** | 4.05 **7.21** | 3.20 **5.10** | 2.81 **4.24** | 2.57 **3.76** | 2.42 **3.44** | 2.30 **3.22** | 2.22 **3.05** | 2.14 **2.92** | 2.09 **2.82** | 2.04 **2.73** | 2.00 **2.66** | 1.97 **2.60** |
| **48** | 4.04 **7.19** | 3.19 **5.08** | 2.80 **4.22** | 2.56 **3.74** | 2.41 **3.42** | 2.30 **3.20** | 2.21 **3.04** | 2.14 **2.90** | 2.08 **2.80** | 2.03 **2.71** | 1.99 **2.64** | 1.96 **2.58** |
| **50** | 4.03 **7.17** | 3.18 **5.06** | 2.79 **4.20** | 2.56 **3.72** | 2.40 **3.41** | 2.29 **3.18** | 2.20 **3.02** | 2.13 **2.88** | 2.07 **2.78** | 2.02 **2.70** | 1.98 **2.62** | 1.95 **2.56** |
| **55** | 4.02 **7.12** | 3.17 **5.01** | 2.78 **4.16** | 2.54 **3.68** | 2.38 **3.37** | 2.27 **3.15** | 2.18 **2.98** | 2.11 **2.85** | 2.05 **2.75** | 2.00 **2.66** | 1.97 **2.59** | 1.93 **2.53** |
| **60** | 4.00 **7.08** | 3.15 **4.98** | 2.76 **4.13** | 2.52 **3.65** | 2.37 **3.34** | 2.25 **3.12** | 2.17 **2.95** | 2.10 **2.82** | 2.04 **2.72** | 1.99 **2.63** | 1.95 **2.56** | 1.92 **2.50** |
| **65** | 3.99 **7.04** | 3.14 **4.95** | 2.75 **4.10** | 2.51 **3.62** | 2.36 **3.31** | 2.24 **3.09** | 2.15 **2.93** | 2.08 **2.79** | 2.02 **2.70** | 1.98 **2.61** | 1.94 **2.54** | 1.90 **2.47** |
| **70** | 3.98 **7.01** | 3.13 **4.92** | 2.74 **4.08** | 2.50 **3.60** | 2.35 **3.29** | 2.32 **3.07** | 2.14 **2.91** | 2.07 **2.77** | 2.01 **2.67** | 1.97 **2.59** | 1.93 **2.51** | 1.89 **2.45** |
| **80** | 3.96 **6.96** | 3.11 **4.88** | 2.72 **4.04** | 2.48 **3.56** | 2.33 **3.25** | 2.21 **3.04** | 2.12 **2.87** | 2.05 **2.74** | 1.99 **2.64** | 1.95 **2.55** | 1.91 **2.48** | 1.88 **2.41** |
| **100** | 3.94 **6.90** | 3.09 **4.82** | 2.70 **3.98** | 2.46 **3.51** | 2.30 **3.20** | 2.19 **2.99** | 2.10 **2.82** | 2.03 **2.69** | 1.97 **2.59** | 1.92 **2.51** | 1.88 **2.43** | 1.85 **2.36** |
| **125** | 3.92 **6.84** | 3.07 **4.78** | 2.68 **3.94** | 2.44 **3.47** | 2.29 **3.17** | 2.17 **2.95** | 2.08 **2.79** | 2.01 **2.65** | 1.95 **2.56** | 1.90 **2.47** | 1.86 **2.40** | 1.83 **2.33** |
| **150** | 3.91 **6.81** | 3.06 **4.75** | 2.67 **3.91** | 2.43 **3.44** | 2.27 **3.13** | 2.16 **2.92** | 2.07 **2.76** | 2.00 **2.62** | 1.94 **2.53** | 1.89 **2.44** | 1.85 **2.37** | 1.82 **2.30** |
| **200** | 3.89 **6.76** | 3.04 **4.71** | 2.65 **3.38** | 2.41 **3.41** | 2.26 **3.11** | 2.14 **2.90** | 2.05 **2.73** | 1.98 **2.60** | 1.92 **2.50** | 1.87 **2.41** | 1.83 **2.34** | 1.80 **2.28** |
| **400** | 3.86 **6.70** | 3.02 **4.66** | 2.62 **3.83** | 2.39 **3.36** | 2.23 **3.06** | 2.12 **2.85** | 2.03 **2.69** | 1.96 **2.55** | 1.90 **2.46** | 1.85 **2.37** | 1.81 **2.29** | 1.78 **2.23** |
| **1000** | 3.85 **6.66** | 3.00 **4.62** | 2.61 **3.80** | 2.38 **3.34** | 2.22 **3.04** | 2.10 **2.82** | 2.02 **2.66** | 1.95 **2.53** | 1.89 **2.43** | 1.84 **2.34** | 1.80 **2.26** | 1.76 **2.20** |
| **∞** | 3.84 **6.64** | 2.99 **4.60** | 2.60 **3.78** | 2.37 **3.32** | 2.21 **3.02** | 2.09 **2.80** | 2.01 **2.64** | 1.94 **2.51** | 1.88 **2.41** | 1.83 **2.32** | 1.79 **2.24** | 1.75 **2.18** |

*Degrees of Freedom for Denominator*

*Degrees of Freedom for Numerator*

| | 14 | 16 | 20 | 24 | 30 | 40 | 50 | 75 | 100 | 200 | 500 | ∞ |
|---|---|---|---|---|---|---|---|---|---|---|---|---|
| **42** | 1.94<br>**2.54** | 1.89<br>**2.46** | 1.82<br>**2.35** | 1.78<br>**2.26** | 1.73<br>**2.17** | 1.68<br>**2.08** | 1.64<br>**2.02** | 1.60<br>**1.94** | 1.57<br>**1.91** | 1.54<br>**1.85** | 1.51<br>**1.80** | 1.49<br>**1.78** |
| **44** | 1.92<br>**2.52** | 1.88<br>**2.44** | 1.81<br>**2.32** | 1.76<br>**2.24** | 1.72<br>**2.15** | 1.66<br>**2.06** | 1.63<br>**2.09** | 1.58<br>**1.92** | 1.56<br>**1.88** | 1.52<br>**1.82** | 1.50<br>**1.78** | 1.48<br>**1.75** |
| **46** | 1.91<br>**2.50** | 1.87<br>**2.42** | 1.80<br>**2.30** | 1.75<br>**2.22** | 1.71<br>**2.13** | 1.65<br>**2.04** | 1.62<br>**1.98** | 1.57<br>**1.90** | 1.54<br>**1.86** | 1.51<br>**1.80** | 1.48<br>**1.76** | 1.46<br>**1.72** |
| **48** | 1.90<br>**2.48** | 1.86<br>**2.40** | 1.79<br>**2.28** | 1.74<br>**2.20** | 1.70<br>**2.11** | 1.64<br>**2.02** | 1.61<br>**1.96** | 1.56<br>**1.88** | 1.53<br>**1.84** | 1.50<br>**1.78** | 1.47<br>**1.73** | 1.45<br>**1.70** |
| **50** | 1.90<br>**2.46** | 1.85<br>**2.39** | 1.78<br>**2.26** | 1.74<br>**2.18** | 1.69<br>**2.10** | 1.63<br>**2.00** | 1.60<br>**1.94** | 1.55<br>**1.86** | 1.52<br>**1.82** | 1.48<br>**1.76** | 1.46<br>**1.71** | 1.44<br>**1.68** |
| **55** | 1.88<br>**2.43** | 1.83<br>**2.35** | 1.76<br>**2.23** | 1.72<br>**2.15** | 1.67<br>**2.06** | 1.61<br>**1.96** | 1.58<br>**1.90** | 1.52<br>**1.82** | 1.50<br>**1.78** | 1.46<br>**1.71** | 1.43<br>**1.66** | 1.41<br>**1.64** |
| **60** | 1.86<br>**2.40** | 1.81<br>**2.32** | 1.75<br>**2.20** | 1.70<br>**2.12** | 1.65<br>**2.03** | 1.59<br>**1.93** | 1.56<br>**1.87** | 1.50<br>**1.79** | 1.48<br>**1.74** | 1.44<br>**1.68** | 1.41<br>**1.63** | 1.39<br>**1.60** |
| **65** | 1.85<br>**2.37** | 1.80<br>**2.30** | 1.73<br>**2.18** | 1.68<br>**2.09** | 1.63<br>**2.00** | 1.57<br>**1.90** | 1.54<br>**1.84** | 1.49<br>**1.76** | 1.46<br>**1.71** | 1.42<br>**1.64** | 1.39<br>**1.60** | 1.37<br>**1.56** |
| **70** | 1.84<br>**2.35** | 1.79<br>**2.28** | 1.72<br>**2.15** | 1.67<br>**2.07** | 1.62<br>**1.98** | 1.56<br>**1.88** | 1.53<br>**1.82** | 1.47<br>**1.74** | 1.45<br>**1.69** | 1.40<br>**1.62** | 1.37<br>**1.56** | 1.35<br>**1.53** |
| **80** | 1.82<br>**2.32** | 1.77<br>**2.24** | 1.70<br>**2.11** | 1.65<br>**2.03** | 1.60<br>**1.94** | 1.54<br>**1.84** | 1.51<br>**1.78** | 1.45<br>**1.70** | 1.42<br>**1.65** | 1.38<br>**1.57** | 1.35<br>**1.52** | 1.32<br>**1.49** |
| **100** | 1.79<br>**2.26** | 1.75<br>**2.19** | 1.68<br>**2.06** | 1.63<br>**1.98** | 1.57<br>**1.89** | 1.51<br>**1.79** | 1.48<br>**1.73** | 1.42<br>**1.64** | 1.39<br>**1.59** | 1.34<br>**1.51** | 1.30<br>**1.46** | 1.28<br>**1.43** |
| **125** | 1.77<br>**2.23** | 1.72<br>**2.15** | 1.65<br>**2.03** | 1.60<br>**1.94** | 1.55<br>**1.85** | 1.49<br>**1.75** | 1.45<br>**1.68** | 1.39<br>**1.59** | 1.36<br>**1.54** | 1.31<br>**1.46** | 1.27<br>**1.40** | 1.25<br>**1.37** |
| **150** | 1.76<br>**2.20** | 1.71<br>**2.12** | 1.64<br>**2.00** | 1.59<br>**1.91** | 1.54<br>**1.83** | 1.47<br>**1.72** | 1.44<br>**1.66** | 1.37<br>**1.56** | 1.34<br>**1.51** | 1.29<br>**1.43** | 1.25<br>**1.37** | 1.22<br>**1.33** |
| **200** | 1.74<br>**2.17** | 1.69<br>**2.09** | 1.62<br>**1.97** | 1.57<br>**1.88** | 1.52<br>**1.79** | 1.45<br>**1.69** | 1.42<br>**1.62** | 1.35<br>**1.53** | 1.32<br>**1.48** | 1.26<br>**1.39** | 1.22<br>**1.33** | 1.19<br>**1.28** |
| **400** | 1.72<br>**2.12** | 1.67<br>**2.04** | 1.60<br>**1.92** | 1.54<br>**1.84** | 1.49<br>**1.74** | 1.42<br>**1.64** | 1.38<br>**1.57** | 1.32<br>**1.47** | 1.28<br>**1.42** | 1.22<br>**1.32** | 1.16<br>**1.24** | 1.13<br>**1.19** |
| **1000** | 1.70<br>**2.09** | 1.65<br>**2.01** | 1.58<br>**1.89** | 1.53<br>**1.81** | 1.47<br>**1.71** | 1.41<br>**1.61** | 1.36<br>**1.54** | 1.30<br>**1.44** | 1.26<br>**1.38** | 1.19<br>**1.28** | 1.13<br>**1.19** | 1.08<br>**1.11** |
| **∞** | 1.69<br>**2.07** | 1.64<br>**1.99** | 1.57<br>**1.87** | 1.52<br>**1.79** | 1.46<br>**1.69** | 1.40<br>**1.59** | 1.35<br>**1.52** | 1.28<br>**1.41** | 1.24<br>**1.36** | 1.17<br>**1.25** | 1.11<br>**1.15** | 1.00<br>**1.00** |

*Degrees of Freedom for Denominator*

# Critical Values of the Studentized Range Statistic

| df for MSerror | α | \multicolumn{9}{c}{k = number of means} |
| | | 2 | 3 | 4 | 5 | 6 | 7 | 8 | 9 | 10 |
|---|---|---|---|---|---|---|---|---|---|---|
| 1 | .05 | 18.00 | 27.00 | 32.80 | 37.10 | 40.40 | 43.10 | 45.40 | 47.40 | 49.10 |
|   | .01 | 90.00 | 135.00 | 164.00 | 186.00 | 202.00 | 216.00 | 227.00 | 237.00 | 246.00 |
| 2 | .05 | 6.09 | 8.30 | 9.80 | 10.90 | 11.70 | 12.40 | 13.00 | 13.50 | 14.00 |
|   | .01 | 14.00 | 19.00 | 22.30 | 24.70 | 26.60 | 28.20 | 29.50 | 30.70 | 31.70 |
| 3 | .05 | 4.50 | 5.91 | 6.82 | 7.50 | 8.04 | 8.48 | 8.85 | 9.18 | 9.46 |
|   | .01 | 8.26 | 10.60 | 12.20 | 13.30 | 14.20 | 15.00 | 15.60 | 16.20 | 16.70 |
| 4 | .05 | 3.93 | 5.04 | 5.76 | 6.29 | 6.71 | 7.05 | 7.35 | 7.60 | 7.83 |
|   | .01 | 6.51 | 8.12 | 9.17 | 9.96 | 10.60 | 11.10 | 11.50 | 11.90 | 12.30 |
| 5 | .05 | 3.64 | 4.60 | 5.22 | 5.67 | 6.03 | 6.33 | 6.58 | 6.80 | 6.99 |
|   | .01 | 5.70 | 6.97 | 7.80 | 8.42 | 8.91 | 9.32 | 9.67 | 9.97 | 10.20 |
| 6 | .05 | 3.46 | 4.34 | 4.90 | 5.31 | 5.63 | 5.89 | 6.12 | 6.32 | 6.49 |
|   | .01 | 5.24 | 6.33 | 7.03 | 7.56 | 7.97 | 8.32 | 8.61 | 8.87 | 9.10 |
| 7 | .05 | 3.34 | 4.16 | 4.69 | 5.06 | 5.36 | 5.61 | 5.82 | 6.00 | 6.16 |
|   | .01 | 4.95 | 5.92 | 6.54 | 7.01 | 7.37 | 7.68 | 7.94 | 8.17 | 8.37 |
| 8 | .05 | 3.26 | 4.04 | 4.53 | 4.89 | 5.17 | 5.40 | 5.60 | 5.77 | 5.92 |
|   | .01 | 4.74 | 5.63 | 6.20 | 6.63 | 6.96 | 7.24 | 7.47 | 7.68 | 7.87 |
| 9 | .05 | 3.20 | 3.95 | 4.42 | 4.76 | 5.02 | 5.24 | 5.43 | 5.60 | 5.74 |
|   | .01 | 4.60 | 5.43 | 5.96 | 6.35 | 6.66 | 6.91 | 7.13 | 7.32 | 7.49 |
| 10 | .05 | 3.15 | 3.88 | 4.33 | 4.65 | 4.91 | 5.12 | 5.30 | 5.46 | 5.60 |
|   | .01 | 4.48 | 5.27 | 5.77 | 6.14 | 6.43 | 6.67 | 6.87 | 7.05 | 7.21 |
| 11 | .05 | 3.11 | 3.82 | 4.26 | 4.57 | 4.82 | 5.03 | 5.20 | 5.35 | 5.49 |
|   | .01 | 4.39 | 5.14 | 5.62 | 5.97 | 6.25 | 6.48 | 6.67 | 6.84 | 6.99 |
| 12 | .05 | 3.08 | 3.77 | 4.20 | 4.51 | 4.75 | 4.95 | 5.12 | 5.27 | 5.40 |
|   | .01 | 4.32 | 5.04 | 5.50 | 5.84 | 6.10 | 6.32 | 6.51 | 6.67 | 6.81 |
| 13 | .05 | 3.06 | 3.73 | 4.15 | 4.45 | 4.69 | 4.88 | 5.05 | 5.19 | 5.32 |
|   | .01 | 4.26 | 4.96 | 5.40 | 5.73 | 5.98 | 6.19 | 6.37 | 6.53 | 6.67 |
| 14 | .05 | 3.03 | 3.70 | 4.11 | 4.41 | 4.64 | 4.83 | 4.99 | 5.13 | 5.25 |
|   | .01 | 4.21 | 4.89 | 5.32 | 5.63 | 5.88 | 6.08 | 6.26 | 6.41 | 6.54 |
| 16 | .05 | 3.00 | 3.65 | 4.05 | 4.33 | 4.56 | 4.74 | 4.90 | 5.03 | 5.15 |
|   | .01 | 4.13 | 4.78 | 5.19 | 5.49 | 5.72 | 5.92 | 6.08 | 6.22 | 6.35 |
| 18 | .05 | 2.97 | 3.61 | 4.00 | 4.28 | 4.49 | 4.67 | 4.82 | 4.96 | 5.07 |
|   | .01 | 4.07 | 4.70 | 5.09 | 5.38 | 5.60 | 5.79 | 5.94 | 6.08 | 6.20 |
| 20 | .05 | 2.95 | 3.58 | 3.96 | 4.23 | 4.45 | 4.62 | 4.77 | 4.90 | 5.01 |
|   | .01 | 4.02 | 4.64 | 5.02 | 5.29 | 5.51 | 5.69 | 5.84 | 5.97 | 6.09 |
| 24 | .05 | 2.92 | 3.53 | 3.90 | 4.17 | 4.37 | 4.54 | 4.68 | 4.81 | 4.92 |
|   | .01 | 3.96 | 4.54 | 4.91 | 5.17 | 5.37 | 5.54 | 5.69 | 5.81 | 5.92 |
| 30 | .05 | 2.89 | 3.49 | 3.84 | 4.10 | 4.30 | 4.46 | 4.60 | 4.72 | 4.83 |
|   | .01 | 3.89 | 4.45 | 4.80 | 5.05 | 5.24 | 5.40 | 5.54 | 5.66 | 5.76 |
| 40 | .05 | 2.86 | 3.44 | 3.79 | 4.04 | 4.23 | 4.39 | 4.52 | 4.63 | 4.74 |
|   | .01 | 3.82 | 4.37 | 4.70 | 4.93 | 5.11 | 5.27 | 5.39 | 5.50 | 5.60 |
| 60 | .05 | 2.83 | 3.40 | 3.74 | 3.98 | 4.16 | 4.31 | 4.44 | 4.55 | 4.65 |
|   | .01 | 3.76 | 4.28 | 4.60 | 4.82 | 4.99 | 5.13 | 5.25 | 5.36 | 5.45 |
| 120 | .05 | 2.80 | 3.36 | 3.69 | 3.92 | 4.10 | 4.24 | 4.36 | 4.48 | 4.56 |
|   | .01 | 3.70 | 4.20 | 4.50 | 4.71 | 4.87 | 5.01 | 5.12 | 5.21 | 5.30 |
| ∞ | .05 | 2.77 | 3.31 | 3.63 | 3.86 | 4.03 | 4.17 | 4.29 | 4.39 | 4.47 |
|   | .01 | 3.64 | 4.12 | 4.40 | 4.60 | 4.76 | 4.88 | 4.99 | 5.08 | 5.16 |

From Table II.2 in Harter, H.L., Clemm, D.S. & Guthrie, E.H. (1959). *The probability integrals of the range and of the Studentized range.* Wright Air Development Center Tech. Rep. 58-484, Vol.2. Used with permission.

# Critical Values of Chi Square

## Level of Significance

| df | .10 | .05 | .02 | .01 |
|----|-----|-----|-----|-----|
| 1 | 2.706 | 3.841 | 5.412 | 6.635 |
| 2 | 4.605 | 5.991 | 7.824 | 9.210 |
| 3 | 6.251 | 7.815 | 9.837 | 11.341 |
| 4 | 7.779 | 9.488 | 11.668 | 13.277 |
| 5 | 9.236 | 11.070 | 13.388 | 15.086 |
| 6 | 10.645 | 12.592 | 15.033 | 16.812 |
| 7 | 12.017 | 14.067 | 16.622 | 18.475 |
| 8 | 13.362 | 15.507 | 18.168 | 20.090 |
| 9 | 14.684 | 16.919 | 19.679 | 21.666 |
| 10 | 15.987 | 18.307 | 21.161 | 23.209 |
| 11 | 17.275 | 19.675 | 22.618 | 24.725 |
| 12 | 18.549 | 21.026 | 24.054 | 26.217 |
| 13 | 19.812 | 22.362 | 25.472 | 27.688 |
| 14 | 21.064 | 23.685 | 26.873 | 29.141 |
| 15 | 22.307 | 24.996 | 28.259 | 30.578 |
| 16 | 23.542 | 26.296 | 29.633 | 32.000 |
| 17 | 24.769 | 27.587 | 30.995 | 33.409 |
| 18 | 25.989 | 28.869 | 32.346 | 34.805 |
| 19 | 27.204 | 30.144 | 33.687 | 36.191 |
| 20 | 28.412 | 31.410 | 35.020 | 37.566 |
| 21 | 29.615 | 32.671 | 36.343 | 38.932 |
| 22 | 30.813 | 33.924 | 37.659 | 40.289 |
| 23 | 32.007 | 35.172 | 38.968 | 41.638 |
| 24 | 33.196 | 36.415 | 40.270 | 42.980 |
| 25 | 34.382 | 37.652 | 41.566 | 44.314 |
| 26 | 35.563 | 38.885 | 42.856 | 45.642 |
| 27 | 36.741 | 40.113 | 44.140 | 46.963 |
| 28 | 37.916 | 41.337 | 45.419 | 48.278 |
| 29 | 39.087 | 42.557 | 46.693 | 49.588 |
| 30 | 40.256 | 43.773 | 47.962 | 50.892 |

From Ronald A. Fisher, *Statistical Methods for Research Workers*, 14th Ed., Table III, p. 113.
Copyright © 1970 by University of Adelaide. Used with permission.

# Index